24

Y0-BCW-763

cu ft Page 461
Square ft. 458

WHEN we build, let us think that we build forever. Let it not be for present delight nor for present use alone. Let it be such work as our descendants will thank us for; and let us think, as we lay stone on stone, that a time is to come when those stones will be held sacred because our hands have touched them, and that men will say, as they look upon the labor and wrought substance of them, "See! This our father did for us."

—*John Ruskin.*

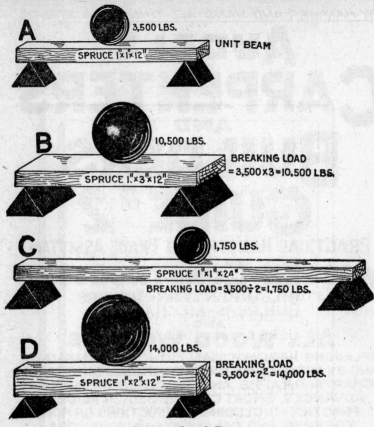

Strength of Beams

It has been found by experiment that the strength of a beam is proportional: 1, *to its breadth,* 2, *to the square of its depth, and* 3, *inversely proportional to its length.* The strength also depends on: 1, the method of suspension (whether supported or fixed ends), and 2, the nature of the load (whether concentrated, or distributed). The above examples show method of calculating a beam's strength taking the value of breaking load for the unit beam as given in fig. **A**, as a basis. This value, 3,500 lbs., has been found by experiment to be the load required to break a 1″×1″×12″ or unit spruce beam supported at the ends and loaded in the middle.

The breaking load depends not only on the size and method of suspension of the beam but also upon the kind of wood. Thus breaking loads for unit beams of various kind of wood are Norway red pine, 4,000 lbs.; Georgia pitch pine, 5,000 lbs.; white oak, 5,500 lbs.; ash. 7,000 lbs.; teak, 8,000 lbs.

Strength of beams is explained at length in the chapter on Strength of Timbers.

AUDELS
CARPENTERS
AND
BUILDERS
GUIDE #2

A PRACTICAL ILLUSTRATED TRADE ASSISTANT
ON
MODERN CONSTRUCTION

FOR CARPENTERS- JOINERS
BUILDERS -MECHANICS
AND
ALL WOOD WORKERS

EXPLAINING IN PRACTICAL, CONCISE LANGUAGE
AND BY WELL DONE ILLUSTRATIONS, DIAGRAMS
CHARTS, GRAPHS AND PICTURES, PRINCIPLES
ADVANCES, SHORT CUTS-BASED ON MODERN
PRACTICE - INCLUDING INSTRUCTIONS ON HOW
TO FIGURE AND CALCULATE VARIOUS JOBS

BY
FRANK D. GRAHAM – CHIEF
THOMAS J. EMERY-ASSOCIATE

THEO. AUDEL & CO – PUBLISHERS
49 WEST 23RD ST., NEW YORK, U.S.A.

COPYRIGHT, 1923, 1939

BY

THEO. AUDEL & COMPANY

Printed in United States

Reprinted 1947

Foreword

"The Audel's Guides to the Building Trades" are a practical series of educators on the various branches of Modern Building Construction and are dedicated to <u>Master Builders and their Associates.</u>

These Guides are designed to give technical trade information in concise, accurate, plain language.

The Guides illustrate the hows and whys, short cuts, modern ways and methods of the foundation principles of the art.

Each book in the series is fully illustrated and indexed for readiest form of <u>reference and study.</u>

The Guides will speak for themselves—and help to increase the reader's knowledge and skill in the Building Trades.

—Publishers.

OUTLINE OF CHAPTERS

READY REFERENCE INDEX

How to Use the Index.—By intelligent use of the index, the reader will have no difficulty in finding any item, and if he will carefully read the index he will be amazed at the vast amount of information to be found in this book, and will in this way find numerous items he would like to look up. This constitutes one method of study—*a reference method.*

The making of an index is an art which requires long experience, the indexes for these Guides being made by specialists in that line.

An index is said to be "full" when each item is indexed in two or more ways. For a practical example, the item "Rip saw," may be indexed either as "Rip saw," or "Saw(s), rip." This method of entering each item in two or more ways constitutes a *full index.*

In the *Carpenters' and Builders' Guides* the author has *abridged* the index to gain more space for the main text, by largely avoiding the unnecessary cross indexing.

Accordingly, if you do not find the item "Rip saw" in the letter R, turn over to S, and look for "Saw(s), rip."

In case the item be not found under either heading, look up some *associated heading,* as, for instance, "Tools," and follow down the indented items under this heading, looking for the desired item, "rip saw."

It should be noted that when there is a main heading with comma, followed by indented items, the main heading should be connected with each indented item, thus:

> Plane(s), ills., 259-290
> block, ills., 265, 284

the last item being read in full, "Plane, block, 265, 284."

Finally, if an item be not found in one Guide, look for it in the other volumes of the set. For instance, the *steel square* is explained in Guide No. 1, and its application to roof framing treated at length in Guide No. 3.

CHAPTER 26

Mathematics for Builders and Carpenters

An elementary knowledge of mathematics is essential to the carpenter in order that he may successfully solve the numerous problems encountered in almost any branch of carpentry. The branches of mathematics of which the carpenter should possess at least an elementary knowledge are:

1. Arithmetic.
2. Geometry.
3. Trigonometry.

Such knowledge will be found very useful especially in making up estimates, solving steel square problems, etc.

1. ARITHMETIC

By definition arithmetic is *the science of numbers and the art of reaching results by their use.*

Scheme of Arithmetic.—An interesting notion of what arithmetic consists of is given in Funk & Wagnall's Standard Dictionary in the following scheme or summary:

Scheme of Arithmetic

Notation

Basis — **1** — unit

Arithmetic Alphabet

0 1 2 3 4 5 6 7 8 9

Increased			*Diminished*		
By tens			*By tens*		
1, 10, 100, 1,000, etc.			1, .1, .01, .001, etc.		
By varying scales			By varying scales		
1 oz.	1 lb.	1 cwt.	¼	⁶/₇	⅓ oz, ¹¹/₂₃ etc.
1 pt.	1 qt.	1 gal.	⅙ lb.	⁹/₈ oz.	⅜ cwt.
1 in.	1 ft.	1 yd.		etc.	

According to the Four Ground Rules

Addition Subtraction	Multiplication Division
By involution (powers)	By evolution (roots)

Relations Expressed by

Ratios   2 : 3   5 : 6   8 : 9   etc.

Proportion (equality of ratios) 2 : 3 : : 4 : 6 etc.

Practical Applications

Percentage, interest, profit and loss, reduction of weights and measures, mensuration, etc.

Arithmetic Alphabet.—In arithmetic figures are used to represent quantities or magnitudes, thus:

cipher	one	two	three	four	five	six	seven	eight	nine
0	1	2	3	4	5	6	7	8	9

A number is one or a collection of these figures to represent a definite quantity or magnitude as 1 21 517 43,988, etc.

There are various kinds of numbers as, simple, compound, integer, abstract, concrete, odd, even, prime, composite, etc., later explained.

Notation and Numeration.—By definition, *notation* in arithmetic is *the writing down of figures to express a number*, and numeration of *the reading of the number or collection of figures already written*.

By means of the ten figures given above any number can be expressed.

Figures have two values, simple and local. The simple value of a figure is its value when standing in units' place. The local value of a figure is the value which arises from its location.

When one of the figures stands by itself, it is called a *unit;* but if two of them stand together, the right hand one is still called a unit, but the left hand one is called *tens;* thus, 79 is a collection of 9 units and 7 sets of ten units each, or of 9 units and 70 units, or of 79 units, and is read as seventy-nine.

If three of them stand together, then the left hand one is called *hundreds;* thus 279 is read two hundred and seventy-nine.

To express larger numbers other orders of units are formed, the figure in the 4th place denoting *thousands;* in the 5th place, *ten thousands;* these are called units of the fifth order.

The sixth place denotes hundred thousands, the seventh place denotes millions, etc.

The French method (which is the same as that used in the U. S.) of writing and reading large numbers is shown in the following

NUMERATION TABLE

Names of periods.	Billions.			Millions.			Thousands.			Units.				Thousandths.		
Order of Units	Hundred-billions.	Ten-billions.	Billions.	Hundred-millions.	Ten-millions.	Millions.	Hundred-thousands.	Ten-thousands.	Thousands.	Hundreds.	Tens.	Units.	Decimal point.	Tenths.	Hundredths.	Thousandths.
	8	7	6,	5	4	3,	2	0	1,	2	8	2,	•	4	8	9

This system is called Arabic notation, and is the system in ordinary every day use.

NOTE.—*Roman Notation.* This system is occasionally used as, in the Bible, for chapter headings, corner stones, etc. The method of expressing numbers is by letters, thus:

Roman Table

I denotes One	XII denotes Twelve	L denotes Fifty
II denotes Two	XIII denotes Thirteen	LX denotes Sixty
III denotes Three	XIV denotes Fourteen	LXX denotes Seventy
IV denotes Four	XV denotes Fifteen	LXXX denotes Eighty
V denotes Five	XVI denotes Sixteen	XC denotes Ninety
VI denotes Six	XVII denotes Seventeen	C denotes One hundred
VII denotes Seven	XVIII denotes Eighteen	D denotes Five hundred
VIII denotes Eight	XIX denotes Nineteen	M denotes One thousand
IX denotes Nine	XX denotes Twenty	$\bar{\text{X}}$ denotes Ten thousand
X denotes Ten	XXX denotes Thirty	$\bar{\text{M}}$ denotes One million
XI denotes Eleven	XL denotes Forty	

In the Roman notation, when any character is placed at the right hand of a larger numeral, its value is added to that of such numeral; as, VI, that is, V + I; XV, that is, X + V; MD, that is, M + D; and the like. I, X, and rarely C, are also placed at the left hand of other and larger numerals, and when so situated their value is subtracted from that of such numerals as, IV, that is, V — 1; XC, that is, C — X; and the like. Formerly the smaller figure was sometimes repeated in such a position twice, its value being in such cases subtracted from the larger; as, IIX, that is, X — II XXC, that is, C — XX; and the like. Sometimes after the

Symbol 👉 ✚

Addition.—Uniting two or more numbers or groups of objects of the same kind into one is called *addition*, and the number obtained by adding is called the *sum*.

The sign of addition is + and is read "plus", thus 7 + 3 is read "seven plus three."

Rule A.—*Write the numbers to be added so that like orders of units stand in the same column.*

B.—*Commencing with the lowest order, or at the right hand, add each column separately, and if the sum can be expressed by one figure, write it under the column added.*

C.—*If the sum of any column contain more than one figure, write the unit figure under the column added, and add the remaining figure or figures to the next column.*

EXAMPLES FOR PRACTICE

7,060	248,124	13,579,802
9,420	4,321	93
1,743	889,866	478,652
4,004	457,902	87,547,289
22,227 Ans.		

NOTE.—*Continued from page* 434.

sign IↃ for D, the character Ↄ was repeated one or more times, each repetition having the effect to multiply IↃ by ten; as, IↃↃ, 5,000; IↃↃↃ, 50,000; and the like. To represent numbers twice as great as these, C was repeated as many times before the stroke I, as the Ↄ was after it; as, CCIↃↃ, 10,000; CCCIↃↃↃ, 100,000; and the like. *The ridiculous custom* of using the Roman notation for chapter numbers, year of copyright, sections, etc., should be discontinued.

Use great care in placing the numbers in vertical lines, as irregularity in writing them down is one cause of mistakes.

Symbol 🖝 ▬

Subtraction.—By definition subtraction consists in *taking one number from another*. The result obtained or "answer" is called the *difference* or *remainder*.

The sign of subtraction is − and is read "minus," thus 10 − 7 is read "ten minus seven" or "seven from ten."

Rule—A. *Write down the sum so that the units stand under the units, the tens under the tens, etc., etc.*

B. *Begin with the units, and take the under from the upper figure, and put the remainder beneath the line.*

C. *But if the lower figure be the larger, add ten to the upper figure, and then subtract and put the remainder down—this borrowed ten must be deducted from the next column of figures where it is represented by 1.*

EXAMPLES FOR PRACTICE

$$
\begin{array}{r}
892 \\
46 \\
\hline
\end{array}
$$

846 remainder.

$$
\begin{array}{r}
89{,}672 \\
46{,}379 \\
\hline
\end{array}
$$

$$
\begin{array}{r}
89{,}642{,}706 \\
48{,}765{,}421 \\
\hline
\end{array}
$$

Symbol 🖝 X

Multiplication.—This process consists in finding the amount of one number increased as many times as there are units in another.

The number to be multiplied or increased is called the *multiplicand;* the number by which the multiplicant is multiplied is called the *multiplier;* and the result thus obtained, the *product.*

The multiplier and multiplicand which produce the product are called its *factors.* This is a word frequently used in mathematical works and its meaning should be remembered.

The sign of multiplication is $\times$ and is read "times" or multiplied by; thus 6×8 is read, 6 times 8 is 48, or, 6 multiplied by 8 is 48.

The principle of multiplication is the same as addition, thus $3 \times 8 = 24$ is the same as $8 + 8 + 8 = 24$.

Rule.—*Place the unit figure of the multiplier under the unit figure of the multiplicand and proceed as in the following examples:*

Example.—Multiply 846 by 8; and 478,692 by 143. Arrange them thus:

$$
\begin{array}{r}
846 \\
8 \\
\hline
6,768
\end{array}
\qquad
\begin{array}{r}
487,692 \\
143 \\
\hline
1463076 \\
1950768 \\
487692 \\
\hline
69,739,956
\end{array}
$$

Rule.—*If the multiplier have ciphers at its end, place it as in the following examples*:

Example.—Multiply 83567 by 50; and 898 by 2800.

$$
\begin{array}{r}
898 \\
2800 \\
\hline
718400 \\
\end{array}
$$

$$
\begin{array}{r}
83567 \\
50 \\
\hline
4{,}178{,}350 \\
\end{array}
\qquad
\begin{array}{r}
718400 \\
1796 \\
\hline
2{,}514{,}400 \\
\end{array}
$$

Symbol

Division.—*This operation consists in finding the value of one of a given number of equal parts into which a quantity is to be divided.*

When one number is divided by another number, the first one is called the *dividend*, and the second one, the *divisor*, the result thus obtained is called the *quotient*.

The sign of division is ÷ and is read "divided by," thus 8 ÷ 2 is read "eight divided by two."

There are two methods of division known as:

1. Short.
2. Long.

In the method of short division the continued subtraction is effected mentally, the quotient alone being set down without any working. Evidently this method is suitable only for small divisors, as 8 ÷ 2, 1,272 ÷ 12.

In the method of long division the operations are written down in full, the method being applied with large divisors of two or more figures as 13,765 ÷ 126. To apply short division with such a large divisor would involve too great a mental process.

1. *Short division.*

To divide by any number up to 12.

Rule.—*Put the dividend down with the divisor to the left of it, with a small curved line separating it, as in the following:*

Example.—Divide 7,865,432 by 6.

$$6)\overline{7,865,432}$$
$$1,310,905 — 2$$

Here at the last we have to say 6 into 32 goes 5 times and 2 over; always place the number that is over as above, as a fraction, thus, $^2/_6$ the top figure being the remainder and the bottom figure the divisor, when it should be put close to the quotient; thus 1,310,905 $^2/_6$.

To divide any number up to 12 with a cipher or ciphers after it as 20, 70, 500, 7,000, etc.

Rule.—*Place the sum down as in the last example, then mark off from the right of the dividend as many figures as there are ciphers in the divisor; also mark off the ciphers in the divisor; then divide the remaining figures by the number remaining in the divisor, thus:*

Example.—Divide 9,876,804 by 40.

$$40)\overline{9,876,804}$$
$$246,920 \; ^4/_{40}$$

2. *Long division.*

To divide any number by a large divisor of two or more figures.

Example.—Divide 18,149 by 56.

$$56)\overline{18149}(324\,^{5}/_{56}$$
$$\underline{168}$$
$$134$$
$$\underline{112}$$
$$229$$
$$\underline{224}$$
$$5$$

In the above operation the process is as follows: As neither 1 nor 18 will contain the divisor, take three figures 181, for the first *partial* dividend. 56 is contained in 181 three times, and a remainder. Write the B, as the first figure in the quotient, and then multiply the divisor by this quotient figure thus: 3 times 56 is 168, which when subtracted from 181 leaves 13. To this remainder annex or "bring down" 4 the next figure in the dividend thus forming 134, which is the next partial dividend. 56 is contained in 134 two times and a remainder. Thus 2 times 56 is 112, which subtracted from 134 leaves 22. To the remainder bring down 9 the last figure in the dividend, forming 229, the last partial dividend. 56 is contained in 229 four times and a remainder. Thus: $4 \times 56 = 224$, which, subtracted from 229, gives 5, the final remainder which write in the quotient with the division below it, thus completing the operation of long division.

Exact Divisor.—A *divisor which is contained into a dividend a whole number of times is called an exact divisor.*

Thus, 5 is contained into 20 four times and is an exact divisor. 6, for instance, is contained into 20 three times with 2 left over and is therefore not an exact divisor.

Factors.—By definition a factor is *one of two or more quantities which, when multiplied together produce a given quantity.*

Thus, 4 and 5 are factors of 20 because 4 multiplied by 5 equals 20.

A prime factor of a number is *one which cannot be separated into factors.*

Thus 4 is a factor of 20 but is not a prime factor because it is made up of two factors two and two; that is, $2 \times 2 = 4$.

Apply the following rule to obtain the prime factors of a given number.

Rule.—*Divide the given number by any prime factor; divide the quotient in the same manner, and so continue the division until the quotient is a prime number. The several divisors and the last quotient will be the prime factors required.*

Example.—What are the prime factors of 798?

$$
\begin{array}{r|r}
2 & 798 \\
3 & 399 \\
7 & 133 \\
19 & 19 \\
& 1
\end{array}
$$

Since the given number is even, divide by 2, and obtain the odd number 399 for a quotient. Then divide by the prime number 3, 7, and 19 as above the last quotient being 1. The divisions 2, 3, 7, and 19 then are the prime factors of 798.

Greatest Common Divisor.—By definition, the greatest common divisor of two or more numbers is *the greatest number that will exactly divide each of them.*

To find the greatest common divisor.

Rule.—**1.** *Write the numbers in a line, with a vertical line at the left, and divide by any factor common to all the numbers.* **2.** *Divide the quotient in like manner, and continue the dividend till a set of quotients is obtained that are prime to each other.* **3.** *Multiply all the divisors together and the product will be the greatest common divisor sought.*

Example.—What is the greatest common divisor of 72, 120 and 440?

```
4 | 72   120   440
2 | 18    30   110
      9    15    55
```

4 will exactly divide each of the given numbers, and 2, each of the quotients obtained by dividing by 4. The last quotients 9, 15 and 55 are prime to each other, hence greatest common divisor is $4 \times 2 = 8$.

Least Common Multiple.

Least Common Multiple.—By definition the least common multiple of two or more numbers is *the least number exactly divisible by those numbers*.

To find the least common multiple.

Rule.—1. *Resolve the given numbers into their prime factors.* **2.** *Multiply together all the prime factors of the largest number, and such prime factors of the other numbers as are not found in the largest number. Their product will be the least common multiple.* **3.** *When a prime factor is repeated in any of the given numbers it must be taken as many times in the multiple, as the greatest number of times it appears in any of the given numbers.*

Example.—Find the least common multiple of 60, 84 and 132.

$$60 = 2 \times 2 \times 3 \times 5$$
$$84 = 2 \times 2 \times 3 \times 7$$
$$132 = 2 \times 2 \times 3 \times 11$$
$$(2 \times 2 \times 3 \times 11) \times 5 \times 7 = 4,620$$

The factor 2 appears twice in each number, hence, applying **3,** of the rule it is written down in the least common multiple twice. By inspection the factors not found in the largest number are 7 and 5, these are written down as above together with the factors of 132, giving 4,620 the least common multiple.

Fractions.—By definition a fraction is *a quantity less than a unit.*

Fractions take their *name* and *value* from the *number* of parts into which the unit is divided. Thus, if the unit be divided into 2 equal parts, one of these parts is called *one-half*, as **M**, in fig. 1,231; if divided into 3 equal parts, one of these parts is called *one-third*, as **S**, in fig. 1,232.

Evidently from the figures one-half or **M** is larger than one-third or **S**.

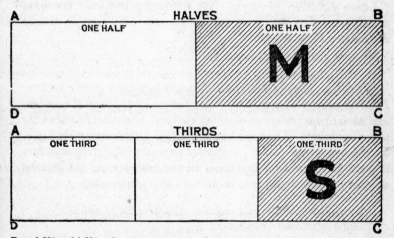

FIGS. 1,231 and 1,232.—Graphic representation of fractional parts. The figures show a rectangle ABCD, representing a unit divided into two equal parts or halves (fig. 1,231) and into three equal parts or thirds (fig. 1,232). Evidently the shaded section **M**, or one half is larger than the shaded section **S**, or one third.

To express a fraction by figures two numbers are required: one to express the number of parts into which the unit is divided and the other to express the number of these parts, making up the fraction.

The number expressing the number of parts taken called the *numerator* is written *above* a diagonal or horizontal line and that expressing the number of parts into which the unit is divided called the *denominator* is written below the line, thus:

| one-half | two-thirds | five-eighths | eleven-sixteenths |

is written

| ½ | ⅔ | ⅝ | $^{11}/_{16}$ |

The line as stated may be either diagonal or horizontal, thus one-half is written either ½ or ½. The horizontal line is more conveniently used where the numerator and denominator contain several figures as $\dfrac{256}{785}$

The terms of a fraction are the numerator and denominator taken together, and for convenience in calculation a fraction should be "reduced to its lowest terms" later explained.

Definitions

Complex Fraction.—One whose numerator or denominator is a fraction.

Compound Fraction.—A fraction of a fraction.

Improper Fraction.—One whose numerator equals or exceeds its denominator.

Partial Fractions.—Fractions where sum may be reduced to the original fraction.

Proper Fraction.—One whose numerator is less than its denominator.

Simple Fraction.—One whose numerator and denominator are whole numbers.

Vulgar Fraction.—One expressed by a numerator and denominator as distinguished from a decimal fraction.

The following general principles should be noted:

1. *A change in the numerator produces a like change in the value of the fraction.*

2. *Multiplying the denominator divides the fraction and dividing the denominator multiplies the fraction.*

3. *Multiplying or dividing both terms of the fraction by the same number does not alter the value of the fraction.*

To reduce a fraction to its lowest terms.

Rule.—*Divide both numerator and denominator by their greatest common divisor.*

Example.—Reduce $^{20}/_{40}$ to its lowest terms.

A Find greatest common divisor:

$$
\begin{array}{r|rr}
2 & 20 & 40 \\
\hline
2 & 10 & 20 \\
\hline
5 & 5 & 10 \\
\hline
& 1 & 2
\end{array}
$$

B Divide both terms by **greatest** common divisor:

$$\frac{20|20}{20|40} = \tfrac{1}{2}$$

$2 \times 2 \times 5 = 20$ greatest common divisor

Find the greatest common divisor 20 as at **A**, divide both **terms by 20** as at **B**, obtaining ½ which is the lowest terms of $^{20}/_{40}$.

To change an improper fraction to a mixed number.

Rule.—*Divide the numerator by the denominator.*

Example.—Change $^{49}/_{5}$ to a mixed number.

$$^{49}/_{5} = 49 \div 5 = 9\,^{4}/_{5}$$

To change a mixed number to an improper fraction.

Rule.—*Multiply the whole number by the denominator of the fraction; to the product add the numerator and place the sum over the denominator.*

Example.—Change $12\tfrac{5}{8}$ to an improper fraction.

multiply whole number by denominator $12 \times 8 = 96$
add the numerator $\underline{\hspace{1.2cm}5}$
sum 101

place sum over denominator $\dfrac{101}{8}$

To reduce fractions to a common denominator.

Rule.—*Multiply each numerator by all of the denominators* *except its own for the new numerator and all the denominators together for the common denominator.*

Example.—Reduce ½, ⅓ and ⅗ to a common denominator.

New numerator of first fraction $= 1 \times 3 \times 5 = 15$
New numerator of second fraction $= 1 \times 2 \times 5 = 10$
New numerator of third fraction $= 3 \times 3 \times 2 = 18$
Common denominator $= 2 \times 3 \times 5 = 30$

from which the fractions become

$$\frac{15}{30} \quad \frac{10}{30} \quad \frac{18}{30}$$

To add fractions.

Rule.—*Reduce them to a common denominator, add the numerators and place their sum over the common denominator.*

Example.—Add ½, ⅓ and ⅗

A Reduce to common denominator:

$1 \times 3 \times 5 = 15$
$1 \times 2 \times 5 = 10$
$3 \times 3 \times 2 = 18$
$2 \times 3 \times 5 = 30$

B Add numerators:

15
10
18
43 (sum)

C Place sum over common denominator:

$$\frac{43}{30}$$

The sum of the fractions ($^{43}/_{30}$) is an improper fraction, hence, reduce to mixed number.

$$^{43}/_{30} = 43 \div 30 = 1\,^{13}/_{30}$$

To subtract fractions.

Rule.—*Reduce them to a common denominator, subtract the numerators and place the difference over the common denominator.*

Example.—Subtract $^{3}/_{7}$ from $^{4}/_{5}$.

A Reduce to common denominator

$3 \times 5 = 15$
$4 \times 7 = 28$
$7 \times 5 = 35$

B Subtract the numerators

28
15
13 (difference)

C Place difference over the common denominator

$$\frac{13}{35}$$

To multiply fractions.

Rule.—(*Case I. Multiplying by a whole number.*) *Multiply the numerator or divide the denominator by the whole number.*

Example.—Multiply $7/12$ by 4.

A Multiplying numerator
$$7/12 \times 4 = 28/12 = 2\,4/12 = 2\tfrac{1}{3}$$

B Dividing denominator
$$7/12 \times 4 = 7/3 = 2\tfrac{1}{3}$$

Rule.—(*Case II. Multiplying by a fraction.*) *Multiply the numerators for a new numerator and the denominators for a new denominator.*

Example.—Multiply $3/4$ by $5/7$.

$$3/4 \times 5/7 = \frac{3 \times 5}{4 \times 7} = \frac{15}{28}$$

Division of fractions.

Rule.—(*Case I. Dividing by a whole number.*) *Divide the numerator, or multiply the denominator by the whole number.*

Example.—Divide $10/13$ by 5.

A Dividing numerator
$$10/13 \div 5 = 2/13$$

B Multiplying denominator
$$10/13 \div 5 = 10/65 = 2/13$$

Rule.—(*Case II. Dividing by a fraction.*) *Invert the divisor and proceed as in multiplication.*

Example.—Divide $3/4$ by $5/7$.

A Invert divisor
$5/7$ inverted is $7/5$

B Multiply by inverted divisor
$$3/4 \times 7/5 = 21/20 = 1\tfrac{1}{20}$$

The two operations are expressed thus:

$$3/4 \div 5/7 = 3/4 \times 7/5 = 21/20 = 1\,1/20$$

Symbol 👉 ● (decimal point)

Decimal Fractions.—A decimal fraction is *one or more of the decimal divisions of a unit*.

The word decimal means *ten* and decimal fractions are usually called simply *decimals*. In the formation of a fraction a single unit is divided into 10 parts as in fig. 1,233.

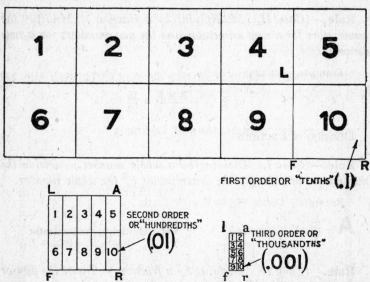

FIRST ORDER OR "TENTHS" **(.1)**

SECOND ORDER OR"HUNDREDTHS" **(.01)**

THIRD ORDER OR "THOUSANDTHS" **(.001)**

FIGS. 1,233 to 1,235.—Graphic representation of decimal fractions. Fig. 1,233, a unit divided into ten parts—1st order or "tens"; fig. 1,234 one of the "tens" as LARF, divided into ten parts—2nd order or "hundredths"; fig. 1,235, one of the "hundredths" as *larf*, divided into ten parts—3rd order or thousandths. Similarly the process of division may be continued indefinitely.

Here the big rectangle or unit is divided into ten parts, then any one of these parts as LARF, is 1/10 of the unit. In the decimal system however it is not necessary to write the denominator because the same law of local value governs the decimals as the integral numbers. The *"decimal point"*

(.) is always placed before the decimal figures to distinguish them from integers.

The law of local value, for decimals assigns:

The first place at the right of the decimal point to 10ths—(1st order) the second place at the right of the decimal point to 100ths—(2nd order)

The third place at the right of the decimal point to 1,000ths—(3rd order)

Thus in fig. 1,233 LARF, or $^1/_{10}$ of the unit is written .1. Fig. 1,234, shows section LARF of fig. 1,233 divided into 10 parts. Evidently one of these parts is equal to one hundredth of the unit and is expressed as .01.

Similarly one of the ten parts of *larf* (fig. 1,235) is equal to one thousandth of the unit and is expressed as .001. Evidently if several of the parts were taken they would be expressed for instance, as .2, .03, .009. The decimal may include parts of the several orders as .23. .145, etc.

Any decimal or combination of a decimal and integer may be read by applying the following table:

Numeration of Decimals

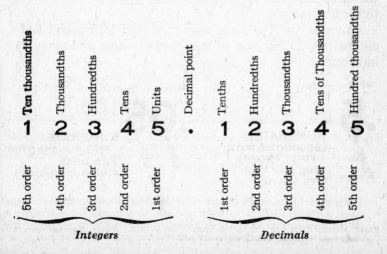

Ten thousandths	Thousandths	Hundredths	Tens	Units	Decimal point	Tenths	Hundredths	Thousandths	Tens of Thousandths	Hundred thousandths
1	2	3	4	5	•	1	2	3	4	5
5th order	4th order	3rd order	2nd order	1st order		1st order	2nd order	3rd order	4th order	5th order
Integers						*Decimals*				

There are several methods of numerating or reading decimals; one method is to *numerate* **toward** *the decimal point numerating each figure and the decimal point* as shown in figs. 1,236 and 1,237. A second method, numerating *from* the decimal point (beginning with the first order), is shown in figs. 1,238 and

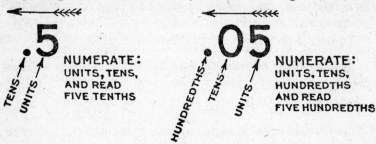

FIGS. 1,236 and 1,237.—How to read decimals (*first method*).   *Rule.— Numerate toward the decimal point (units, tens, hundredths, etc.; numerating each order and the decimal point.*

1,239. It is immaterial which method be used, the result is the same although some theoretical highbrows might object to the first method.

A number may be made up of one or more integers and a decimal as 23.35; this is read twenty-three and thirty-five hundredths.

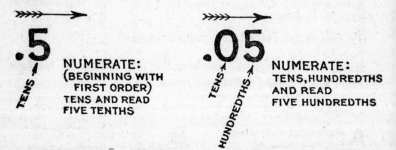

FIGS. 1,238 and 1,239.—How to read decimals (*second method*).   *Rule.— Numerate from the decimal point, beginning with the first order "tens".*

The practice of putting a cipher to the left of the decimal when there is no integer, as, for instance, 0.5, is unnecessary.

The important thing about decimals is to *always plainly put down the decimal point.* And in case of a column of figures as in addition, care should be taken to have all the decimal points exactly under each other.

To reduce decimals to a common denominator:

Rule.—*Annex ciphers after each decimal so that each will have the same number of figures or places thus:*

$$
\left.\begin{matrix} .5 \\ .27 \\ .325 \end{matrix}\right\}
\quad \begin{matrix} \text{annexing ciphers} \\ \text{for same number} \\ \text{of places become} \end{matrix} \quad
\left\{\begin{matrix} .500 \\ .270 \\ .325 \end{matrix}\right.
$$

that is to say

$$
\left.\begin{matrix} .5 &=& .500 \\ .27 &=& .270 \\ .325 &=& .325 \end{matrix}\right\}
\text{ which is read }
\left\{\begin{matrix} \text{five tenths} = \text{five hundred thousandths} \\ \text{twenty-seven hundredths} = \text{two hundred} \\ \text{and seventy thousandths.} \\ \left.\begin{matrix} \text{three hundred} \\ \text{and twenty-five} \\ \text{thousandths.} \end{matrix}\right\} = \left\{\begin{matrix} \text{three hundred} \\ \text{and twenty-five} \\ \text{thousandths.} \end{matrix}\right. \end{matrix}\right.
$$

in other words *adding ciphers after a decimal does not change its value.* This is apparent from figs. 1,240, to 1,242. The practice of adding ciphers after decimals is quite unnecessary except perhaps in a very large column of figures to be added.

To reduce a decimal to a common fraction.

Rule.—*Write down the denominator and reduce the common fraction thus obtained to its lowest terms.*

Example.—Reduce .25 to a common fraction.

A Write down denominator

$$.25 = \frac{25}{100}$$

B Reduce to lowest terms

$$5 \overline{\smash{\big)}\,\frac{25}{100}} = \frac{5}{20} \quad 5 \overline{\smash{\big)}\,\frac{5}{20}} = \frac{1}{4}$$

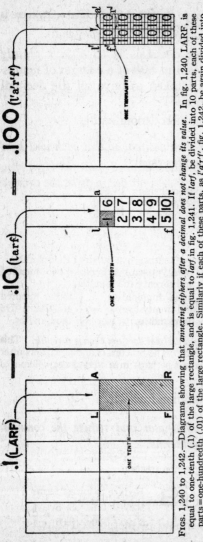

FIGS. 1,240 to 1,242.—Diagrams showing that *annexing ciphers after a decimal does not change its value.* In fig. 1,240, LARF, is equal to one-tenth (.1) of the large rectangle, and is equal to *larf* in fig. 1,241. If *larf*, be divided into 10 parts, each of these parts = one-hundredth (.01) of the large rectangle. Similarly if each of these parts, as *l'a'r'f'*, fig. 1,242, be again divided into 10 parts, each of the parts thus obtained = one-thousandth (.001) of the large rectangle. Hence .1 = .10 = .100.

To add decimals.

Rule. — *Place the numbers in a column with the decimal points under each other and add as in whole numbers*

To subtract decimals.

Rule. — *Place the numbers so that the decimal points are under each other and proceed as in simple subtraction.*

Examples.

Addition

```
  . 5
  .25
 1.75
─────
 2.50
```

Subtraction

```
 1.25
  .72
─────
  .53
```

To multiply decimals.

Rule.—*Proceed as in simple multiplication and point off as many places as there are in multiplier and multiplicand.*

Thus

$$.1 \times .0025 = .00025$$

Here there is one place in multiplicand and four in multiplier, or five altogether.

To divide decimals.

Rule.—*Proceed as in simple division, and from the right hand of the quotient point off as many places for decimals as the decimal places in the dividend exceed those in the divisor.*

Examples.

$$1.50 \div .25 = 6.$$
$$.10 \div .3 = .3(+)$$

To reduce common fractions to decimals.

Rule.—*Divide the numerator by the denominator and carry out the division to as many decimal places as desired.*

Examples.

$^4/_5$ to decimal
```
    4
  5)4.0
    .8
```

$^5/_8$ to decimal
```
    5
  8)5.000
    .625
```

The table of decimal equivalents on page 454 of common fractions will be found very useful especially in problems of the steel square.

Fractional Inch Decimal Equivalent

All the eights equivalents should be memorized thus:

8ths

Fraction	1/8	2/8	3/8	4/8	5/8	6/8	7/8
Decimal	.125	.25	.375	.5	.625	.75	.875

FRACTIONS OF AN INCH, AND DECIMAL EQUIVALENTS

8ths	16ths	32nds	64ths	Decimal
			1/64	.015625
		1/32		.03125
			3/64	.046875
	1/16			.0625
			5/64	.078125
		3/32		.09375
			7/64	.109375
1/8				.125
			9/64	.140625
		5/32		.15625
			11/64	.171875
	3/16			.1875
			13/64	.203125
		7/32		.21875
			15/64	.234375
1/4				.250
			17/64	.265625
		9/32		.28125
			19/64	.296875
	5/16			.3125
			21/64	.328125
		11/32		.34375
			23/64	.359375
3/8				.375
			25/64	.390625
		13/32		.40625
			27/64	.421875
	7/16			.4375
			29/64	.453125
		15/32		.46875
			31/64	.484375
1/2				.500
			33/64	.515625
		17/32		.53125
			35/64	.546875
	9/16			.5625
			37/64	.578125
		19/32		.59375
			39/64	.609375
5/8				.625
			41/64	.640625
		21/32		.65625
			43/64	.671875
	11/16			.6875
			45/64	.703125
		23/32		.71875
			47/64	.734375
3/4				.750
			49/64	.765625
		25/32		.78125
			51/64	.796875
	13/16			.8125
			53/64	.828125
		27/32		.84375
			55/64	.859375
7/8				.875
			57/64	.890625
		29/32		.90625
			59/64	.921875
	15/16			.9375
			61/64	.953125
		31/32		.96875
			63/64	.984375
				1.0000

Compound Numbers.—A compound number expresses *units of two or more denominations of the same kind*, as five yards, one foot and four inches.

The process of changing the denomination in which a quantity is expressed without changing its value is called *reduction*.

Thus 1 yard and 2 ins. = 38 ins., or 25 inches = 2 feet and 1 inch, are examples of reduction. Problems of reduction occur and are explained with the various measures and weights.

Measures.—By definition a measure is *that by which the extent, quantity, capacity, volume or dimensions in general is ascertained by some fixed standard.* There are several kinds of measure as:

1. Linear (length).
2. Square (area).
3. Cubic (volume).
4. Weight.
5. Time.
6. Angular.

etc.

Linear Measure.—There are several kinds of linear measure known as: 1, long; 2, surveyors' or land; 3, nautical.

TABLE

Long Measure

12 inches (ins. or ″) make 1 foot
3 feet make 1 yard (yd.)
5½ yards or 16½ feet make 1 rod (rd.)
40 rods make 1 furlong (fur.)
8 furlongs or 320 rods make 1 statute mile (mi.)

Unit equivalents

									ft.		ins.
				yd.	1			=	3	=	36
			rd.	1	=	5½	=	16½	=	198	
	fur.	1	=	40	=	220	=	660	=	7,920	
mi.	1	=	8	=	320	=	1,760	=	5,280	=	63,360

and yd. row: yd. 1 = 12 (ins)

Scale—ascending, 12, 3, 5½, 40, 8; descending, 8, 40, 5½, 3. 12.

To reduce a compound number to a lower denomination—
Reduction descending.

Rule.—*Multiply the highest denomination of the given number by that number of the scale will reduce it to the next lower denomination and add to the product the given number, if any, of that lower denomination, continuing until the number is reduced to the denomination required.*

Examples.—Reduce 1 yd., 8 ft. and 7 ins. to ins.

    1 yd. 8 ft. 7 ins.
      3 (scale factor 3 ft. = 1 yd.)
    —————
      3 ft.
      8 ft. to be added   **Reduction descending**
    —————
    11 ft.
    12 (scale factor 12 ins. = 1 ft.)
    —————
    132 ins.
      7 ins. to be added
    —————
    139 ins. total

To reduce a denominate number to a compound number **of** higher denominations—**Reduction ascending.**

Rule.—*Divide the denominate number by that number of the ascending scale which will reduce it to the next higher denomination; the quotient is in the higher denomination and the remainder if any, in the lower denomination. Continue the division until the number is reduced to the highest denomination required.*

Example.—Reduce 139 ins. to a compound number of higher denominations.

    $139 \div 12^* = 11$ ft., 7 ins.

————

*NOTE.—12 is scale number to reduce ins. **to** ft.

Reduction ascending

11 — 3 = 3* yds. 2 ft.

'NOTE.—3 is scale number to reduce ft. to yds.

Answer—3 yds. 2 ft. 7 ins.

In any of the measures which follow the compound numbers may be reduced by following the rules given above.

TABLE

Surveyors' or Old Land Measure

7.92 ins.	make 1 link (l.)
25 links	make 1 rod (rd.)
4 rods or 66 ft.	make 1 chain (ch.)
80 chains	make 1 mile (mi.)

Unit equivalents

				l.		ins.
		rd.	1	=		7.92
	ch.	1	=	25	=	198
mi.	1	=	4	=	100	=	792
1	=	80	=	320	=	8,000	=	63,360

Scale—ascending, 7.92, 25, 4, 80; descending, 80, 4, 25, 7.92.

NOTE.—The denomination *rods* is seldom used in chain measure, distances being taken in chains and links.

TABLE

Nautical Measure

6,080.26 ft. or 1.15156 statute miles = 1 nautical mile or knot*
3 nautical miles = 1 league
60 nautical miles or 69.168 statute miles = 1 degree (at the equator)
360 degrees = circumference of earth at equator

---

*NOTE.—The British Admiralty take the round figure 6,080 ft. for length of the "measured rule" in trials of vessels. The value varies from 6080.26 to 6088.44 ft. according to different measures of the earth's diameter. Some writers hold that the word *knot* should be used only to denote a rate of speed. The length between knots on the log line is $1/100$ of a nautical mile, or 50.7 feet when a half-minute glass is used; thus a speed of 10 knots is equal to 10 nautical miles per hour. A marine measure for ropes and cables is: 1 fathom = 6 ft; 1 cable's length = 120 fathoms.

Square Measure.—This kind of measure is used to measure the area of a surface; it involves two dimensions, length and breadth, that is:

$$\text{area} = \text{length} \times \text{breadth}$$

The dimensions length and breadth may be taken in any denomination as inches, feet, yards, etc., but both must be

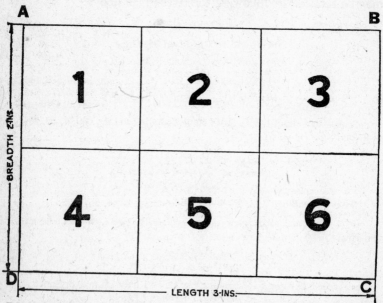

Fig. 1,243.—Diagram illustrating square measure. If the rectangle ABCD, measure 2 ins. on one side and 3 ins. on the other, and lines be drawn at each inch division, then each of the small squares will have an area of 1 sq. in. and the area of the rectangle will be area ABCD = breadth × length = 2 × 3 = 6 sq. ins.

taken in the same denominations. The word "square" is used to denote the product of the two dimensions, thus:

inches (length) × inches (breadth) = **square** *inches*

Square measure is shown graphically in fig. 1,243.

TABLE
Square Measure

144 square inches (sq. ins.) make 1 square foot (sq. ft.)
9 sq. ft. make 1 square yard (sq. yd.)
30¼ sq. yds. make 1 square rod or perch (sq. rd. or P.)
40 rods make 1 rood (R)
4 roods make 1 acre (A)
640 acres make 1 square mile (sq. mi.)

Unit equivalents

						sq. yd.		sq. ft.		sq. ins.
								1	=	144
						1	=	9	=	1,296
		sq. rd.		1	=	30¼	=	272¼	=	39,204
	R	1	=	40	=	1,210	=	10,890	=	1,568,160
	A	1 = 4	=	160	=	4,840	=	43,560	=	6,272,640
sq. mi.	1	=640	=2,560	=102,400	=3,097,600	=27,878,400	=	4,014,489,600

Scale—ascending, 144, 9, 30¼, 40, 4, 640; descending, 640, 4, 40, 30¼, 9, 144.

TABLE
Surveyors' Square Measure

625 square links (sq. l.) make 1 pole (P)
16 poles make 1 square chain (sq. ch.)
10 square chains make 1 acre (A)
640 acres make 1 square mile (sq. mi.)
36 square miles (6 miles square make 1 township (Tp.)

Unit equivalents

						P.
				sq. ch.		1 = 625
		A		1	=	16 = 10,000
	sq. mi.	1	=	10	=	160 = 100,000
Tp.	1	= 640	=	6,400	=	102,400 = 64,000,000
1	=	36	=23,040	=230,400	=3,686,400	=2,304,000,000

Scale—ascending, 625, 16, 640, 36; descending, 36, 640, 10, 16, 625.

Cubic Measure.—This measure is used to find the volume or

NOTE.—The denomination *rood* is practically obsolete. An acre equals a square whose side is 208.71 feet.

amount of space within the boundary surfaces of a cube or body having six equal square sides. It involves three dimensions, that is:

$$\text{volume} = \text{length} \times \text{breadth} \times \text{thickness}$$

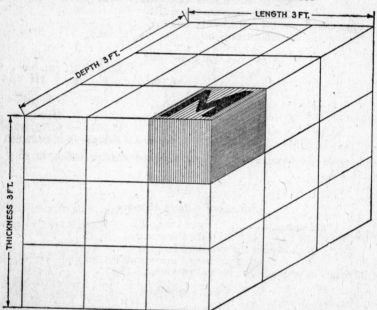

Fig. 1,244.—Diagram illustrating cubic measure. If each side of the cube measure 3 ft. and it be cut as indicated by the lines, each little cube as **M**, will have each of its sides 1 ft. long and will contain $1 \times 1 \times 1 = 1$ cu. ft. Accordingly the large cube will contain $3 \times 3 \times 3 = 27$ cu. ft. or 1 cu. yd.

As in square measure these dimensions may be taken in any denomination but all must be of the same denomination.

The word "cubic" is used to denote the product of the three dimensions, thus:

inches (length) × inches (breadth) × inches (thickness) = *cubic inches*

Cubic measure is shown graphically in fig. 1,244.

TABLE

Cubic Measure

1,728 cubic inches (cu. in.) make 1 cubic foot (cu. ft.)

27 cubic feet make 1 cubic yard (cu. yd.)

40 cubic feet of round timber or ⎱ make 1 ton or load (T)
5 cubic feet of hewn timber ⎰

16 cubic feet make 1 cord foot (cd. ft.)

8 cord feet or ⎱ make 1 cord of wood (Cd.)
128 cubic feet ⎰

24¾ cubic feet make 1 perch of stone masonry or (Pch.)

Scale—Most of the unit equivalents are fractional except 1,728 and 27, and are therefore omitted.

There are other kinds of cubic measure known collectively as measures of capacity. These are divided into two classes:

1. Liquid.
2. Dry.

Liquid measure also known as wine measure is used in measuring various liquids as water, molasses, liquors, etc.

TABLE

Board Measure

1 board 1 in. thick × 1 ft. wide × 1 ft. long = 1 ft. board measure (B. M.)
1 board 2 in. thick × 1 ft. wide × 1 ft. long = 2 ft. board measure
1 board ½ in. thick × 1 ft. wide × 1 ft. long = 1 ft. board measure

etc.

from which follows

Board Measure Rule.—*Multiply length in ft. by width in ft. of the board and multiply this product by 1 for board an inch or less than an inch in thickness, and by the thickness in inches and fractions of an inch for board over 1 in. in thickness.*

Example.—How many feet board measure (B. M.) in a board 12 ft. long by 18 ins. wide by ½ in. thick?; by 1¾ in. thick?

$$18 \text{ ins.} = 18 \div 12 = 1\frac{1}{2} \text{ ft.}$$

board ½ in. thick $= 12 \times 1\frac{1}{2} \times 1 = 18$ ft. B. M.
board 1¾ in. thick $= 12 \times 1\frac{1}{2} \times 1\frac{3}{4}$
$$= 12 \times 1.5 \times 1.75 = 31.5 \text{ ft. B. M.}$$

TABLE

Liquid measure

4 gills (gi.)	make 1 pint (pt.)
2 pints	make 1 quart (qt.)
4 quarts	make 1 gallon (gal.)*
31½ gallons	make 1 barrel (bbl.)
2 barrels or 63 gallons	make 1 hogshead (hhd.)

Unit equivalents

							pt.		gi.
				qt.		1	=	4
			gal.	1	=	2	=	8
		bbl.	1	=	4	=	8	=	32
	hhd.	1	=	31½	=	126	=	252	=	1,008
	1	=	2	=	63	=	252	=	504	=	2,016

Scale—ascending, 4, 2, 4, 31½, 2; descending, 2, 31½, 4, 2, 4.

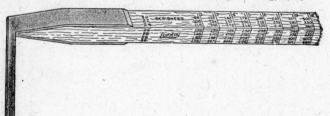

FIG. 1,245.—Lufkin Pacific coast log rule for large timber especially adapted to Pacific coast requirements, ⅛ in. square, and has 12 ins. forged steel hook (Seattle pattern). Marking is Scribner's scale for even length logs 20 to 48 ft. inclusive.

*NOTE.—There are two kinds of gallons: the U. S. gallon = 231 cu. ins.; the British Imperial gallon = 277.274 cu. ins.

Dry measure is used for measuring such articles as grain, salt, fruit, ashes, etc.

TABLE

Dry measure

2 pints (pt.) make 1 quart (qt.)
8 quarts   make 1 peck (pk.)
4 pecks   make 1 bushel (bu.)*

Unit equivalents

		qt.	pt.
pk.	1	=	2
bu.	1	= 8	= 16
1	= 4	= 32	= 64

Scale—ascending, 2, 8, 4: descending, 4, 8, 2.

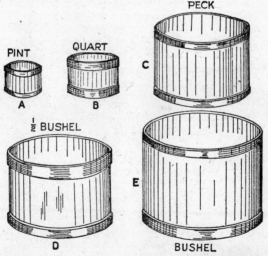

FIGS. 1,246 to 1,250.—Various dry measure containers. **A,** pint; **B,** quart; **C,** peck; **D,** ½ bushel; **E,** bushel basket.

*NOTE.—The standard U. S. bushel is the Winchester bushel, which is, in cylinder form, 18½ ins. in diameter and 8 ins. deep; it contains 2150.42 cu. ins. A struck bushel contains 2150.42 cu. in. or 1.2445 cu. ft. A heaped bushel is a cylinder 18½ ins. in diameter and 8 ins. deep, with a heaped cone not less than 6 ins. high. The British Imperial bushel = 8 imperial gallons = 2218.192 cu. ins. or 1.2837 cu. ft.

Measures of Weight.—By definition, weight is *the measure of the force with which bodies tend toward the earth's center; the downward pressure due to gravity minus the centrifugal force due to the earth's rotation.* Weight differs from gravity in being the effect of gravity or the downward pressure of a body under the influence of gravity. Weight is *the measure of the quantity of matter a body contains.* Three scales of weight are used in the U.S.:

1. Troy (for weighing gold silver, etc.).

2. Apothecaries (used by druggists in compounding medicines).

3. Avoirdupoise (for all ordinary purposes).

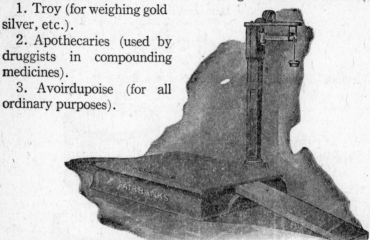

Fig. 1,251.—Fairbanks platform scale with incline brackets especially adapted to weighing wheelbarrow loads or for general use. The brackets cast on the ends of the frame form rests for incline planks so that the wheelbarrow loads may be easily run on and off the scale.

Fig. 1,252.—Fairbanks wagon scale especially adapted for weighing wagon loads.

TABLE

Avoirdupois weight

16 drachms (dr.) or 437.5 grains (gr.)	make 1 ounce (oz.)
16 ounces	make 1 pound (lb.)
100 pounds	make 1 hundred weight (cwt.)
2,000 pounds	make 1 short ton
2,240 pounds	make 1 long ton

Unit equivalents

						oz.		dr.
				lb.	1	=		16
			cwt.	1	=	16	=	256
	T.	1	=	100	=	1,600	=	25,600
1	=	20	=	2,000	=	32,000	=	512,000

Scale—ascending, 16, 16, 100, 20; descending, 20, 100, 16, 16.

Long ton Table

28 lbs.	make 1 quarter (qr.)
4 quarters	make 1 hundred weight (cwt.)
20 hundred weight	make 1 ton (T.)

				gr.		lbs.
		cwt.	1	=	28
	T. =	1	=	4	=	112
1	=	20	=	80	=	2,240

Scale—ascending, 28, 4, 20; descending, 20, 4, 28.

Time Measure.—By definition time is *a measure of duration.* The unit is ordinarily the day. The *civil* day begins at midnight and the *astronomical* day (used by astronomers in dating events) at noon. The civil year is composed of civil days.

NOTE.—Formerly, 112 pounds, or 4 quarters of 28 pounds each, were reckoned a hundredweight, and 2240 pounds a ton, now called the long ton. This is now seldom employed in this country, except *at the mines for coal,* or at the United States Custom-houses for goods imported from Great Britain, in which country such weight continues to be used.

TABLE

Time

60 seconds (sec.″)	make 1 minute (min.′)
60 minutes	make 1 hour (hr.)
24 hours	make 1 day (da.)
365 days	make 1 common year (yr.)
366 days	make 1 leap year
12 calendar months	make 1 year
100 years	make 1 century (C.)

Unit equivalents

				min.		sec.
			hr.	1	=	60
		da.	1	= 60	=	3,600
	wk.	1	= 24	= 1,440	=	86,400
	1 =	7	= 168	= 10,080	=	604,800
yr.	mo.	{ 365	= 8,760	= 525,600	=	31,536,000
1 = 12 =	{ 366	8,784	= 527,040	= 31,622,400		

Scale—ascending, 60, 60, 24, 7; descending, 7, 24, 60, 60.

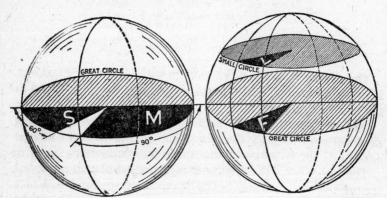

FIGS. 1,253 and 1,254.—Globes illustrating circular measure. Fig. 1,253 shows a great circle, or circle passing through the center of the globe. In contrast with this is the small circle shown in fig. 1254. In circular measure each of these circles is divided into 360°. Fig. 1,253 shows a quadrant M, made up of two radii and a 90° arc, also a sextant S, measured with a 60° arc. Note in fig. 1,253, the angles L, and F, are the same and accordingly have the same number of degrees, but the length of each degree of L, is less than that of F.

Circular Measure.—This measure is used in astronomy, surveying, geography and in navigation. In principle, every circle great or small (see figs 1,253 and 1,254) is divisible into the same number of parts as degree minutes, etc., hence the parts of different circles although having the same names, are of different lengths. The value of angles is stated in terms of this measure:

TABLE

Circular measure

60 seconds (")	make 1 minute (')
60 minutes	make 1 degree (°)
30 degrees	make 1 sign (S)
360 degrees	make 1 circle (C)

Unit equivalents

				1	=	60	
S		1	=	60	=	3,600	
C	1	30	=	1,800	=	108,000	
1	= 12	= 360	=	21,600	=	1,296,000	

Scale—ascending, 60, 60, 30, 12; descending, 12, 30, 60, 60.

The Metric System.—This system was adopted in France in 1795 and its use was authorized in Great Britain in 1864, and in the United States in 1866.

The important feature of the metric is that it is based upon the decimal scale, hence, the student should first acquire a knowledge of decimals before taking up the metric system.

The *meter* is the base or unit of the system and is defined the one ten-millionth part of the distances on the earth's surface from the equator to either pole. Its value in inches should be remembered.

1 meter = 39.37079 ins.

It must be apparent that the meter is used like the yard in measuring cloths and short distances.

Units of other denominations are named by prefixing to the word *meter* the Latin numerals for the lower denominations and Greek numerals for the higher denominations.

Lower denomination		*Higher denomination*	
Deci	= $1/10$	Decka	= 10
Centi	= $1/100$	Hecto	= 100
Milli	= $1/1000$	Kilo	= 1,000
		Myria	= 10,000

Thus one decimeter = $1/10$ of a meter; 1 millimeter = one-thousandth of of a meter and one kilometer = one-thousand meters. From this the linear table which follows is easily understood.

Metric Table of Linear Measure

Metric Denomination		*Meter*		U. S. value
	1 millimeter =	.001	=	.0394 in.
10 millimeters	= 1 centimeter =	.01	=	.3937 in.
10 centimeters	= 1 decimeter =	.1	=	3.937 in.
10 decimeters	= 1 *meter* =	1.	=	39.3707 ins.
10 meters	= 1 dekameter =	10.	=	32.809 ft.
10 dekameters	= 1 hectometer =	100.	=	328.09 ft.
10 hectometers	= 1 kilometer =	1,000.	=	.62138 mi.
10 kilometers	= 1 myriameter =	10,000.	=	6.2138 mi.

The kilometer is commonly used for measuring long distances. The square meter is the unit for measuring ordinary surfaces; as flooring, ceilings, etc.

Metric Table of Square Measure

100 sq. millimeters (sq. mm.)	= 1 sq. centimeter	=	.155+ sq. in.
100 sq. centimeters (sq. cm.)	= 1 sq. decimeter	=	15.5 + sq. in.
100 sq. decimeters (sq. dm.)	= 1 sq. meter (sq. m.)	=	1.196+ sq. yd.

The acre is the unit of land measure, and is a square whose side is 10 meters, equal to a square dekameter, or 119.6 sq. yds.

Metric Table of Land Measure

1 centiare (ca.)	= (1 sq. meter)	=	1.196034 sq. yd.
100 centiares (ca.)	= 1 are	=	119.6034 sq. yd.
100 ares (A.)	= 1 hectare	=	2.47114 acres
100 hectares (ha.)	= 1 sq. kilometer	=	.3861 sq. mi.

The cubic meter is the unit for measuring ordinary solids; as excavations, embankments, etc.

Metric Table of Cubic Measure

1,000 cu. millimeters (cu. mm.)	= 1 cu. centimeter	= .061+ cu. in.
1,000 cu. centimeters (cu. cm.)	= 1 cu. decimeter	= 61.026+ cu. in.
1,000 cu. decimeters (cu. dm.)	= 1 cu. meter	= 35.316+ cu. ft.

The stere is the unit of wood or solid measure, and is equal to a cubic meter or .2759 cord.

Metric Table of Wood Measure

	1 decistere	= 3.531+ cu. ft.
10 decisteres (dst.)	= 1 stere	= 35.316+ cu. ft.
10 steres (st.)	= 1 dekastere (dst.)	= 13.079+ cu. yd.

The liter is the unit of capacity, both of liquid and of dry measures, and is a vessel whose volume is equal to a cube whose edge is one-tenth of a meter, equal to 1.05673 qt. liquid measure, and .9081 qt. dry measure.

Metric Table of Capacity

10 milliliters (ml.)	= 1 centiliter
10 centiliters (cl.)	= 1 deciliter
10 deciliters (dl.)	= 1 liter
10 liters (l.)	= 1 dekaliter
10 dekaliters (dl.)	= 1 hectoliter
10 hectoliters (hl.)	= 1 kiloliter, or stere
10 kiloliters (kl.)	= 1 myrialiter (ml.)

The hectoliter is the unit in measuring liquids, grain, fruit, and roots in large quantities.

1 myrialiter	= 10 cubic meters	= 283.72+ bu.	=2641.7+ gal.
1 kiloliter	= 1 cubic meter	= 28.372+ bu.	= 264.17 gal.
1 hectoliter	= $^1/_{10}$ cubic meter	= 2.8372+ bu.	= 26.417 gal.
1 decaliter	= 10 cu. dm.	= 9.08 quarts	= 2.6417 gal.
1 liter	= 1 cu. dm.	= .908 quart	= 1.0567 qt.
1 deciliter	= $^1/_{10}$ cu. dm.	= 6.1022 cu. in.	= .845 gil.
1 centiliter	= 10 cu. cm.	= .6102 cu. in.	= .338 fluid oz.
1 milliliter	= 1 cu. cm.	= .061 cu. in.	= .27 fluid dr.

The gram is the unit of weight, and equal to the weight of a cube of distilled water, the edge of which is one hundred of a meter, equal to 15.432 Troy grains.

Metric Table of Weight Measure

10 milligrams (mg.)	= 1 centigram	=	.15432+ gr. troy
10 centigrams (cg.)	= 1 decigram	=	1.54324+ gr. troy
10 decigrams (dg.)	= 1 gram	=	15.43248+ gr. troy
10 grams (g.)	= 1 dekagram	=	.35273+ oz. avoir.
10 dekagrams (Dg.)	= 1 hectogram	=	3.52739+ oz. avoir.
10 hectograms (hg.)	= 1 kilogram or kilo	=	2.20462+ lb. avoir.
10 kilograms (kg.)	=1 myriagram	=	22.04621+ lb. avoir.
10 myriagrams (Mg.) or 100 kilograms	= 1 quintal	=	220.46212+ lb. avoir.
10 quintals or 1,000 kilos	= 1 tonneau, or 1 ton	=	2204.62125+ lb. avoir.

Symbol 🖘 ⋮

Ratio.—By definition, *ratio is the relation of one number to another, as obtained by dividing the first number by the second.* Thus the ratio of 2 to 4 is expressed as 2 : 4, the symbol : being read "to" in the case of a ratio and "so is" in case of a proportion—it is equivalent to "divided by," hence:

$$2 : 4 = 2 = \tfrac{1}{2}$$

The first term of a ratio is the *antecedent* and the second term the *consequent* thus:

$$\text{antecedent} \quad \text{consequent}$$
$$2 \quad : \quad 4$$

Since a ratio is virtually a fraction it follows that *if both terms be multiplied or divided by the same number the value of the ratio is not altered.* Thus:

$$2 : 4 = 2 \times 2 : 4 \times 2 = 2 \div 2 : 4 \div 2$$

Rule.—*Two quantities of* **different** *kinds cannot form the terms of a ratio.*

Thus no ratio can exist between $5 and 1 day, but can exist between $5 and $2, or between 1 day and 10 days.

Symbols 👉 ∷ or ══

Proportion.—When two ratios are equal, the four terms form a proportion. A proportion is therefore expressed by putting the sign = or ∷ between two ratios, thus:

$$\text{(expressed)} \quad 4 : 8 :: 2 : 4$$

$$\text{(read) as 4 is to 8 so is 2 to 4}$$

the same thing is also expressed, thus:

$$^4/_8 = {}^2/_4$$

The first and last terms of a proportion are called the *extremes* and the middle terms the *means*, thus:

$$\text{extremes} \quad \text{means} \quad \text{extremes}$$
$$4 : 8 \quad :: \quad 2 : 4$$

Rule.—*The product of the extremes equals the product of the means.*

Thus in the proportion

$$4 : 8 = 2 : 4$$

$$4 \times 4 = 8 \times 2$$

Since the equation is not altered by dividing both sides by the same number, the value of any term can be obtained thus:

$$\frac{4 \times 4}{4} = \frac{8 \times 2}{4}$$

$$\text{or } 4 = 2 \times 2 = 4$$

"Rule of Three."—When three terms of a proportion are given, the method of finding the fourth term is called the *"rule of three."*

Example.—If five bundles of shingles cost $16, what will 25 bundles cost?

Let X, represent the unknown term in the proportion, and, remembering that each ratio must be made up of quantities of like kind—that is, put dollars on one side of the equal sign and bundles on the other, thus:

$$5 \text{ bundles} : 25 \text{ bundles} = 16 \text{ ($)} : X \text{ ($)}$$

Multiplying extremes by means

$$5 \times X = 25 \times 16$$

$$X = \frac{25 \times 16}{5} = \$80$$

Symbol 👉 %

Percentage.—By definition, percentage means *rate per*

hundred, or, *proportion in a hundred parts*. Thus, $1/100$ of a number is called one per cent, $2/100$, 2 per cent. The symbol % is used for per cent, thus 1%, 2%.

Note carefully the following with respect to the symbol %

5% means $5/100$ which when reduced to a decimal (as is necessary in making a calculation) becomes .05, but .05% has a quite different value, thus

.05% means $^{.05}/_{100}$ which when reduced to a decimal becomes .0005, that is, $5/100$ of 1%.

Rule.—*If the decimal have more than two places, the figures that follow the hundredths place signify parts of* 1%.

> *Example.*—If the list price of Perfection shingles be $16 per 1,000, what is the net cost with 5% discount for cash?

A Reduce rate % to decimal
$5\% = {}^5/_{100} = .05$

B Multiply decimal by list price
$16 \times .05 = .80c$

C Subtract product obtained in B, from list price
$\$16 - .80c = \$15.20$

Symbol 🖝 Exponent

Powers of Numbers (Involution).—The word *involution* means *the multiplication of a quantity by itself any number of times*, and a *power* as here applied is the product arising from this multiplication.

Involution then is *the process of raising a number to a given power*. The "square" of a number is its second power; the "cube," its third power. Thus:

square of 2 = 2 × 2 = 4
cube of 2 = 2 × 2 × 2 = 8

The power to which a number is raised is indicated by a small "superior" figure called an "exponent." Thus:

ROOT EXPONENT   ROOT TAKEN TWO TIMES   POWER

$$2^2 = 2 \times 2 = 4$$

from which it is seen that the exponent indicates the number of times the number or "root" has been taken.

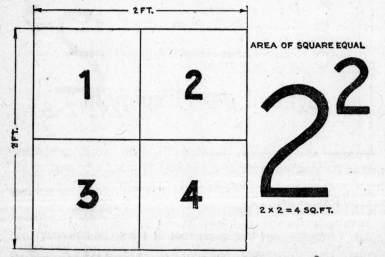

Fig. 1.255.—Two foot square illustrating the square of a number.

Symbol 👉 √

Roots of Numbers (Evolution).—The word *evolution* means *the operation of extracting a root.* The root here is a factor repeated to produce a power. Thus in the equation $2 \times 2 \times 2 = 8$, 2 is the root from which the power (8) is produced. This number is indicated by the symbol √ called the radical sign,

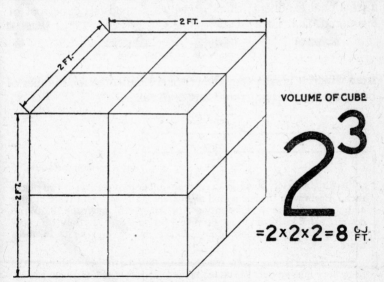

VOLUME OF CUBE

$$2^3$$

$$=2 \times 2 \times 2 = 8 \text{ CU. FT.}$$

Fig. 1,256.—Two foot cube illustrating the cube of a number.

which placed over a number means that the root of the number is to be extracted. Thus:

$\sqrt{4}$ means that the *square* root of 4 is to be extracted

The *index* of the root is a small figure placed over the radical sign which denotes what root is to be taken. Thus $\sqrt[3]{9}$ indicates the cube root of 9; $\sqrt[4]{16}$, the fourth root of 16. *When there is* **no index** *the radical sign alone always means the* **square root.**

Sometimes the number under the radical sign is to be raised to a power before extracting the root, thus:

$$\sqrt[3]{4^3} = \sqrt[3]{4 \times 4 \times 4} = \sqrt[3]{64} = 4$$

The power and the root are often combined and expressed as a fractional exponent, thus $8^{2/3}$ which is read the cube root of 8 squared, that is:

$$8^{2/3} = \sqrt[3]{8^2} = \sqrt[3]{64} = 4$$

Example.—Extract the square root of 186,624.

```
        18'66'24)432
        16
     83)266
        249
    862) 1724
         1724
```

From right to left point off the given number into periods of two places each. Begin with the last period pointed off (18). Largest square in 18 is 4; put this down in the quotient and the square (16) under the 18. Write down remainder (2) and bring down next period (66). Multiply 4 (in quotient) by 2 for first number of next divisor and say 8 goes into 26, three times.

Place 3 after 4 in quotient and also after 8 in the divisor. Multiply the 83 by 3, placing product 249 under 266 and subtract obtaining remainder 17. Bring down last period 24 and proceed as before, obtaining 432 as the square root of 186,624.

Extracting the cube root is a more complicated though similar process, as indicated by the rule following.

Rule.—*(Cube root).* **1.** *Separate the number into groups of* *three figures each, beginning at the units.* **2.** *Find the greatest cube in the left hand group and write its root for the first figure of the required root.* **3.** *Cube this root, subtract the result from the left hand group, and to the remainder annex the next group for a dividend.* **4.** *For a partial divisor, take three times the square of the root already found, considered as tens, and divide the dividend by it. The quotient (or the quotient diminished) will be the second figure of the root.* **5.** *To this partial divisor add three times the product of the first figure of the root considered as tens by the second figure, and also the square of the second figure. This sum will be the complete divisor.* **6.** *Multiply the complete divisor by the second figure of the root, subtract the product from the dividend, and to the remainder annex the next group for a new dividend.* **7.** *Proceed in this manner until all the groups have been annexed. The result will be the cube root required.*

2. GEOMETRY

By definition, geometry is *that branch of pure mathematics that treats of space and its relations.*

In other words, it is the science of the mutual relations of points, lines, angles, surfaces and solids, considered as having no properties except those arising from extension and difference of situation.

Lines.—There are two kinds of lines: straight and curved. A straight line is *the shortest distance between two points.* A curved line is *one which changes its direction at every point.* Two lines are said to be parallel *when they have the same direction.* A horizontal line is *one parallel to the horizon or surface of the water.* A line is perpendicular with another line *when it inclines no more to one side than the other.*

Angles.—An angle is *the difference in direction of two lines proceeding from the same point called the vertex.*

Angles are said to be, *right*, when formed by two perpendicular lines;

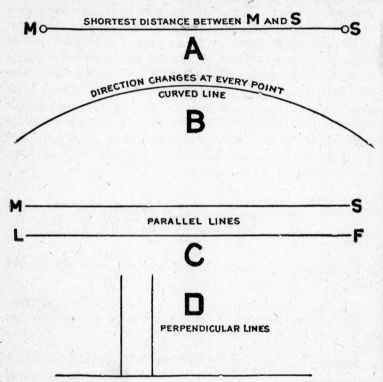

M○——————SHORTEST DISTANCE BETWEEN M AND S——————○S

A

DIRECTION CHANGES AT EVERY POINT
CURVED LINE

B

M————————————————————————————————S

PARALLEL LINES

L————————————————————————————————F

C

D

PERPENDICULAR LINES

FIGS. 1,257 to 1,260.—Various lines. **A,** straight; **B,** curved; **C,** parallel; **D,** perpendicular.

acute, when less than a right angle, and *obtuse,* when greater than a right. All angles except right (or 90°) angles are called *oblique* angles.

Angles are usually measured in degrees (circular measure).

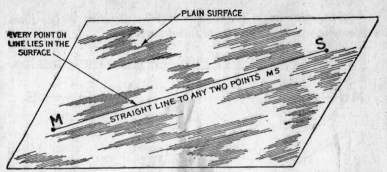

PLAIN SURFACE

EVERY POINT ON
LINE LIES IN THE
SURFACE

S.

STRAIGHT LINE TO ANY TWO POINTS MS

M

FIG. 1,261.—Proper conception of a "plane" or *plane surface*. A surface such that *every point on a straight line joining any two points in the surface, lies in the surface.*

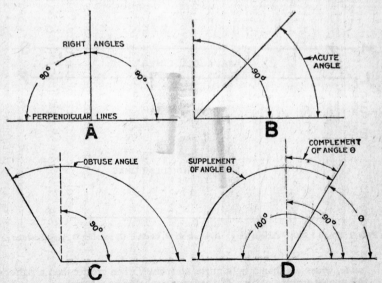

RIGHT ANGLES

90°   90°

PERPENDICULAR LINES

A

90°

ACUTE ANGLE

B

OBTUSE ANGLE

90°

C

SUPPLEMENT OF ANGLE θ

COMPLEMENT OF ANGLE θ

180°   90°   θ

D

FIGS. 1,262 to 1,265.—Various angles **A**, right, **B**, acute; **C**, obtuse; **D**, complement and supplement of an angle.

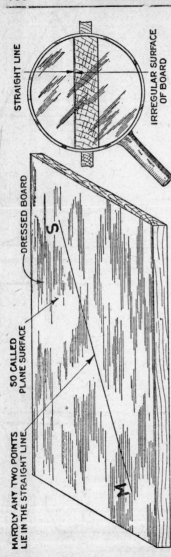

FIGS. 1,266 and 1,267.—Popular and erroneous conception of a plane or plane surface. The microscopic view, fig. 1,267, indicates that the surface is not plane or flat but is made up of a multiplicity of irregularities so that hardly any two points lie in a straight line joining any two points, as M and S.

The *complement* of an angle is the difference between 90° and the angle; the *supplement* of the angle, the difference between the angle and 180°. These relations are shown in figs. 1,262 to 1,265.

Plane Figures.—The term plane figures denotes *a plane surface bounded by straight or curved lines.* A proper conception of the term "plane" is essential. A plane or plane surface is *one such that any straight line joining any two points lies wholly in the surface.*

Fig. 1,261 defines a plane surface, and figs. 1,266 and 1,267 the ordinary and erroneous idea of such surface. There is a great variety of plane figures, known as *polygons* when their sides are straight lines. The sum of

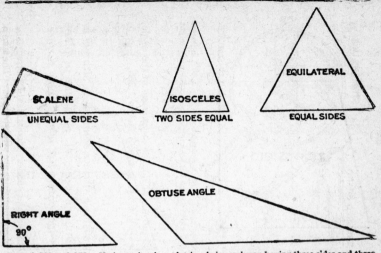

FIGS. 1,268 to 1,272.—Various triangles. A triangle is a polygon having three sides and three angles. By altering the angles and sides a great variety of triangles may be obtained.

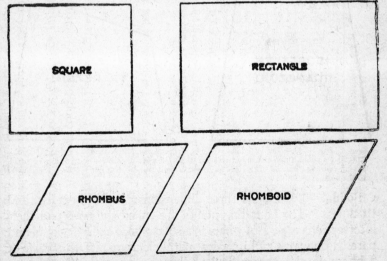

FIGS. 1,273 to 1,276.—Various quadrilaterals I. All sides parallel.

the sides is called the *perimeter*. A regular polygon has all its sides and angles equal. Plane figures of three sides are known as triangles; of four sides, *quadrilaterals*, etc. Various plane figures are formed of curved sides as *circles*, *ellipses*, etc.

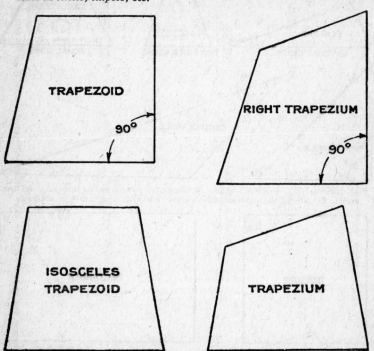

FIGS. 1,277 to 1,280.—Various equilaterals II. Trapezoids and trapeziums. A quadrilateral is called a *trapezoid* if two and only two sides be parallel; a *trapezium* if no two sides be parallel; an *isosceles trapezoid*, if the legs be equal; a right trapezoid, if one leg be perpendicular to the bases.

Solids.—These have three dimensions: length, breadth, and thickness. The bounding planes are called the *faces* and their intersections *edges*. A *prism* is a solid whose ends are equal and parallel polygons and its sides, parallelograms. The *altitude* of a prism is the perpendicular distance its opposite sides or

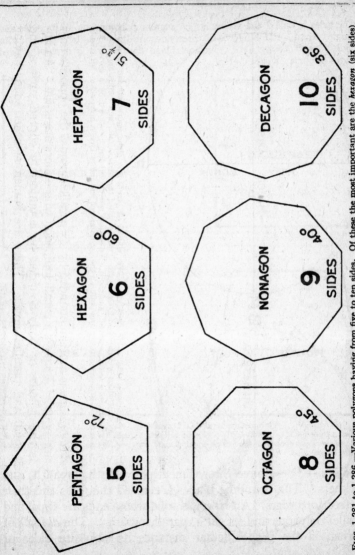

FIGS. 1,281 to 1,286.—Various polygons having from five to ten sides. Of these the most important are the *hexagon* (six sides) and the *octagon* (eight sides).

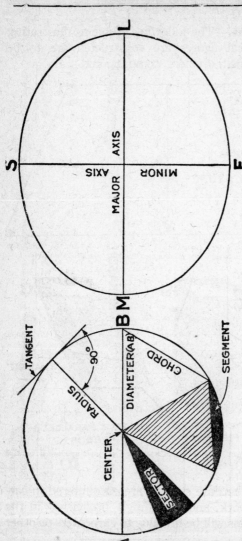

FIGS. 1,287 and 1,288.—Curved figures. Fig. 1,287, circle; fig. 1,288, ellipse. *A circle* is a plane figure bounded by a uniformly curved line, every point of which is equidistant from a point O within called the center. OR, is a radius and AB, a diameter. The figure also illustrates a sector, segment, and chord. *An ellipse* is a curved figure enclosed by a curved line which is such that the sum of the distances between any point on the circumference and the two foci is invariable. ML, major axis; SF, minor axis.

bases. A *parallelopipedon* is a prism bounded by six parallelograms, the opposite ones being parallel and equal. A *cube* is a parallelopipedon whose faces are equal. An important solid is the cylinder or body bounded by a uniformly curved surface and having its ends equal and parallel circles. There are numerous other solids having curved surfaces such as cones, spheres, etc.

Geometrical Problems.—The following problems illustrating how various geometrical figures are constructed are to be solved by the use of pencil, dividers, compass, and scale.

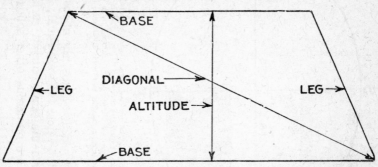

FIG. 1,289.—Quadrilateral illustrating legs, bases, etc. The parallel sides are the *bases;* the distance between the bases, the *altitude*, a line joining two opposite vertices, a *diagonal*.

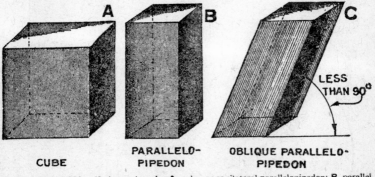

FIGS. 1,290 to 1,292.—Various prisms I. **A,** cube, or equilateral parallelopipedon; **B,** parallel opipedon; **C,** oblique parallelopipedon.

Many of these problems are such as are encountered in carpentry in laying out work, and according?y proficiency in the solution of such problems will be of value to carpenters or other wood workers.

Problem 1.—*To bisect or divide into two equal parts a straight line or arc of a circle.*

In fig. 1,296, from the ends A, B, as centers, describe arcs cutting each other at C, and D, and draw CD, which cuts the line at E, or the arc at F.

Problem 2.—*To draw a perpendicular to a straight line, or a radial line to an arc.*

In fig. 1,296, the line CD, is perpendicular to AB, moreover, the line CD, is radial to the arc AB.

PENTAGONAL PRISM   **TRIANGULAR PRISM**   **CYLINDER**

Figs. 1,293 to 1,295.—Various solids II. **A**, pentagonal prism; **B**, triangular prism; **C**, cylinder.

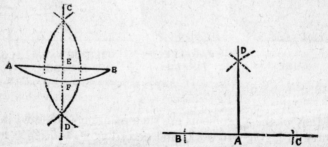

FIG. 1,296.—*Problem 1 To bisect a straight line or arc of a circle.*

FIG. 1,297.—*Problem 3. To erect a perpendicular to a straight line, from a given point in that line.*

Problem 3.—To erect a perpendicular to a straight line, from a given point in that line.

In fig. 1,297 with any radius from any given point A, in the line BC, describe arcs cutting the line at B and C. Next, with a longer radius describe arcs with B, and C, as centers, intersecting at D, and draw the perpendicular DA.

Second method.—In fig. 1,298, from any center F, above BC, describe a circle passing through the given point A, and cutting the given line at D; draw DF, and produce it to cut the circle at E; and draw the perpendicular AE.

Third method (boat builders' laying down method).—In fig. 1,929 let MS be the given line and A, the given point. From A, measure off a distance

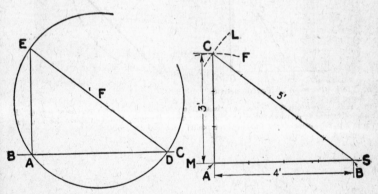

Fig. 1,298.—*Problem 3* Second method.

Fig. 1,299.—*Problem 3.* Third method (boat builder's laying down method).

AB, say 4 ft. With centers A, and B, and radii of 3 and 5 ft. respectively, describe arcs L, and F, intersecting at C. Draw a line through A and C, which will be the perpendicular required.

Fourth method.—In fig. 1,300, from A, describe an arc EC, and from E, with the same radius, the arc AC, cutting the other at C; through C, draw a line ECD, and set off CD, equal to CE, and through D, draw the perpendicular AD.

Problem 4.—*To erect a perpendicular to a straight line from any point without the line*

In fig. 1,301, from the point A, with a sufficient radius cut the given line at F, and G; and from these points describe arcs cutting at E. Draw the perpendicular AE.

Second method.—In fig. 1,302, from any two points BC, at some distance apart, in the given line, and with the radii BA, CA, respectively, describe arcs cutting at A and D. Draw the perpendicular AD.

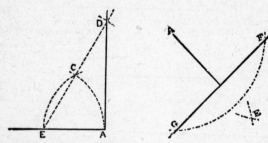

FIG. 1,300.—*Problem 3.* Fourth method.

FIG. 1,301.—*Problem 4. To erect a perpendicular to a straight line from any point without the line.* If there be no room below the line, the intersection may be taken above the line, that is to say, between the line and the given point.

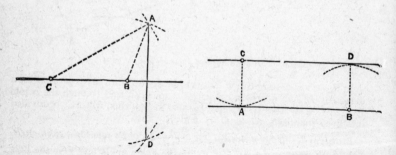

FIG. 1,302.—*Problem 4.*—Second method.

FIG. 1,303.—*Problem 5.*—*Through a given point to draw a line parallel to a given line.*

Problem 5.—*Through a given point to draw a line parallel to a given line.*

In fig. 1,303, with C, as center describe an arc tangent to the given line AB; the radius will then equal distance from given point to the given line. Take a point B, on line remote from C, and describe an arc. Draw a line through C, tangent to this arc and it will be parallel to the given line AB.

Second method.—In fig. 1,304, from A, the given point, describe the arc FD, cutting the given line at F; from F, with the same radius, describe the arc E, A, and set off FD, equal to EA. Draw the parallel through the points AD.

Problem 6.—*To divide a line into a number of equal parts.*

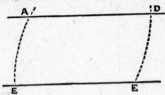

Fig. 1,304.—*Problem 5.* Second method.

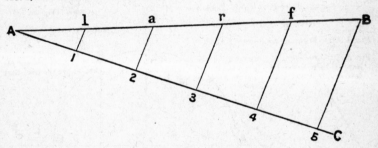

Fig. 1,305.—*Problem 6.* *To divide a line into a number of equal parts.*

In fig. 1,305, assuming line AB, is to be divided into say 5 parts, draw a diagonal line AC, of five units' length. Join BC, and through the points 1, 2, 3, 4, draw lines 1*l*, 2*a*, etc., parallel to BC, then will AC, be divided into five equal parts, A*l*, *la*, *ar*, *rf*, and *f*B.

Problem 7.—*Upon a straight line to draw an angle equal to a given angle.*

In figs. 1,306 and 1,307, let A, be the given angle and FG, the line. With any radius from the points A, and F, describe arcs DE, IH, cutting the sides of the angle A, and the line FG.

Set off the arc IH, equal to DE, and draw FH. The angle F, is equal to A, as required.

Problem 8.—*To bisect an angle.*

In fig. 1,308, let ACB, be the angle; with center C, describe an arc cutting the sides at A and B. On A, and B, as centers describe arcs cutting at D. A line through C and D will divide the angle into two equal parts.

Problem 9.—*To find the center of a circle.*

In fig. 1,309 draw any chord as MS. With M, and S, as centers and any radius, describe arcs L, F, and L′, F′, and a line through their intersection, giving a diameter AB. Applying same construction with centers A, and B,

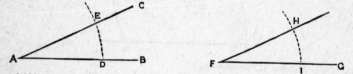

FIGS. 1,306 and 1,307.—**Problem 7.** *Upon a straight line to draw an angle equal to a given angle*

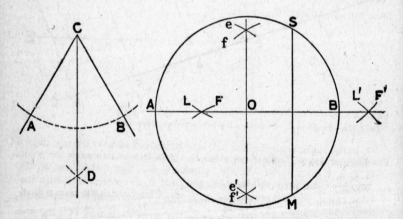

FIG. 1,308.—**Problem 8.** *To bisect an angle.*

FIG. 1,309.—**Problem 9.** *To find the center of a circle.*

describe arcs *lf*, and *l'f'*. A line drawn through the intersections of these arcs will cut AB, at O, the center of the circle.

Problem 10.—*Through two given points to describe an arc of a circle with a given radius.*

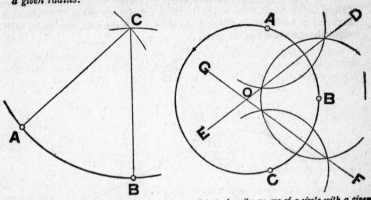

Fig. 1,310.—Problem 10. *Through two given points to describe an arc of a circle with a given radius.*

Fig. 1,311.—Problem 10. Second method.

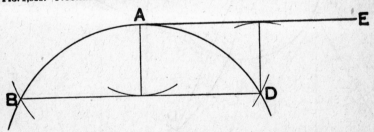

Fig. 1,312.—Problem 11. *To describe a circle passing through three given points.*

In fig. 1,310, take the given points A, and B, as centers, and, with the given radius, describe arcs cutting at C; and from C, with the same radius, describe an arc AB, as required.

Second method.—In fig. 1,311, for a circle or an arc, select three points ABC, in the circumference, well apart; with the same radius; describe arcs from these three points cutting each other, and draw two lines DE, FG, through their intersections. The point where they cut is the center of the circle or arc.

Problem 11.—To describe a circle passing through three given points.

In fig. 1,311, let A,B,C, be the given points and proceed as in last problem to find the center O, from which the circle may be described. This problem is useful in such work as laying out object of large diameter as an arch, when the span and rise are given.

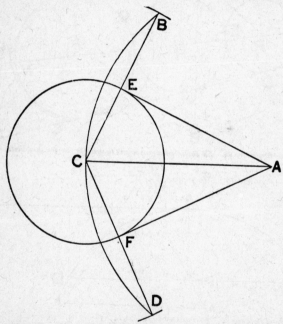

FIG. 1,313.—Problem 12. *To draw a tangent to a circle from a given point in the circumference of the circle.* **Problem 13.** *To draw tangents to a circle from points without.*

Problem 12.—To draw a tangent to a circle from a given point in the circumference.

In fig. 1,312, from A, set off equal segments AB, AD, join BD, and draw AE, parallel to it, for the tangent.

Problem 13.—*To draw tangents to a circle from points without.*

In fig. 1,313, from A, and with the radius AC, describe an arc BCD, and from C, with a radius equal to the diameter of the circle, cut the arc at BD; join BC, CD, cutting the circle at EF, and draw AE, AF, the tangents.

Problem 14.—*Between two inclined lines to describe a series of circles tangent to these lines and tangent to each other.*

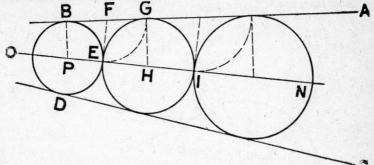

FIG. 1,314.—**Problem 14.** *To describe tangent circles tangent to two inclined lines.*

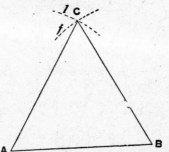

FIG. 1,315.—**Problem 15.** *To construct an equilateral triangle on a given base.*

In fig. 1,314, bisect the inclination of the given lines AB, CD, by the line NO. From a point P, in this line draw the perpendicular PB, to the line AB, and on P, describe the circle BD, touching the lines and cutting the center line at E. From E, draw EF, perpendicular to the center line, cutting AB, at F, and from F, describe an arc EG, cutting AB, at G. Draw GH, parallel to BP, giving H, the center of the next circle, to be described with the radius HE, and so on for the next circle IN.

Problem 15.—*To construct an equilateral triangle on a given base.*

In fig. 1,315, with A, and B, as centers and radius equal to AB, describe arcs *l* and *f*. At their intersection C, draw lines CA, and CB, sides of the required triangle. If the sides be unequal, the process is the same, taking for radii the lengths of the two sides to be drawn.

Problem 16.—*To construct a square on a given base.*

In figs. 1,316, with end points A, and B, of base as centers and radius equal to AB, describe arcs cutting at C; on C, describe arcs cutting the others at DE; and on D, and E, cut these at FG. Draw AFBG, and join the intersections HI.

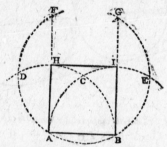

FIG. 1,316.—*Problem 16. To construct a square on a given base.*

Problem 17.—*To construct a rectangle on a given base.*

In fig. 1,316, let AB, be given base. Erect perpendicular at A and B, equal to altitude of the rectangle, and join their end D and C, by line DC, ABCD, is the rectangle required.

Problem 18.—*To construct a parallelogram having given the sides and an angle.*

In figs. 1,317 to 1,320, let A and B, be the given sides and HGI, the given angle. Draw DE, equal to A, and at D, an oblique line making with ED, the given angle HGI. On the oblique line lay off DF, equal to the given line B. With F, as center and radius equal to A, describe an arc *m*, and with E, as center and radius equal to B, describe another arc *s*, intersecting *m* at C. Draw FC and EC, completing the parallelogram. *Another method*. From the points E and F, draw lines parallel respectively to DF and ED, intersecting at C, completing the parallelogram.

Problem 19.—*To describe a circle about a triangle.*

In fig. 1,321, bisect two sides AB, AC, of the triangle at E and F, and from these points draw perpendiculars intersecting at K. From the center K, with the radius KA, describe the circle ABC.

Problem 20. *To circumscribe and inscribe a circle about a square.*

In fig. 1,323, draw the diagonals AB, and CD, intersecting at E. With radius EA, circumscribe the circle. To inscribe a circle let fall from the center (as just found) a perpendicular to one side of the square as OM, in fig. 1,323. With radius OM, inscribe the circle.

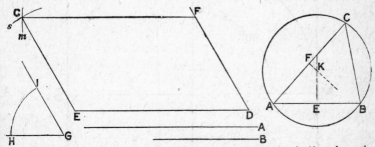

FIGS. 1,317 to 1,320.—*Problem 18. To construct a parallelogram having given the sides and an angle.*

FIG. 1,321.—*Problem 19. To describe a circle about a triangle.*

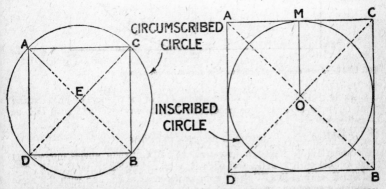

CIRCUMSCRIBED CIRCLE

INSCRIBED CIRCLE

FIGS. 1,322 and 1,323.—*Problem 20. To circumscribe (fig. 1,322) and inscribe (fig. 1,323) a circle about a square.*

Problem 21.—*To circumscribe a square about a circle.*

In fig. 1,324, draw diameters MS and LF, at right angles to each other. At the points M, L, S, F, where these diameters cut the circle, draw tangents that is, lines perpendicular to the diameter, thus obtaining the sides of the circumscribed square ABCD.

Problem 22.—*To inscribe a circle in a triangle.*

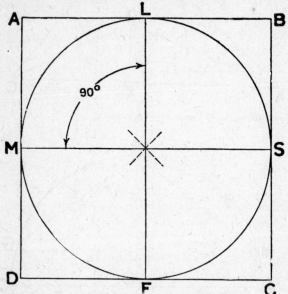

Fig. 1,324.—*Problem 21.—To circumscribe a square about a circle.*

In fig. 1,325, bisect two of the angles AC, of the triangle by lines cutting at D; from D, draw a perpendicular DE, to any side, and with DE, as radius describe a circle.

Problem 23.—*To inscribe a pentagon in a circle.*

In fig. 1,326, draw two diameters, AC, BD, at right angles intersecting at O; bisect AO, at E, and from E, with radius EB, cut AC, at F, and from B, with radius BF, cut the circumference at GH, and with the same radius step round the circle to I and K; join the points so found to form the pentagon.

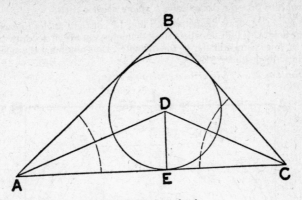

FIG. 1,325.—*Problem 22. To inscribe a circle in a triangle.*

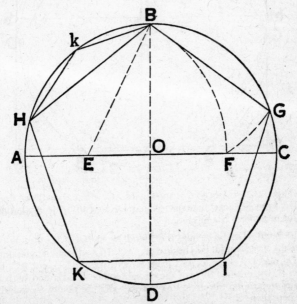

FIG. 1,326.—*Problem 23. To inscribe a pentagon in a circle.*

Problem 24.—*To construct a hexagon upon a given straight line.*

In fig. 1,327, from A and B, the ends of the given line describe arcs intersecting at g, from g; with the radius gA, describe a circle. With the same radius set off the arcs AG, GF and BD, DE. Join the points so found to form the hexagon.

Problem 25.—*To inscribe a hexagon in a circle.*

In fig. 1,328, draw a diameter ACB; from A and B, as centers with the

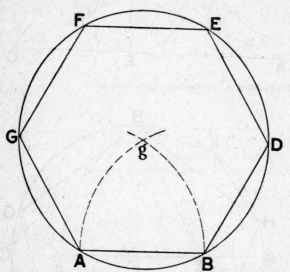

FIG. 1,327.—**Problem 24.** *To construct a hexagon upon a given straight line.*

radius of the circle AC, cut the circumference at D, E, F, G, and draw AD, DE, etc., to form the hexagon.

The points DE, etc., may be found by stepping the radius (with the dividers) six times round the circle.

Problem 26.—*To describe an octagon on a given straight line.*

In fig. 1,329, produce the given line AB, both ways, and draw perpendiculars AE, BF; bisect the external angles A and B, by the lines AH, BC, which make equal to AB. Draw CD and HG, parallel to AE and equal to

AB; from the center GD, with the radius AB, cut the perpendiculars at EF, and draw EF, to complete the hexagon.

Problem 27.—To inscribe an octagon in a square.

In fig. 1,330, draw the diagonals of the square intersecting at *e;* from the

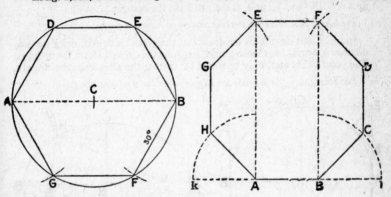

FIG. 1,328.—*Problem 25.—To inscribe a hexagon in a circle.*

FIG. 1,329.—*Problem 26.—To describe an octagon on a given straight line.*

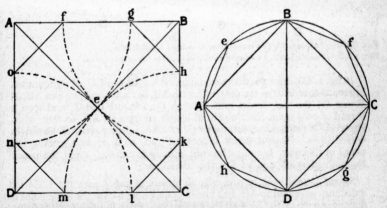

FIG. 1,330.—*Problem 27.—To inscribe an octagon in a square.*

FIG. 1,331.—*Problem 28. To inscribe an octagon in a circle.*

corners A,B,C,D, with A*e*, as radius, describe arcs cutting the sides at *g*, *h*, etc.; and join the points so found to complete the octagon.

Problem 28.—*To inscribe an octagon in a circle.*

In fig. 1,331, draw two diameters AC, BD, at right angles; bisect the arcs AB, BC and C, at *e*, *f*, etc., to form the octagon.

Problem 29.—*To circumscribe an octagon about a circle.*

In fig. 1,332, describe a square about the given circle AB, draw perpendiculars *h*, *k* and C to the diagonals, touching the circle, to form the octagon. The points *h*, *k*, etc., may be found by cutting the sides from the corners.

Problem 30.—*To describe an ellipse when the two axes are given.*

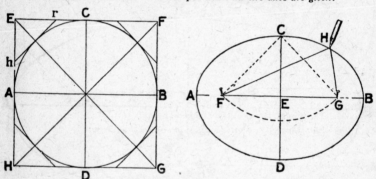

FIG. 1,332.—*Problem 29. To circumscribe an octagon about a circle.*
FIG. 1,333.—*Problem 30. To describe an ellipse when the two axes are given.*

In fig. 1,333, draw the major and minor axes AB and CD, at right angles, intersecting at E. On the center C, with AE, as radius, cut the axis AB, at F and G, the *foci;* insert pins through the axis at F and G, and loop a thread or cord upon them equal in length to the axis AB, so that when stretched it reaches the extremity C, of the *conjugate axis,* as shown in dotted lines. Place a pencil inside the cord, as at H, and guiding the pencil in this way, keeping the cord equally in tension, carry the pencil round the pins FG, and so describe the ellipse.

Second Method.—Along the edge of a piece of paper mark fig. 1,334 off a distance *ac*, equal to AC, half the major axis, and from the same point a distance *ab*, equal to CD, half the minor axis. Place the slips so as to bring the point *b*, on the line AB, or major axis, and the point *c*, on the line DE, or minor axis. Set off the position of the point *a*. Shifting the slip, so that the point *b*, travels on the major axis, and the point *c*, on the minor axis, any number of points in the curve may be found through which the curve may be traced.

Mensuration.—Briefly, by definition, mensuration is *the act, art, or process of measuring.*

It is that branch of mathematics that has to do with: finding the length of lines, the area of surfaces, and the volume of solids.

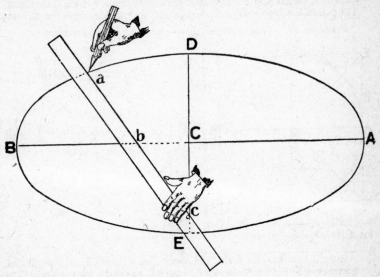

Fɪɢ. 1,334.—*Problem 30.* Second method.

Accordingly the problems which follow will be divided into three groups, as:

1. Measurement of lines.

    a. One dimension—*length*

2. Measurement of surfaces (*areas*).

    a. Two dimensions—*length* and *breadth*

3. Measurement of solids (*volumes*).

    a. Three dimensions—*length*, *breadth*, and *thickness*

1.   Measurement of Lines
(length)

Problem 1.—To find the length of any side of a right triangle, the other two sides being given.

Rule.—*Length of hypothenuse equals square root of the sum of*

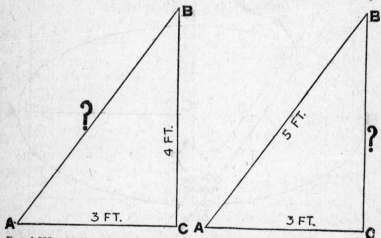

FIGS. 1,335 and 1,336.—*Problem 3.* *To find the length of any side of a right triangle.*

the squares of the two legs; length of either leg equals square root of the difference of the square of the hypothenuse and the square of the other leg.

    Example.—The two legs of a right triangle measure 3 and 4 ft.; find length of hypothenuse. If the length of hypothenuse and one leg be 5 and 4 ft. respectively, what is the length of the other leg.

    In fig. 1,335

$$AB = \sqrt{3^2 + 4^2} = \sqrt{25} = 5$$

In fig. 1,336 BC = $\sqrt{5^2 - 3^2} = \sqrt{25 - 9} = \sqrt{16} = 4$

Problem 2.—To find length of circumference of a circle.

Rule.—*Multiply the diameter by* 3.1416.

Example.—What length of moulding strip is required for a circular window 5 ft. in diameter?

$$5 \times 3.1416 = 15.7 \text{ ft.}$$

As the carpenter does not ordinarily measure feet in tenths, the .7 should be reduced to inches; it corresponds to 8½ ins. from the table below. That is the length of moulding required in 15 ft. 8½ ins.

Decimals of a Foot and Inches

Inch	0"	1"	2"	3"	4"	5"	6"	7"	8"	9"	10"	11"
0	.0	.0833	.1677	.2500	.3333	4167	.5000	.5833	.6667	.7500	.8333	.9167
1–16	.0052	.0885	.1719	.2552	.3385	.4219	.5052	.5885	.6719	.7552	.8385	.9219
1–8	.0104	.0937	.1771	2604	.3437	.4271	.5104	.5937	.6771	.7604	.8437	.9271
3–16	.0156	.0990	.1823	.2656	.3490	.4323	.5156	.5990	.6823	.7656	.8490	9323
1–4	.0208	.1042	.1875	.2708	.3542	.4375	.5208	.6042	.6875	.7708	.8542	.9375
5–16	0260	1094	.1927	.2760	.3594	.4427	.5260	.6094	.6927	.7760	.8594	.9427
3–8	0312	.1146	.1979	2812	.3646	.4479	.5312	6146	.6979	.7812	.8646	.9479
7–16	.0365	.1198	.2031	.2865	.3698	.4531	.5365	.6198	.7031	.7865	.8698	.9531
1–2	.0417	.1250	2083	.2917	.3750	.4583	.6250	.7083	.7917	.8750	.9583	
9–16	.0469	.1302	.2135	.2969	.3802	.4635	5469	.6302	.7135	.7969	.8802	.9635
5–8	.0521	.1354	.2188	3021	.3854	.4688	.5521	.6354	.7188	.8021	.8854	9688
11–16	.0573	.1406	.2240	.3073	.3906	.4740	.5573	.6406	.7240	.8073	.8906	.9740
3–4	.0625	.1458	.2292	3125	.3958	.4792	.5625	.6458	.7292	8125.	.8958	.9792
13–16	.0677	.1510	.2344	.3177	4010	.4844	.5677	6510	.7344	.8177	.9010	.9844
7–8	.0729	.1562	.2396	.3229	4062	.4896	5729	.6562	.7396	.8229	.9062	.9896
15–16	.0781	.1615	.2448	.3281	4115	.4948	.5781	6615	.7448	.8281	9115	.9948

Problem 3.—To find the length of an arc of a circle.

Rule.—*As 360° is to the number of degrees of the arc so is the length of the circumference to the length of the arc.*

Example.—If the circumference of a circle be 6 feet, what is the length of 60° arc?

Let X = length of the arc, solving for X,

$$360 : 60 = 6 : X = \frac{60 \times 6}{360} = \frac{360}{360} = 1 \text{ft.}$$

Problem 4.—To find the rise of an arc.

Rule 1.—*The rise of an arc is equal to the square of the chord of half the arc divided by the diameter.*

Rule 2.—*Length of the chord subtending an angle at the center is equal to twice the sine of half the angle.*

Example.—A circular porch 10 ft. in diam. has six plate forms. Find width of board required for these forms allowing 3 ins. margin for joints as in fig. 1,337.

Each plate will subtend an angle of 360 ÷ 6 = 60°

here the "chord of half the arc" (mentioned in rule 1) will subtend 60 ÷ 2 = 30°.

Applying rule 2, "half the angle" = 30° ÷ 2 = 15°.

From table of "trigonometrical functions" (page 522), sine of 15° = .259, which with radius of 5 ft., becomes

$$\sin 15° \text{ (on 10-ft. circle)} = 5 \times .259 = 1.295$$

Applying rule 2 Length of chord ML, = 2 × 1.295 = 2.59

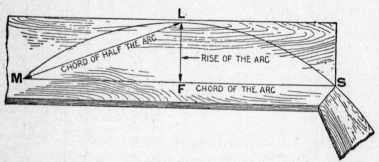

Fig. 1,337.—*Problem 4. To find width of board required for plate form of circular porch.*

Applying rule 1 rise of arc MS, = 2.59^2 ÷ 10 = .671 ft. or 8½ ins. (approx.)

Add to this 3 ins. margin for joints and obtain

width of board 8⅛ + 3 = 11⅛, — use 12 in. board

2. Measurement of Surfaces
(areas)

Problem 5.—To find the area of a square.

Rule.—*Multiply the base by the height.*

Example.—What is the area of a square whose side is 5 ft. as in fig. 1,338?

$$5 \times 5 = 25 \text{ sq. ft.}$$

Problem 6.—To find the area of a rectangle.

Rule.—*Multiply the base by the height (i. e., width by length).*

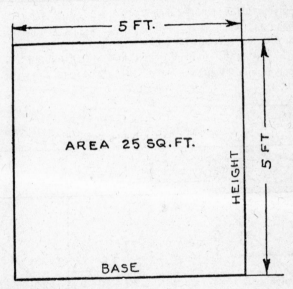

FIG. 1,338.—*Problem 5. Area of square.*

Example.—What is the floor area of a porch 5 ft. wide and 12 ft. long, as in fig. 1,339?

$$5 \times 12 = 60 \text{ sq. ft.}$$

Problem 7.—To find the area of a parallelogram.

Rule.—*Multiply base by perpendicular height.*

Example —What is the area of the 5 × 12 parallelogram shown in fig. 1,340?

$$5 \times 12 = 60 \text{ sq. ft.}$$

Problem 8.—To find the area of a triangle.

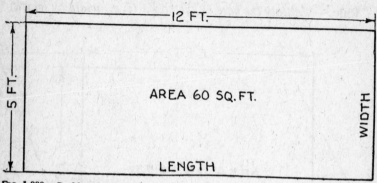

FIG. 1,339.—*Problem 6. Area of rectangle.*

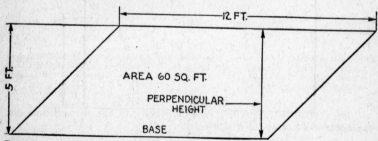

FIG. 1,340.—*Problem 7. Area of parallelogram.*

Rule.—*Multiply the base by half the altitude.*

Example —How many sq. ft. of sheathing are required to cover a church steeple having four triangular sides, as shown in fig. 1,341?

$$\frac{1}{2} \text{ of altitude} = 15 \text{ ft.}$$

$$\text{area of one side} = 12 \times 15 = 180 \text{ sq. ft.}$$

Total area (four sides) $4 \times 180 = 720$ sq. ft.

Problem 9.—To find the area of a trapezoid.

Rule.—*Multiply one-half the sum of the two parallel sides by the perpendicular distance between them.*

Example —What is the area of the trapezoid shown in fig. 1,343?

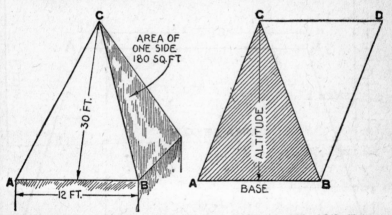

Figs. 1,341 and 1,342.—*Problem 8. Area of triangle.* An inspection of fig. 1,342 will show that area of triangle = base $\times$ ½ altitude because constructing a parallelogram ABCD, it is made up of two equal triangles and its area = base $\times$ altitude. Hence ½ altitude is taken in finding area of a triangle.

Here LA and FR, are the parallel sides and MS, the perpendicular distance between them. Applying rule

$$\text{area} = \tfrac{1}{2} \, (LA + FR) \times MS$$
$$= \tfrac{1}{2} \, (8 + 12) \times 6 = 60 \text{ sq. ft.}$$

Problem 10.—To find the area of a trapezium.

Rule.—*Draw a diagonal, dividing figure into triangles; measure diagonal and altitudes and find area of the triangles.*

Example —What is the area of the trapezium shown in fig. 1,344, for the dimensions given? Draw diagonal LR, and altitudes AM, and FS.

area triangle ALR = $12 \times {}^6/_2 = 36$ sq. ft.
area triangle LRF = $12 \times {}^9/_2 = 54$ sq. ft.

area trapezium LARF = ...90 sq. ft.

Problem 11.—To find the area of any irregular polygon.

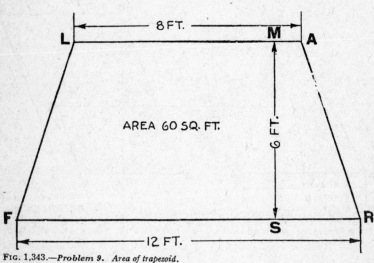

FIG. 1,343.—*Problem 9. Area of trapezoid.*

Rule.—*Draw diagonal dividing the figures into triangles and find the sum of the areas of these triangles.*

Problem 12.—To find the area of any regular polygon when length of side only is given.

Rule.—*Multiply the square of the sides by the figure for "area, side = 1" opposite to the polygon in the table following:*

Table of Regular Polygons

Number of sides	3	4	5	6	7	8	9	10	11	12
Area when side = 1.........	.433	1.	1.721	2.598	3.634	4.828	6.181	7.694	9.366	11.196

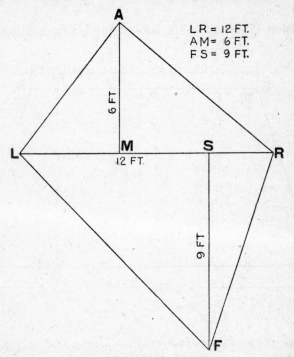

L R = 12 FT.
A M = 6 FT.
F S = 9 FT.

6 FT

M

12 FT.

S

9 FT

Fig. 1,344.—*Problem 10.   Area of trapezium.*

Example.—What is the area of an octagon (8-sided polygon) where sides measure 4 ft.

In the above table under 8, find 4.828.   Multiply this by the square of one side.

$$4.828 \times 4^2 = 77.25 \text{ sq. ft.}$$

Problem 13.—To find the area of a circle.

Rule.—*Multiply square of diameter by .7854.*

Example—How many square feet of floor surface in a 10 ft. circular floor?

$$10^2 \times .7854 = 78.54 \text{ sq. ft.}$$

Figs. 1,345 and 1,346 show why the decimal .7854 is used in finding the area of a circle.

Problem 14.—To find the area of a sector of a circle.

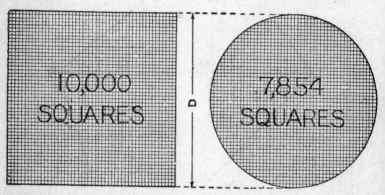

Figs. 1,345 and 1,346.—Diagram illustrating why the decimal .7854 is used to find the area of a circle. If the square be divided into 10,000 parts or small squares, a circle having a diameter D, equal to a side of the large square will contain 7,854 small squares, hence, if the area of the large square be 1 sq. in., then the area of the circle will be 7854 ÷ 10,000 or .7854 sq. ins., that is, area of the circle = .7854 × D × D = .7854 × 1 × 1 = .7854 sq. ins.

Rule.—*Multiply the arc of the sector by half the radius.*

Example.—How much tin is required to cover a 60° section of a 10-foot circular deck?

$$\text{length of } 60° \text{ arc} = \frac{60}{360} \text{ of } 3.1416 \times 10 = 5.24 \text{ ft.}$$

The reason for the above operation should be apparent without any explanation.

Applying rule

tin required for 60° sector = 5.24 × ½ of 5 = 13.1 sq. ft.

Problem 15.—To find the area of a segment of a circle.

Rule.—*Find the area of the sector which has the same arc and also the area of the triangle formed by the radii and chord; take the sum of these areas if the segment be greater than 180°; take the difference if less.*

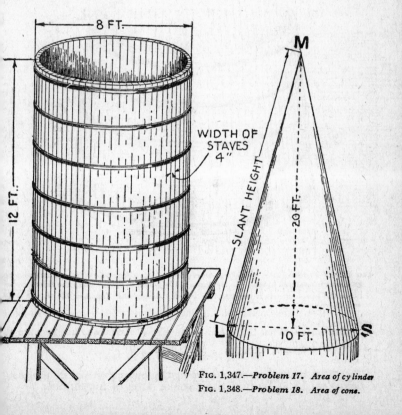

FIG. 1,347.—*Problem 17. Area of cylinder*
FIG. 1,348.—*Problem 18. Area of cone.*

Problem 16.—To find the area of a ring.

Rule.—*Take the difference between the areas of the two circles.*

Problem 17.—To find the area of an ellipse.

Rule.—*Multiply the product of the two diameters by .7854.*

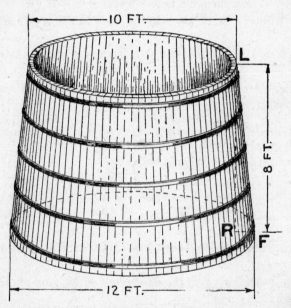

Fig. 1,349.—*Problem 19.—Area of frustum of a cone.* This is the shape of the ordinary wooden tank seen in windmill towers. In the figure LR = height of tank. Since the difference between the two diameters is two feet, RF = 1 ft. Hence slant height or LF = $\sqrt{1^2 + 8^2}$ = 8.06.

Example.—What is the area of an ellipse where two diameters are 10 and 6 inches?

$$10 \times 6 \times .7854 = 47.12 \text{ sq. ins.}$$

Problem 18.—To find the circular area of a cylinder.

Rule.—*Multiply* 3.1416 *by the diameter and by the height.*

Example.—How many sq. ft. of lumber are required for the sides of a cylindrical tank 8 ft. in diameter and 12 ft. high; how many pieces 4″ × 12′ will be required?

cylindrical surface 3.1416 × 8 × 12 = 302 sq. ft.

circumference of tank = 3.1416 × 8 = 25.1 ft.

Number 4″ × 12′ pieces 25.1 ÷ $^4/_{12}$ = 25.1 × 3 = 75.3, say **76.**

Problem 19.—To find the slant area of a cone.

Rule.—*Multiply* 3.1416 *by diameter of base and by one-half the slant height.*

Example.—A conical spire having a base 10 ft. diameter and altitude of 20 ft. is to be covered. Find area of surface to be covered.

In fig. 1,348, first find slant height, thus

slant height = $\sqrt{5^2 + 20^2}$ = $\sqrt{425}$ = 20.62 ft.

circumference of base = 3.1415 × 10 = 31.42 ft.

area of conical surface = 31.42 × ½ of 20.62 = 314 sq. ft.

Problem 20.—To find the (slant) area of the frustum of a cone.

Rule.—*Multiply half the slant height by the sum of the circumferences.*

Example.—A tank is 12 ft. in diameter at the base, 10 ft. at the top, and 8 ft. high. What is the area of the slant surface?

circumference 10 ft. circle = 3.1416 × 10 = 31.42 ft.

circumference 12 ft. circle = 3.1416 × 12 = 37.7 ft.

sum of circumferences = 69.1 ft.

slant height = $\sqrt{1^2 + 8^2}$ = $\sqrt{65}$ = 8.06

slant surface = sum of circumferences × ½ slant height

= 69.1 × ½ of 8.06 = 278.5 sq. ft.

3. Measurement of Solids

(volumes)

Problem 21.—To find the volume of a rectangular solid.

Rule.—*Multiply length, breadth and thickness together.*

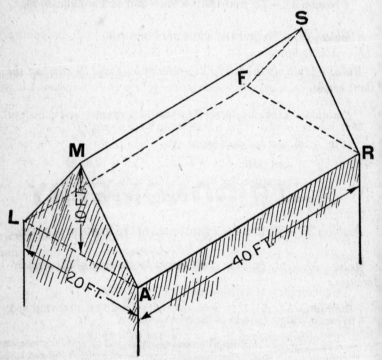

FIG. 1,350.—*Problem 20. Volume of rectangular wedge.*

Example.—What is the volume of a timber $4'' \times 8'' \times 12'$? Before applying rule first reduce all dimensions to ft. thus,

$$4'' = {}^4/_{12} \text{ ft.} = \tfrac{1}{3} \text{ ft.}$$
$$8'' = \tfrac{2}{3} \text{ ft.}$$

volume of timber $= \tfrac{1}{3} \times \tfrac{2}{3} \times 12 = 2.67$ cu. ft.

If the timber be a piece of oak weighing 48 lbs. per cu. ft. the **total weight** would be

$$48 \times 2.67 = 128 \text{ lbs.}$$

Problem 22.—To find the volume of a rectangular wedge.

Rule.—*Find the area of one of the triangular ends and multiply by distance between ends.*

Example.—A barn attic has the shape of a rectangular wedge. What volume storage capacity would there be for the proportions shown in fig. 1,350?

In the figure, the boundary of the attic is LARFMS.

Area triangular end MLA $= 20 \times {}^{10}/_2 = 100$ sq. ft.
volume of attic $= 100 \times 40 = 4{,}000$ cu. ft.

3. TRIGONOMETRY

By definition trigonometry is *that branch of mathematics which treats of the relations of the sides and angles of triangles and applies them to other figures involving or containing triangles.*

Trigonometry is divided into two branches:
1. Plane.
2. Spherical.

Plane trigonometry deals with plane triangles, and spherical trigonometry with spherical triangles, the difference being shown in figs. 1,351 and 1,352. Evidently the kind of trigonometry the carpenter is interested in is **plane** trigonometry. Spherical trigonometry is useful in navigation.

Every triangle has six parts:

1. Three angles.
2. Three sides.

When any three of these parts are given, provided **one of them** be a side, the other parts may be determined. The determination of the unknown parts is called the *solution of triangles*.

Measurement of Angles.—In trigonometry the arcs of circles are used to measure angles. The unit of measurement of angles

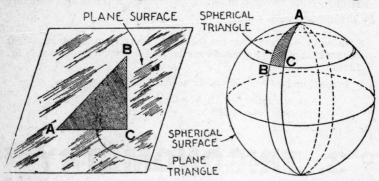

Figs. 1,351 and 1,352.—Plane and spherical triangles illustrating *plane* and *spherical* branches of trigonometry.

is the *degree* (°). In this system of measurement, the arc of every circle is supposed to be divided into 360 equal parts, called degrees; thus, a degree is $1/360$ of the circumference of any circle. A degree is divided into 60 parts called minutes expressed by ('), and each minute is divided into 60 seconds, expressed by ("), so that the circumference of any circle contains 21,600 minutes or 1,296,000 seconds.

Evidently, then the length of a degree depends upon the diameter of the circle as shown in fig. 1,353.

The *complement* of an angle is the difference between 90° and the angle.

the *supplement* of an angle is the difference between 180° and the angle. These terms are illustrated in figs. 1,354 and 1,355.

Trigonometrical Functions.—By definition, a function is a *quantity in mathematics so connected with another quantity that if any alteration be made in the latter there will be a consequent alteration in the former.* The dependent quantity is said to be **a**

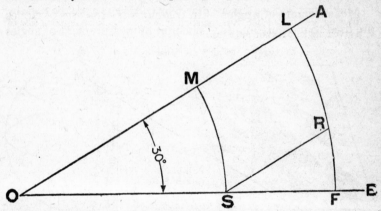

FIG. 1,353.—The length of a degree depends upon the diameter of the circle on which it is measured. Let the angle AOB, be measured on the arc MS, say 30°. Describe with longer radius another arc LF, and draw SR, parallel to MA, then LR, is approximately equal to MS, and LF, are in length ³⁰/₃₆₀ of their respective circles, that is, each contains 30 degrees. Hence LR (approximately equal to MS), does not contain as many degrees as MS, and it follows that each degree on LF, is larger than on MS.

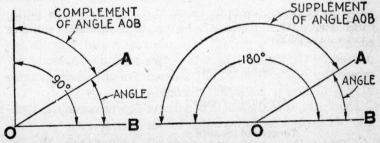

FIGS. 1,354 and 1,355.—*Complement* and *supplement* of an angle.

function of the other. Thus, the circumference of the circle is a function of the diameter.

These functions may consist of:

1. Ratios.
2. Lines ("natural functions").

In the first instance they are defined by referring to a triangle made by drawing (as in fig. 1,356) a perpendicular from any point A, on one side of a given angle, MOS or θ, to the other side, as AB.

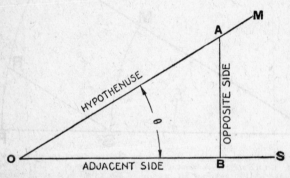

Fig. 1,356.—Angle θ and constructed triangle AOB, for expressing trigonometrical functions as ratios.

It will be noted that the triangle thus formed is a right triangle, that is, angle ABO = 90°. In this triangle the trigonometric functions, exposed as ratios are as follows:

$$\textit{Sine of the angle } \theta' = \frac{AB}{AO} = \frac{\text{opposite side}}{\text{hypothenuse}}$$

$$\textit{Cosine of the angle } \theta = \frac{OB}{OA} = \frac{\text{adjacent side}}{\text{hypothenuse}}$$

$$\textit{Tangent of the angle } \theta = \frac{AB}{OB} = \frac{\text{opposite side}}{\text{adjacent side}}$$

$$\textbf{\textit{Cotangent}} \text{ of the angle } \theta = \frac{OB}{BA} = \frac{\text{adjacent side}}{\text{opposite side}}$$

$$\textbf{\textit{Secant}} \text{ of the angle } \theta = \frac{OA}{OB} = \frac{\text{hypothenuse}}{\text{adjacent side}}$$

$$\textbf{\textit{Cosecant}} \text{ of the angle } \theta = \frac{OA}{AB} = \frac{\text{hypothenuse}}{\text{opposite side}}$$

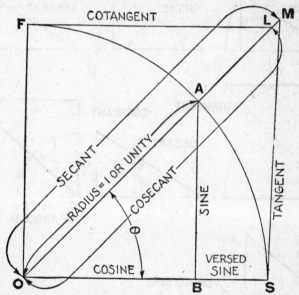

FIG. 1,357.—*Natural trigonometrical functions*, or functions expressed as lines.

For the sake of brevity the names of the functions are contracted, thus: for *sine* θ, write *sin* θ; for cosine θ, write *cos* θ, etc.

The cosine, cotangent (cot.) and cosecant (cosec) of an angle are respectively the sine, tangent and secant of the complement of that angle.

In the second instance the trigonometrical functions are defined by *certain lines* whose lengths depend upon the arc

which measures the angle.   These are virtually ratios but by
taking what corresponds to the hypothenuse OA, of the triangle
AOB, in fig. 1,356 as a *radius of unity length* of a circle the denominators of the ratios are unity or 1, and disappear leaving

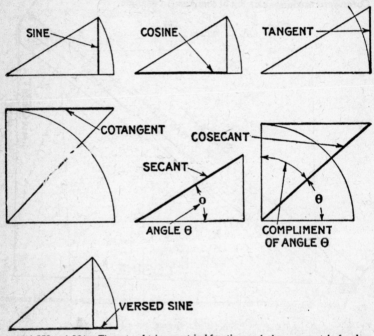

FIGS. 1,358 to 1,364.—The natural trigonometrical functions each shown separately for clearness. As elsewhere stated the cos., cot, and cosec. of an angle are respectively the sine, tan,
and sec. of the complement of the angle.

only the numerators—that is, a line instead of a ratio or function; these lines are the so called *"natural functions,"* thus in
fig. 1,357:

$$\textit{Sine} \text{ angle } \theta = \frac{AB}{\text{radius}} = \frac{AB}{1} = AB$$

Cosine angle $\theta = \dfrac{\text{OB}}{\text{radius}} = \text{OB}$

Tangent angle $\theta = \dfrac{\text{MS}}{\text{OS}} = \dfrac{\text{MS}}{\text{radius}} = \text{MS}$

Cotangent angle θ = tangent of complement of angle

$$\theta = \dfrac{\text{FL}}{\text{OF}} = \dfrac{\text{FL}}{\text{radius}} = \textbf{FL}$$

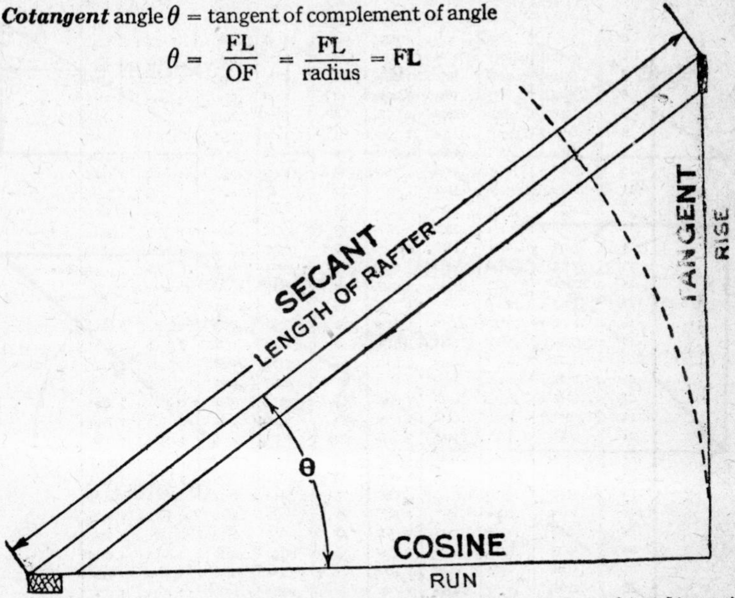

FIG. 1,365.—Common rafter in position between plate and ridge illustrating cosine and tangent.

Secant angle $\theta = \dfrac{\text{OM}}{\text{OS}} = \dfrac{\text{OM}}{\text{radius}} = \text{OM}$

Cosecant angle θ = secant of complement angle $\theta = \dfrac{\text{OL}}{\text{OF}} = \dfrac{\text{OL}}{\text{radius}} = \text{OL}$

Versed sine angle $\theta = \dfrac{\text{BS}}{\text{OS}} = \dfrac{\text{BS}}{\text{radius}} = \text{BS}$

It is these natural trigonometrical functions that are especially useful, rather than the functions expressed as ratios, because, with the aid of the table which follows the exact lengths of the functions for an arc of unity radius can be found.

NATURAL TRIGONOMETRICAL FUNCTIONS

Degree	Sine	Cosine	Tangent	Secant	Degree	Sine	Cosine	Tangent	Secant
0	.00000	1.0000	.00000	1.0000	46	.7193	.6947	1.0355	1.4395
1	.01745	.9998	.01745	1.0001	47	.7314	.6820	1.0724	1 4663
2	.03490	.9994	.03492	1.0006	48	.7431	.6691	1.1106	1.4945
3	.05234	.9986	.05241	1.0014	49	.7547	.6561	1.1504	1.5242
4	.06976	.9976	.06993	1.0024	50	.7660	.6428	1.1918	1.5557
5	.08716	.9962	.08749	1.0038	51	.7771	.6293	1.2349	1 5890
6	.10453	.9945	.10510	1.0055	52	.7880	.6157	1.2799	1 6243
7	.12187	.9925	.12278	1.0075	53	.7986	.6018	1.3270	1 6616
8	.1392	.9903	.1405	1.0098	54	.8090	.5878	1.3764	1.7013
9	.1564	.9877	.1584	1.0125	55	.8192	.5736	1.4281	1 7434
10	.1736	.9848	.1763	1.0154	56	.8290	.5592	1.4826	1.7883
11	.1908	.9816	.1944	1.0187	57	.8387	.5446	1.5399	1 8361
12	.2079	.9781	.2126	1.0223	58	.8480	.5299	1.6003	1.8871
13	.2250	.9744	.2309	1.0263	59	.8572	.5150	1.6643	1.9416
14	.2419	.9703	.2493	1.0306	60	.8660	.5000	1.7321	2.0000
15	.2588	.9659	.2679	1.0353	61	.8746	.4848	1.8040	2.0627
16	.2756	.9613	.2867	1.0403	62	.8829	.4695	1.8807	2.1300
17	.2924	.9563	.3057	1.0457	63	.8910	.4540	1.9626	2.2027
18	.3090	.9511	.3249	1.0515	64	.8988	.4384	2.0503	2.2812
19	.3256	.9455	.3443	1.0576	65	.9063	.4226	2.1445	2.3662
20	.3420	.9397	.3640	1.0642	66	.9135	.4067	2.2460	2.4586
21	.3584	.9336	.3839	1.0711	67	.9205	.3907	2.3559	2.5593
22	.3746	.9272	.4040	1.0785	68	.9272	.3746	2.4751	2.6695
23	.3907	.9205	.4245	1.0864	69	.9336	.3584	2.6051	2.7904
24	.4067	.9135	.4452	1.0946	70	.9397	.3420	2.7475	2.9238
25	.4226	.9063	.4663	1.1034	71	.9455	.3256	2.9042	3.0715
26	.4384	.8988	.4877	1.1126	72	.9511	.3090	3.0777	3.2361
27	.4540	.8910	.5095	1.1223	73	.9563	.2924	3.2709	3.4203
28	.4695	.8829	.5317	1.1326	74	.9613	.2756	3.4874	3.6279
29	.4848	.8746	.5543	1.1433	75	.9659	.2588	3.7321	3.8637
30	.5000	.8660	.5774	1.1547	76	.9703	.2419	4.0108	4.1336
31	.5150	.8572	.6009	1.1666	77	.9744	.2250	4.3315	4.4454
32	.5299	.8480	.6249	1.1792	78	.9781	.2079	4.7046	4.8097
33	.5446	.8387	.6494	1.1924	79	.9816	.1908	5.1446	5.2408
34	.5592	.8290	.6745	1.2062	80	.9848	.1736	5.6713	5.7588
35	.5736	.8192	.7002	1.2208	81	.9877	.1564	6.3138	6.3924
36	.5878	.8090	.7265	1.2361	82	.9903	.1392	7.1154	7.1853
37	.6018	.7986	.7536	1.2521	83	.9925	.12187	8.1443	8.2055
38	.6157	.7880	.7813	1.2690	84	.9945	.10453	9.5144	9.5668
39	.6293	.7771	.8098	1.2867	85	.9962	.08716	11.4301	11.474
40	.6428	.7660	.8391	1.3054	86	.9976	.06976	14.3007	14.335
41	.6561	.7547	.8693	1.3250	87	.9986	.05234	19.0811	19.107
42	.6691	.7431	.9004	1.3456	88	.9994	.03490	28.6363	28.654
43	.6820	.7314	.9325	1.3673	89	.9998	.01745	57.2900	57.299
44	.6947	.7193	.9657	1.3902	90	1.0000	Inf.	Inf.	Inf.
45	.7071	.7071	1.0000	1.4142	—	—	—	—	—

NOTE.—For *intermediate values* interpolate. For *cotangent* take value of tangent of complement of the angle.

Problem 1.—Find length of rafter for 12 ft. run and 8 ft. rise, allowing for 1½ in. ridge board.

$$\text{pitch} = \frac{\text{rise}}{\text{span}} = \frac{\text{rise}}{2 \times \text{run}} = \frac{8}{2 \times 12} = \frac{1}{3}$$

As given in table below, for ⅓ pitch the rafter makes an angle of 34° with the horizontal.

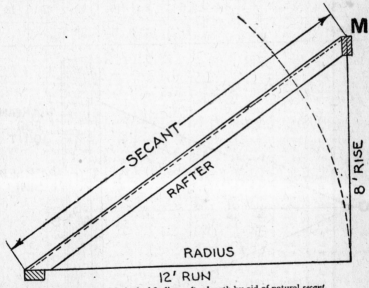

Fig. 1,366.—Problem 1. Method of finding rafter length by aid of natural *secant*.

By comparing fig. 1,366, showing rafter with fig. 1,357, it will be seen that the rafter corresponds to the secant (both figures being lettered the same), hence look in a table of natural trigonometrical functions, giving values for secant, and find 1.2062 value of secant for 34°. Now since the run corresponds (in fig. 1,366) to the unity radius, multiply the value found by 12, thus

artificial length of rafter = 1.2062 × 12 = 14.47 ft.

deducting ½ of ridge board width.

length of rafter = 14.46 — .75 = 13.71 ft.

Pitch Table

Pitch	⅙	¼	⅓	5/12	½	⅝	¾
Run	12	12	12	12	12	12	12
Rise	4	6	8	10	12	15	18
Angle	..	27°	34°	..	45°	..	..

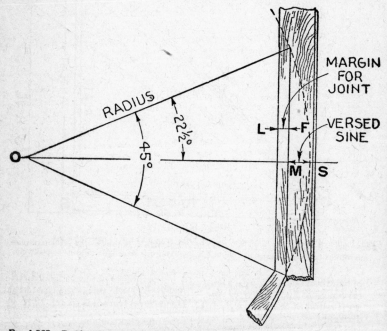

Fig. 1,367.—Problem 2.—Method of finding width of board for cutting circular deck or porch block forms by aid of the *versed sine*.

Problem 2.—What width board is required to cut 45° block forms for a circular deck 12 ft. in diameter allowing margin of 3 ins. for joints.

The width of board = "rise of arc" + margin for joint. In fig. 1,357 (compare with fig. 1,367) the rise of the arc is equal to the *versed sine* MS,

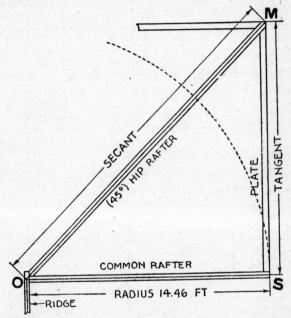

F1G. 1,368.—Problems 3 and 4. Method of finding length of hip rafter and portion of plate intercepted between common and hip rafters by aid of the *secant* and tangent respectively.

of half the angle, or 22½°. Hence look in the table of natural trigonometrical functions and find *versed sine* = .0696 for 22½°; this is the rise of the arc if radius of the porch were 1 ft. Hence for 6 ft. radius (porch 12 ft. in diameter)

rise of arc = .0696 × 6 = .4176 ft. or 5 ins. (approx.)

width of plank = 5 ins. rise + 3 ins. (for joint) = 8 ins.

Problem 3.—If the common rafter on a building as found in problem 1 be 14.46 ft artificial length, what is the artificial length of a 45° hip.

Comparing fig. 1,368 with 1,357, clearly the length of the hip rafter corresponds to the secant of the angle the hip makes with the common rafter. Hence find in table, secant 45° = 1.4142. Multiply by length of common rafter (radius)

artificial length of hip × 1.4142 = 14.46 = 20.45 ft. or 20' 5⅜"

Problem 4.—In the roof construction shown in fig. 1,368 what is the length of the plate intercepted between the common and hip rafters?

Comparing the figure with fig. 1,357 it will be seen that the intercepted plate MS, corresponds to the tangent of the angle between the common and hip rafters.

Hence from table tangent 45° = 1, and from which

length MS, of intercepted plate = 1 × 14.46 = 14.46 ft. or 14' 5½"

Problem 5.—A fancy grill work consisting of radial and vertical pieces is to be constructed in a semi-circular opening having a 6 ft. radius as in fig. 1,369. Find the lengths of the vertical pieces as MS and LF, touching the circumference at 30° and 60° from the horizontal.

Comparing fig. 1,369 with 1,357 it will be seen that the vertical pieces MS and LF, correspond to sine of the angle made by the intersecting radial piece with the horizontal. Accordingly, from table

$$\text{sine} \begin{cases} 30° = .5 \\ 60° = .866 \end{cases}$$

hence length of vertical pieces

MS = .5 × 6 = 3 ft.
LF = .866 × 6 = 5.2 ft. or 5' 2⅜"

Problem 6.—In laying out the grill work fig. 1,369, how far must the foot of the pieces LF and MS, be spaced from the center O, to bring them into a vertical position?

The distances OF and OS, correspond to the cosine of angles 30° and 60° respectively. Accordingly from table

$$\text{Cosine} \begin{cases} 30° = .866 \\ 60° = .5 \end{cases}$$

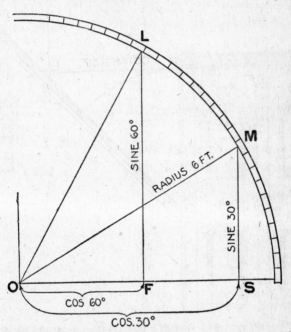

FIG. 1,369.—Problems 5 and 6. Method of finding in a grill work construction length of vertical pieces and their distance from center by aid of sine and cosine respectively of the angle made by intersecting radial pieces with the horizontal.

hence distances

$$OS = .866 \times 6 = 5.2 \text{ ft.} = 5' \, 3\tfrac{3}{8}''$$
$$OF = .5 \times 6 = 3 \text{ ft.}$$

Problem 7.—A bridge is to be constructed from the top of a building to an opening in the roof of an adjacent building as in fig. 1,370. If the rise OF, to the point of entry L, be 15 ft. and the pitch of the roof be ⅓, what length beams FL, are required?

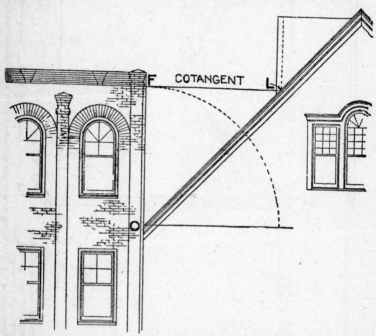

FɪG. 1,370.—Problems 7 and 8. Method of finding length of bridge from side of building to given point on adjacent pitch roof by aid of cotangent, and of finding slant length of roof by aid of cosecant.

Comparing the figure with fig. 1,357, it is seen that the bridge FL, corresponds to the cotangent Now in the table on page 524, ⅓ pitch corresponds to an angle of 34°, and from table (page 522), cotangent of 34° = 1.4 3 Hence, length of beams required, or

$$FL = 1.483 \times 15 = 22.25 \text{ ft. or } 22' 3''$$

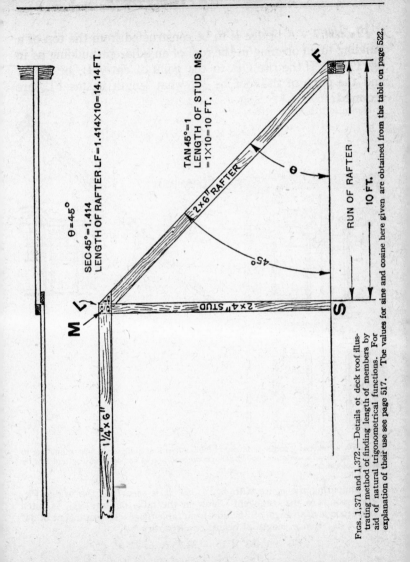

FIGS. 1,371 and 1,372.—Details of deck roof illustrating method of finding length of members by aid of natural trigonometrical functions. For explanation of their use see page 517. The values for sine and cosine here given are obtained from the table on page 522.

θ = 45°

SEC 45° = 1.414
LENGTH OF RAFTER LF = 1.414 × 10 = 14.14 FT.

TAN 45° = 1
LENGTH OF STUD MS.
= 1 × 10 = 10 FT.

RUN OF RAFTER
10 FT.

2 × 6" RAFTER

θ

45°

2 × 4" STUD

F

S

M

1/4 × 6"

Problem 8.—In estimating amount of roofing material necessary to cover side of roof from O to L, in fig. 1, 370 what is the
distance from O to L?

Comparing with fig. 1,357, it is seen that OL, corresponds to the cosecant.
Accordingly from table, cosec 34° = 1.788.
Hence length slant surface or

$$OL = 1.788 \times 15 = 26.82 \text{ or } 26' \ 9\tfrac{7}{8}''$$

CHAPTER 27

Surveying

By definition, the word surveying broadly means the art and science of determining the area and configuration of portions of the surface of the earth and representing them on maps.

FIG. 1,373.—Kolesch Y, level 18 in. telescope; magnifying power about 28 diameters; minimum focus 8 ft. from instrument; bubble, 20 seconds sensitiveness.

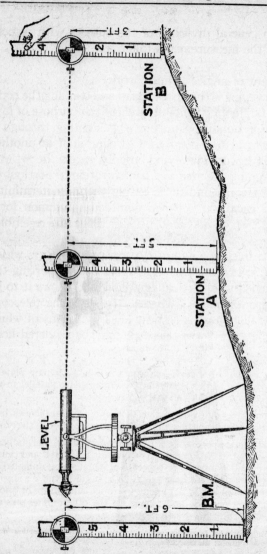

FIG. 1,374.—General principle of leveling: *The elevations of all points above a given starting point of reference called a bench mark* (B. M.) *is obtained.* In the figure, A and B are two points whose levels or difference in level are to be determined. The instrument is placed midway between the B. M. and station A, and the height of the line of sight through the instrument determined with respect to B. M. by leveling the telescope and sighting on a rod divided into feet, inches and fractions of an inch. Say this is 6 ft. Now sighting on the rod placed on station A, and then on station B, readings of 5 ft. and 3 ft. respectively are obtained. Hence, for these readings station A = 6 — 5 = 1 ft. higher than the B. M.; station B is 6 — 3 = 3 ft. higher than the B. M., and the difference in elevation between station A and B, = 5 — 2 (or 3 — 1) = 2 ft. By a similar process the difference in elevation between any number of points is determined.

There are two general divisions of the subject with respect to the nature of the measurements taken as:

1. Leveling
2. Measurement of angles (transit work)

Leveling in surveying is the operation of ascertaining the comparative levels of different points of land for the purpose of laying out a grade or building site, etc., by sighting through a leveling instrument at one point to a leveling staff at another point as shown in fig. 1,374.

The Level.—This instrument is employed for determining the difference in elevation between points. A common form is known as the Y level, so called because its shape resembles the letter Y.

It consists of a telescope mounted upon two supports which from their shape are called Y's. The cross bar supporting the telescope is attached to a vertical spindle which allows it to be turned in a horizontal plane. Directly beneath the telescope and attached parallel to it, is a spirit level by means of which the line of collimation* of the telescope may be rendered horizontal.

Construction of the Y Level.—In construction a circular plate is screwed to a tripod and to this is attached a similar plate parallel to the first and connected with it by a ball and socket joint.

Four screws (sometimes only three) called foot screws or plate screws, hold these plates apart by resting on the lower one and passing through the other.

A vertical spindle in the center of the plates supports a rod, bar, or beam and is used to revolve the instrument. The beam is horizontal and carries at its ends two vertical standards or supports of equal size terminated by two forks of the general form of the letter Y. The inside of the Y's is semicircular. The top of the Y's may be closed by semi-circular straps or bridles called clips, hinged on one side and pinned on the other. The pins are

---

*NOTE.—The line of collimation is the line which would connect the intersection of the cross hairs with the optical center of the objective.

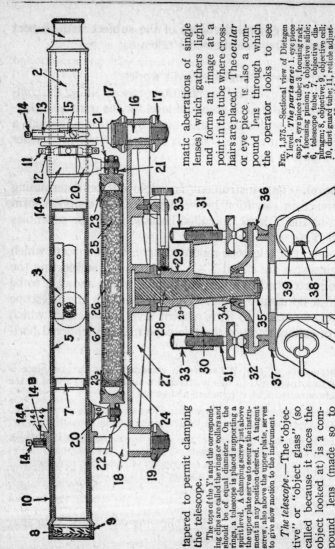

matic aberrations of single lenses) which gathers light and forms an image at a point in the tube where crosshairs are placed. The *ocular* or *eye piece* is also a compound lens through which the operator looks to see

FIG. 1,375.—Sectional view of Dietzgen Y level. *The parts are:* 1, eye piece cap; 2, eye piece tube; 3, focusing rack; 4, focusing pinion; 5, objective slide; 6, telescope tube; 7, objective diaphragm; 8, objective; 9, objective cell; 10, dust guard tube; 11, reticle adjusting screw; 12, reticle screw washer; 13, Y clip; 14, tension regulating screw; 14a, Y collar; 14b, steady pin; 15, Y clip latch; 16, adjusting Y; 17, Y adjusting nut; 18, fixed Y; 19, Y clamp nut; 20, level saddle; 21, vertical level adjustment; 23, level ends; 24, level tubing; 25, level vial; 26, level bubble; 27, Y bar; 28, center spindle; 29, center sleeve; 30, leveling arm; 31, leveling screw; 32, leveling screw ball cups; 33, dust caps; 34, half ball; 35, center nut; 36, leveling screw plate; 37, tripod head; 38, tripod bolt; 39, tripod nut.

tapered to permit clamping the telescope.

The tops of the Y's and the corresponding clips are called the rings or collars and should be of equal diameter. On the rings, a telescope is placed supporting a spirit level. A clamping screw just above the upper plate serves to secure the instrument in any position desired. A tangent screw, also above the upper plate, serves to give slow motion to the instrument.

The telescope.—The "objective" or "object glass" (so called because it faces the object looked at) is a compound lens (made so as to correct spherical and chroa magnified view of the image. Tangent screws may be used to give motion to the tubes carrying the objective and ocular.

The cross hairs.—Either platinum drawn wires or spider's threads attached to a ring within the telescope at the spot where the image is formed. The ring is secured by four capstan headed screws which pass through the telescope tube. There are commonly two hairs, one supposed to be horizontal and the other vertical, with their intersection in the axis of the telescope.

Bubble level.—The spirit level attached to the telescope can be raised

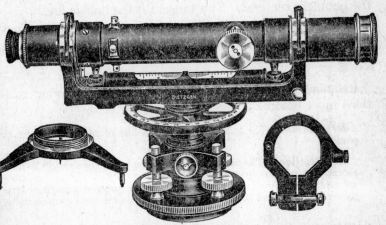

FIGS. 1,376 to 1,378.—Dietzgen builder's Y level, metal trivet (fig. 1,376), and Y adjustment (fig. 1,378). **Specifications:** telescope length 12 ins.; magnifying power 18 to 20 diameters; objective 1⅛ ins.; used full value; erecting eye piece; sensibility 60 seconds; ¹⁄₁₀ in. division; cross bar 7½ ins.; horizontal circle vernier reading to 5 minutes; 4 leveling screws. The metal trivet (fig. 1,377) is for setting level where use of tripod is difficult.

vertically by means of *altitude screws* at the rear end, and may be slightly moved laterally by means of *azimuth screws* at the forward end.

The supports—Form the *Y's* and are supported by the bar to which they are fastened by two nuts, one above and one below. These nuts may be moved by means of an *adjusting pin.*

"Lines" of the Level.—The following are three principal lines of a level.

1. Vertical axis
2. Bubble line
3. Line of collimation

The vertical axis.—This passes through the center of the spindle.

Bubble line.—The metallic supports of the spirit level are equal and the tangent at their top or bottom is horizontal when the bubble is centered. This tangent is the bubble line.

Line of collimation.—The line which would connect the intersection of the cross hairs with the optical center of the objective is the line of collimation.

Relations between the lines of a level.—The following relations must obtain.

1st Relation.—The bubble line and the line of collimation must be parallel.

2nd Relation.—The plane described by the bubble line should be horizontal, that is to say, perpendicular to the vertical axis. These conditions are generally satisfied in a new level. But exposure and usage may alter these relations; hence the necessity of adjusting the instrument occasionally.

Adjustments of the Y Level.—The first relation given above cannot be established directly but requires three adjustments.

First Adjustment.—*Making the line of collimation parallel to the bottom element of the collars, or collimating the instrument.* Clamp the instrument. Unclip the collars. Sight at a distant point (as far as distinct) bringing the horizontal crosshair on it. Carefully turn the telescope in the collars by half a revolution around its axis and sight again. If the horizontal cross hair be still on the sighted point, the telescope is collimated with regard to that cross hair; if it be off the point, bring it half way back by means of the capstan headed screws and the rest of the way by the plate screws. Repeat the operation over another point till satisfactory. Collimate it with regard to the other cross hair. Leave screws at a snug bearing.

Second Adjustment.—*Setting the bubble line in a plane with the bottom element of the collars.* Unclip telescope, clamp the instrument over a pair of plate screws. Center the bubble by means of plate screws. Carefully and slowly turn the telescope in the collars by a small arc to the right, then to the left. If bubble move from center, bring it back by means of the azimuth or side screws.

Third Adjustment.—Setting the bubble line parallel to the bottom element of the collars. Unclip telescope. Clamp the instrument over a pair of plate screws. Center the bubble by means of plate screws. Carefully take

FIGS. 1,379 and 1,380.—Dietzgen builders' convertible Y level with compass. This instrument due to its *convertible feature* can be used for obtaining vertical lines and for sighting objects above or below a horizontal plane. The view shows instrument with telescope inclined when sighting a vertical line. *The compass* affords a ready means of determining the bearing of lines and of measuring angles by the needle.

telescope up, replacing it as carefully in the Y's in the opposite direction, that is to say, the objective sighting in the direction where the eye piece first was. If the bubble has moved bring it back half way by means of the altitude or foot screws of the spirit level and the rest of the way by the plate screws. Repeat in another direction till satisfactory.

The second relation is established by making the bubble line stay in the center of the graduation during a complete revolution of the instrument around its spindle.

Fourth Adjustment.—*Making the axis of the instrument (not of the telescope) vertical.* Pin the clips, clamp and center bubble over a pair of plate screws. Reverse telescope over same pair of plate screws; bring bubble half-way back (if it has moved) by means of plate screws.

Fifth Adjustment.—*Making the bubble remain centered during a full revolution of instrument.* Center bubble and revolve instrument horizontally by a half revolution. If bubble move, correct half way by means of the support screws (at the foot of the Y's).*

Leveling Rod.—This instrument, used in leveling is usually $6\frac{1}{2}$ feet high, graduated to hundredths of a foot and provided with a sliding target. The rod is made in two parts so arranged that its length can be extended to 12 feet.

---

*NOTE.—Should the rings become worn and unequal, use two peg method of the dumpy level.

NOTE.—*Dumpy level* (so named from its compactness). Mostly used in England, and to some extent in the United States on account of the better stability of its adjustments over the Y level from which it mainly differs in that the telescope is permanently attached to the supports or uprights; but these uprights are adjustable.

NOTE.—Drive two stakes (pegs) several hundred feet apart. Set instrument about half way between them. Level up and sight the rod held in succession on each stake. The difference of the readings is the true difference of the elevation of the stakes, even if instrument be not in adjustment. To test the instrument, set it over one of the stakes (the highest one for instance); level up and sight the rod held on the other stake. Subtract the height of the instrument from the reading, the difference should be equal to the difference of elevation of the stakes as previously determined; if not, set the target half way between these readings, sight on it and center bubble by means of altitude screws. Repeat operation till satisfied.

Centering the Objective and Ocular.—These adjustments are made permanently by the maker. Four screws hold the tubes carrying the glasses, their heads passing through the outside tube, where, after permanent adjustment, they are covered by a metallic ring.

Parallax.—Apparent motion of the cross hairs on the object sighted when the eye is moved slightly. This shows imperfect focusing of the ocular over the cross hairs. To correct, hold a white surface as that of a book a little in front of the objective and move the ocular tube to and fro until the cross hairs are perfectly defined.

How to Carry the Level.—The instrument should be properly clamped and screwed down on the tripod which is carried generally on the shoulder, except when going over rough ground and fences or obstructions. Carry it upright on rough surface. Then crossing a fence, carefully pass it over on the other side spreading the legs; the rodman will help if necessary.

The Tripod.—See that the ferrules or shoes are not loose. Tighten the legs securely but not too much. Generally place two shoes in the direction of the line. On side hill work, place the shoe up hill. Don't knock the legs when stepping from side to side.

A sliding disc called a target is provided with a vernier for accurate work, reading to thousandths of a foot.

In using, the rod is held in a vertical position with its lower end resting upon the point, the elevation of which is desired and the target moved up and down until its center coincides with the cross hairs of the telescope of the level.

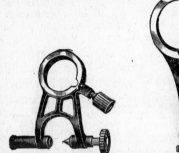

FIGS. 1,381 to 1,383.—Dietzgen clamp and tangent screws. They act entirely on the centers, both the plates are free from strain and can be clamped without affecting the levels. The tangent screw consists of a single screw made of hard bronze or nickel silver with an opposing spiral spring to take up counter motion. Both clamp and tangent screws are accessible. The tangent screw or levels is attached to the cross bar and the clamp revolves with it and is always in the same relative position.

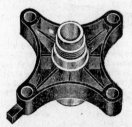

FIG. 1,384.—Dietzgen leveling base. This part to which the leveling screws are filled, is of ribbed design. The leveling screws are made of hard bronze or nickel silver.

The reading of the elevation is made from the rod on a line corresponding with the center line of the target. There are various kinds of rods, some designed to be read by the rod man, others through the telescope of the level.

Methods of Leveling.—The simplest case of leveling is to find the difference in level between two points which are visible from a third point, the difference in level being less than the length of the leveling rod as in fig. 1,385. In case the difference in level be greater than the length of the rod the method shown in fig. 1,386 is used. Usually it is desired to find the relative

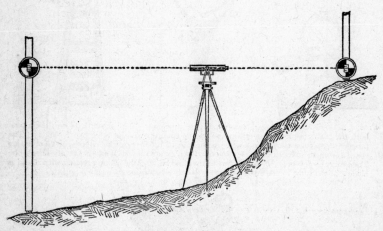

FIG. 1,385.—Leveling. *1.* Between two points whose difference in level is less than length of rod. Set up and level instrument at some point about half way between the two points. Have rod man hold rod vertically on one of the points and move target up and down till its center coincides with the cross wires of the level. Take reading which gives distance A*a*. Similarly, turn telescope on its spindle, hold rod on the other point and take reading which gives the distance B*b*. Evidently the difference in level is equal to the difference in the readings that is A*a* — B*b*

elevations of several points, as in grading work in which case it is necessary to keep more elaborate notes and to measure distances between the stations. The method here employed is shown in fig. 1,387, and the field notes are recorded as follows:

Field Notes

(Corresponding to the operations illustrated in fig. 1,387.)

Station	Distance	Backsight	Height of Instrument	Foresight	Elevation	Remarks
A	0	4.2	104.2	.....	100	Bench-mark, top of hydrant
B	100	.....	....	10.1	94.1	
C	60	.....	....	7.3	96.9	
D	50	.....	....	5.8	98.4	
T	.....	4.1	99.1	9.2	95.1	Turning point
E	70	6.8	....	.....	92.3	
F	110	.....	....	9.5	89.6	
G	80	.....	....	11.5	87.6	

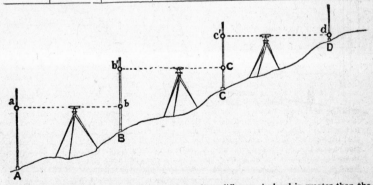

FIG. 1,386.—Leveling. 2. Between two points whose difference in level is greater than the length of the rod. Divide the distance between the two points into sections of such length that the difference in level between the dividing points A, B, C, called *stations*, shall be less than the length of the rod. Set up and level between A and B, and measure distance A*a* called back sight (B. S.), then reverse the telescope and take reading B*b*, called a foresight (F. S.). Next set up the level between B and C, and similarly take readings C*c'* and C*c*. Repeat operation between C and D, taking readings C*c'* and D*d*. Evidently the difference in level between stations A and D, is equal to the *sum of the differences between the intermediate stations*, that is this difference equals (A*a* — B*b*) + (B*b'* — C*c*) + (C*c'* — D*d*) or expressed in another form = (A*a* + B*b'* + C*c'*) — (B*b* + C*c* + D*d*).

Directions for Using the Level.—Note carefully the following mode of procedure in leveling:

1. Center the bubble over a pair of plate screws, then over the other pair. Plate screws should have a snug bearing. When looking at the bubble or at the cross hairs the eyes should look natural, that is, without strain. (Try to observe with both eyes open.)

2. Adjust the eye piece to the cross hairs for parallax.

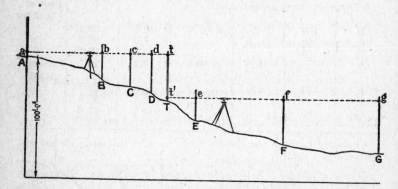

FIG. 1,387.—Leveling. *3.* Finding the relative elevations of several points. Assume a datum or reference line below the elevation of the lowest station and refer all elevations to this line. Start at some permanently fixed point as a mark on building top of hydrant, etc.; this is called a *bench mark.* Let A, be the bench mark and assume datum line 100 feet below level of A. The "field notes" corresponding to the operations are given in the main text. Starting with the instrument between A and B, and taking a back sight on A, the distance A*a* is found to be 4.2 ft., which added to 100 gives the height of the instrument. Next take foresights on B, C and D, and record them in proper column. It is evident from the figure that readings B*b*, C*c*, etc., subtracted from the height of the instrument, will give the elevation at B, C, etc. This is done, and the results recorded in the proper column. The ground falls away so rapidly beyond D, that it is necessary to set up the level further along and establish a new height of instrument. This is done by holding the rod at some convenient point, as at T, called a *turning point,* and taking a fore sight, which measures the distance T*t* (9.2). The level is then set up in its second position between E and F, and a back sight taken on the rod in the same position which gives the distance T*t'* (4.1). Then the distance *t't* = 9.2 — 4.1 = 5.1, and this subtracted from the previous height of instrument gives the new height which is 104.2 — 5.1 = 99.1. A back sight is now taken on E, and fore sights from F, and G. These are recorded in the proper columns, and the elevations found by subtracting these distances from the new height of instrument. The horizontal distances between the stations are measured with a tape, and recorded in the second column. In plotting a cross section from notes kept in this way, the datum line is first drawn, and perpendiculars erected at points corresponding to the different stations. The proper elevations are then indicated on these vertical lines, and a *contour line* drawn through the points so marked.

3. Turn instrument toward target (it is better to level up facing the target).

4. Look again at bubble.

5. Sight the target and have it set right by motions according to a pre-arranged code with the rodman.

6. Look again at bubble.

7. Read rod or direct target from the intersection of cross-hairs only.

8. Approve target when absolutely sure.

9. Have the height of target called out by rodman.

10. Enter it in level book.

11. Quickly make needed calculations and

12. Briskly motion rod man to new station or to stay for a turning point *T. P.* and backsight and move yourself to another position.

The following additional hints will be found useful:

Guarding against the Sun.—Draw the telescope shade, or use an umbrella or a hat.

Length of Sights.—Avoid sights too short and too long. 250 to 350 ft. should be the limits of sights.

Equal Sights.—Length of backsight should practically balance length of foresight; this may be approximated by pacing, or by the stadia cross-hairs in the telescope.

Long Sights.—When sights longer than the maximum allowable are unavoidable, correction should be made for curvature.

Leveling Up or Down a Steep Slope.—The leveler after some practice will place his instrument so as to take a reading near the top or the bottom of the rod (as the case may be), thus gaining vertical distance; but this produces unequal sights. He may also follow a zig-zag course.

Leveling Across a Large Body of Water.—1. *A running stream.* Drive a stake to the water surface on each side of the stream and in a direction normal to the flow (although the line may not run so). Take a *F. S.* on the first, a *B. S.* on the second and continue to and along the line. The elevations of the two stakes may be assumed equal.

2. *Across a Pond.* If a pond or lake be too wide to insure a good sight

across, do as for a stream. Drive stakes on each side and to the water surface; take a *F. S.* on the first and a *B. S.* on the second.

Across a Wall.—Take a *F. S.* on the rod set on a stake, driven to the natural surface on the first side of the wall. Measure the height of the wall above stake and enter it as a *B. S.* Drive a stake also to the natural surface on the second side of the wall, measure the height of the wall on that side above the stake and enter it as a *F. S.* Set the rod on the stake and take a sight on it which will be a *B. S.* and continue.

In Underbrush.—If it cannot be cut down on the line of sights, find a high place or provide one by piling logs, rocks, etc., to set the instrument upon.

Through Swamp.—Push legs of tripod down as far as possible. The leveler lies on his side. Two men may be necessary at the level. If still unsafe drive stakes or piles for supporting instrument.

Elevations to Be Taken at Road Crossings.—Take elevations both ways for some distance.

Elevations to Be Taken at River Crossings.—Take elevations of high water marks, flood marks with dates of same. Question residents for the purpose; also for dates and data of extreme low water.

Proper Length of Sights.—This will depend upon the distance at which the rod appears distinct and upon the precision required. Under ordinary conditions sights should not exceed 300 ft. where elevations are required to the nearest .01 ft. and even at a much shorter distance the boiling of the air may prevent a precision of this degree.

Trigonometric Leveling.—Finding the difference in elevation of two points by means of the horizontal distance between them and the vertical angle is called *trigonometric leveling.* It is used chiefly in determining the elevation of triangulation stations and in obtaining the elevation of a plane table station

---

NOTE.—*Curvature and Refraction Correction.* Since a level line is a curved line which at every point is perpendicular to the direction of gravity and the line of sight of a level is along a tangent to this curve it is necessary to take this into account in the more precise leveling work. This correction is usually combined with that due to the refraction of the atmosphere; and the combined correction, for sights of 300 ft. is about .002 ft; for 500 ft., .005 ft.; for 1,000 ft., .02 ft. These corrections are to be applied to any single rod reading by subtracting from the reading; but if the rod be equally distant from the instrument on the foresight and backsight the effect of curvature and refraction is eliminated from the result.

from any visible triangulation point of known elevation. In triangulation work the vertical angles are usually measured at the same time the horizontal angles are measured, so as to obtain the elevations of triangulation points as well as their horizontal positions. The vertical angle is measured to some definite point on the signal whose height above the center mark of the station was determined when the signal was erected, and the height of the instrument above its station should be measured and recorded. In the most exact work the angles are measured with a special vertical circle instrument. In less precise work an ordinary theodolite whose vertical arc reads by verniers to 30″ or to 20″ may be used, but with such instruments only single readings can be made. The best results with such an instrument are obtained by taking the average of several independent readings half of which are taken with the telescope direct and the other half with the telescope inverted. In every case the index correction, or reading of the vertical arc when the telescope is level, must be recorded.

The Transit.—This instrument is for measuring both horizontal and vertical angles, although for ordinary work the vertical attachment is omitted. This instrument consists of a telescope mounted in standards which are attached to a horizontal plate called the *limb*. Inside of the limb, and concentric with it, is another plate called the *vernier plate*. The lower plate or limb turns on a vertical spindle or axis which fits into a socket in the tripod head. By means of a clamp and tangent screw, it may be clamped fast in any position, and made to move slowly through a small arc. The circumference of this plate is usually graduated in divisions of either one-half or one-third of a degree, and in the common form of transit these divisions are numbered from some one point on the limb in

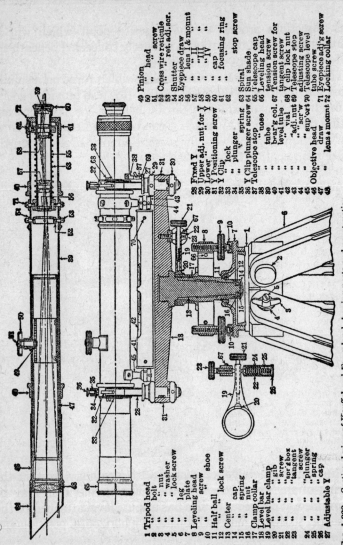

1 Tripod head
2　"　bolt
3　"　nut
4　"　"　washer
5　"　"　lock screw
6　"　leg
7　"　plate
8 Leveling head
9　"　screw
10　"　"　shoe
11 Half ball
12　"　"　lock screw
13 Center
14　"　cap
15　"　spring
16　"　nut
17 Clamp collar
18 Level bar
19 Level bar clamp
20　"　"　gib
21　"　"　screw
22　"　"　box
23　"　"　tangent
　　　　　　screw
24　"　"　plunger
25　"　"　spring
26　"　"　cap
27 Adjustable Y

28 Fixed Y
29 Upper adj. nut for Y
30 Lower　"　"　Y
31 Y Positioning screw
32 Y Clip
33　"　lock
34　"　plunger
35　"　"　spring
36 Y Clip plunger screw
37 Telescope stop
38　"　"　nose
39　"　"　tube
40 b-a-r'g col.
41　"　"　leve. vial
42　"　"　"
43　"　"　adj. nut
44　"　"　"　scr'w
45　"　"　sup'ort
46 Objective head
47　"　"　draw
48　"　"　lens & mount

49 Pinion head
50　"　"　head screw
51　"　"
52 Cross wire reticle
53 Shutter　"　ret. adj. scr.
54　"　"　ret. adj. scr.
55 Eyepiece draw
56　"　lens I & mount
57　"　"　II
58　"　"　III
59　"　"　IV
60　"　cap
61　"　focusing ring
62　"　"
63 Spiral　　　stop screw
64 Sun shade
65 Telescope cap
66 Leveling head
　　　tension screw
67 tension screw for
　　　tangent screw
68 Y clip lock nut
69 Y Telescope stop
70 Telescope level
　　　tube screw
71 Eyepiece adj'z screw
72 Locking collar

Fig. 1,388.—Sectional view of Keuffel and Essex level showing parts and construction.

both directions around to the opposite point which will be 180 degrees. The graduation is generally concealed beneath the plate above it, except at the verniers.

This upper plate is the vernier plate which turns on a spindle fitted into a socket in the lower plate. It is also provided with a clamp by means of which it can be held in any position, and with a tangent screw by which it can be turned through a small arc. A vernier is a device for reading smaller divisions on the scales than could otherwise be done.

Fig. 1,389.—Dietzgen builders convertible Y level. Can be used for leveling and for sighting objects above or below a horizontal plane.

The transit generally is provided with a compass, so that the bearing of any given line with the magnetic meridian may be determined, if desired. It also has a spirit level attached to the telescope, so that it may be brought to a horizontal position and made to serve as a level.

Construction of the Transit.—The general features of transit construction are shown in fig. 1,390. Referring to the figure these are briefly as follows:

Parallel Plates.—There are two plates, upper and lower. *The lower plate A,* is generally formed with two parts. The outside part is a flat ring and is screwed to the tripod head.

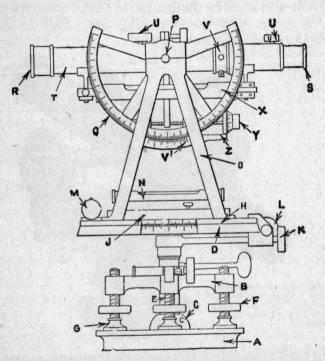

FIG. 1,390.—Transit. *The parts are:* A, lower plate; B, upper plate; C, central dome; D, divided limb; E, spindle; F, foot screws; G, foot screw cups; H, vernier plate; J, compass circle; K, clamp screw vernier plate to divided limb; L, tangent screw; M and N, spirit levels O, standards or supports; P, horizontal shaft; Q, vertical arc; R, objective; S, ocular; T, telescope; U, racks and pinions; V, adjustable cross hair ring; *v,* divided limb vernier; *v',* vertical arc vernier; X, spirit level; Y, gradienter; Z, scaled index. These parts are described in detail in the main text.

The inside part is another flat ring of larger diameter than the opening in the outside part and having a central dome C, perforated on the top.

The inside part is movable and rests on the under side of the outside part.

The upper plate B, is generally made in the form of a central nut, with four arms at right angles (or three at 120°).

> The upper plate carries an inverted conical shell the lower portion of which passes through the perforation in the dome of the inside part of the lower plate where it expands into a spherical shape and thus forms a *ball joint* with the lower plate. This spherical member is perforated in the center to allow the passage of a plumb bob string.

Foot Screws.—The two plates are connected by four (sometimes only three) foot screws F, in order: 1, to clamp the lower and upper plates, making them fast with each other and with the inverted shell, and 2, to serve in leveling the instrument.

> The screws pass through the ends of the arms of the upper plate and are surmounted by dust caps. Their feet fit into small cups G, resting on the top surface of the lower plate to avoid wear.

Shifting Center.—As these cups may be moved as well as the central part of the lower plate (after slightly loosening the foot screws), a slight motion may be given to the instrument for better setting it over a given point of the ground. This arrangement is called a *shifting center.*

Outer Spindle.—In the conical shell attached to the upper plate a second conical shell fits and may revolve. It is the *outer spindle* and carries projections to form attachments with other parts of the transit.

Divided Limb.—The upper portion of the outer spindle terminates in a horizontal (it is intended to be so) disc of plate *D*, the limb of which is divided into 360° sub-divided into half, or third, or quarter degrees. The degrees are numbered every ten, either from 0° to 360° or from 0° to 180° either way; the degree-marks are a little longer than the sub-divisions, and every fifth degree has a mark a little longer yet.

Lower Motion.—The outer spindle and the divided limb are also called the *lower motion.*

Inner Spindle.—A solid inverted cone fits into the outer spindle and may revolve in it; it is the *inner spindle* and, like the outer one, it is provided with some projections for like purposes.

Vernier Plate.—The upper portion of the inner spindle projects further than the divided limb and carries also a horizontal disc *H*, which moves in a plane parallel to the divided limb which it covers, except for two rectangular openings in opposite directions through which the divisions of the limb may be seen. These openings each carry a vernier *v* by means of which the sub-divisions of degrees are again divided. Some verniers read to one minute, others to one-half minute and some to 10 seconds.

To facilitate the reading of the vernier, the openings are sometimes fitted with reflector and magnifying glass.

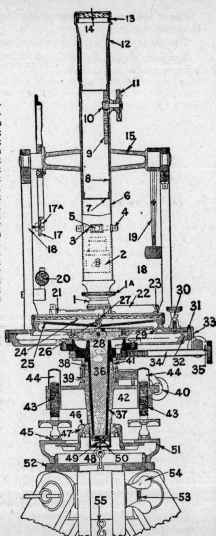

FIG. 1,391.—Sectional view of Dietzgen transit. *The parts are:* 1, eyepiece cap; 2, eye piece tube; 3, cross hair reticle; 4, reticle adjusting screw; 5, washer for reticle adjusting screw; 6, telescope main tube; 7, diaphragm for objective tube; 8, objective slide; 9, focusing rack; 10, focusing pinion; 11, focusing nut; 12, objective head; 13, objective cell; 14, objective; 15, telescope axis; 16, vertical circle; 17, vertical circle; 18, standards; 19, telescope axis clamp; 20, standard level; 21, plate level; 22, vernier shade glass; 23, vernier shade glass frame; 24, compass glass cover; 25, compass needle; 26, needle center; 27, center jewel; 28, needle pivot; 29, needle lifter; 30, needle lifter screw; 31, upper plate with horizontal vernier; 32, lower plate or horizontal limb; 33, tangent hanger; 34, clamp screw for upper vernier plate; 35, plate tangent screw; 36, inner center; 37, intermediate center; 38, outer center; 39, clamp for lower or limb plate; 40, tangent screw for lower or limb plate; 41, clamping collar; 42, leveling base or leveling screw arms; 43, leveling screws; 44, dust caps; 45, leveling screw cups, 46, half ball nut; 47, shifting plate; 48, center nut; 49, center nut spring; 50, dust cap and plumb bob support; 51, leveling screw plate; 52, tripod head; 53, tripod belt; 54, wing nut for tripod bolt; 55, plumb bob chain and hook.

Upper Motion.—The inner spindle and vernier plate *H,* are also called the *upper motion.*

The vernier plate carries a compass circle *J.*

Compass Circle.—A circular box the bottom of which carries at its center a sharp pivot of very hard metal (very hard steel or iridium) upon which a magnetic needle about 5 inches long is balanced by an agate cup fixed in the middle of its length. The needle is very strongly magnetized; its north end is distinguished by color or ornamentation and its balance is regulated by a small coil of fine wire wound around one arm and which can be shifted. The limb formed by the edge of the sides of the box is divided into 360°

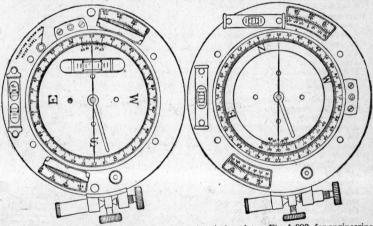

Fig. 1,392 and 1,393.—Dietzgen compass box and variation plate. Fig. 1,392, for engineering transit; fig. 1,393, for surveying transit. The compass circles are numbered in quadrants and graduated to half degrees. The south end of the needle in the northern hemisphere is provided with a coil of fine wire which can be shifted to equalize the difference of attraction. The *variation plate* is provided so that the magnetic declination may be set off accurately; the cardinal points shift with the graduated circle. This latter feature avoids the possibility of an error in reading when the magnetic declination is set off and the needle is at rest between the astronomical north and the magnetic north.

with half degrees shown; they are numbered from two zeros marked at the ends of a diameter to 90° right and left. The bottom of the box is marked with two rectangular diameters corresponding to the graduations 0 and 90° of the vernier and two other diameters at 45° to the first. The forward end of the diameter marked 0 is designated by the letter *N,* and the rear end by the letter *S;* they mean *North* and *South.* The ends of the transverse diameter marked 90° is designated by the letters *E* on the left and *W* on the right; they meaning *East* and *West.* When set to an ordinary surveyor's compass, the forward end of the frame carries a vernier and a tangent screw to read fractions smaller than ½ degree.

Controlling Clamps.—A screw K, permits to clamp the vernier plate H, to the divided limb D. Another screw attached to the upper plate permits to clamp the divided limb to the upper plate.

Tangent Screws.—One tangent or slow motion screw L, accompanies each clamp screw. It is used to complete the clamping at the exact spot where it is to be made.

Spirit Levels.—The spirit levels are attached to the vernier plate, one M, in front (north point of the box) the other N, on the side, thus forming an angle of 90°.

Standards.—The vernier plate carries two vertical standards or supports O-shaped like an inverted V and placed one on each side. the center of their legs being just opposite the 90° graduation of the compass box. They are made equal.

Horizontal Axis.—The standards carry between and on the top of them a movable horizontal axis P.

Vertical Circle.—To this axis is attached, by means of a clamp screw, a vertical circle or arc Q, divided like the horizontal divided circle, and which in its vertical motion, just touches a circular vernier *v*, carried by the left standard together with a slow motion screw.

Telescope.—In the middle of the horizontal axis and perpendicular to it is solidarily attached a telescope T, of a description similar to that of the engineer's level with objective R, and ocular S, racks and pinions U, for their motions, adjustable cross hairs ring V, with ordinary and stadia hairs.

Telescope Level.—An adjustable spirit level X, is also attached to the under part of the telescope as in the engineer's level. This permits of the transit being also used as a leveling instrument if necessary.

Motions of the Telescope.—Being solidary with the vernier plate, the telescope has the full range of the horizon and can measure any horizontal angle. Being on a horizontal axis endowed of free motion, it may move in a vertical plane carrying with it the vertical arc, and it can therefore measure vertical angles.

In the *horizontal motion*, the vertical cross hair of the telescope is brought exactly on the point sighted by means of the slow motion screw L, carried by the vernier plate H.

In the *vertical motion*, the horizontal cross hair of the telescope is brought exactly on the point sighted by means of the slow motion screw carried on the inside of the left hand support and moving the vertical circle.

Surveying

"Lines of a Transit."—The following are the principal lines of a transit:

1. Vertical axis
2. Horizontal axis
3. Plate level line
4. Attached level line
5. Line of collimation

Vertical Axis.—The vertical which passes through the center of the spindle *E*.

Horizontal Axis.—The axis *P*, of the shaft by which the telescope rests on the supports. It must be made horizontal.

Plate Level Line.—The top or bottom lines of the plate level case *N*. These are level when the bubble is centered.

Attached Level Line.—The level line of the bubble level *X*, attached to the telescope. Employed only when the instrument is used as an engineer's level.

Line of Collimation.—Line determined by the optical center of the objective and the intersection of the cross hairs.

Relations between the Lines of a Transit.—The following relations must obtain:

1. The plate levels must be perpendicular to the vertical axis.
2. The line of collimation must be perpendicular to the horizontal axis.
3. The horizontal axis must be perpendicular to the vertical axis.
4. The attached level line and the line of collimation must be parallel.
5. The zero of the vertical circle must correspond to the zero of the vernier when the telescope is horizontal.

Adjustments of the Transit.—The following are the necessary adjustments of the transit.

First Adjustment.—*Making the axis of the spindle vertical and the planes of the plates perpendicular to it.* Set one level over a pair of plate screws; the other level will thus be set over the other pair. Level up both levels by means of the plate screws. Turn the vernier plate around by ½ a revolution; if the bubbles remain centered during the motion, the vernier plate is in adjustment; if they have moved, bring them half way back by means of the adjusting screws and the rest of the way by means of the foot screws. Repeat.

Verify if the bubbles remain centered when revolving the divided circle; if not, the plates are not parallel and the transit must be sent to the maker for repairs.

Second Adjustment.—*Collimating the telescope.* Set up transit in center of open and practically level ground. Carefully level the instrument. Drive a stake or better a chaining pin some 200 or 300 feet away; chain the distance. Take a sight on that point and clamp the plates. Revolve the telescope vertically (in altitude) by half a revolution, thus reversing the line of sight. Chain in that new direction the same distance as first measured and set a pin. Unclamp and revolve the vernier-plate by half a horizontal revolution. Sight again at the first point and clamp. Again revolve the telescope vertically by half a revolution. If the line of sight fall on the pin, the telescope is collimated; if not, set a new pin on the last sight and at the same distance as before and another pin at $\frac{1}{4}$ the distance between the first pin and the second. Move the vertical cross hair by means of the capstan headed screw and an adjusting pin, until the intersection of the cross hairs covers the last pin set. Repeat.

Third Adjustment.—*Adjusting the horizontal axis so that the line of collimation will move in a vertical plane.* Level up carefully and sight on a high, well defined point, as a corner of a chimney, and clamp. Slowly move the telescope down till it sights the ground and drive a pin there. Unclamp; revolve the vernier plate half a revolution and revolve the telescope vertically half a revolution, reversing the line of sight. Look again at the high point and clamp. Slowly move telescope down till it sights the ground. If the intersection of the cross hairs cover the pin, the horizontal axis is in adjustment; if not, correct halfway by means of a support adjusting screw and the rest of the way by means of the plate screws. Repeat.

Fourth Adjustment.—*Making the line of collimation horizontal when the bubble of the attached level is centered.* Drive two stakes 300 or 400 feet apart and set up the instrument about half way between. Level up and take readings on the rod held successively on the two stakes; the difference of the readings is the difference of elevation of the stakes. Next set the transit over one of the stakes, level up and take a reading of the rod held on the other stake; measure the height of the instrument; the difference between this and the last rod reading should equal the difference of elevation as previously determined; if it do not, correct half the error by means of the attached level adjusting screw. Repeat.

Fifth Adjustment.—*Making the vernier of the vertical circle read zero when the bubble of the attached level is centered.* Level up the instrument. Sight on a well defined point and take note of the reading on the vertical circle. Turn vernier plate half a revolution and the telescope also vertically half a revolution and again sight on the same point. Read again the vertical circle. Half the difference of the two readings is the index error which may be corrected by moving either the vernier or the vertical circle;

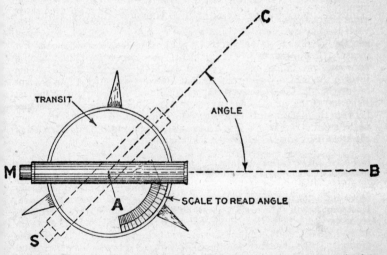

FIG. 1,394.—General principle of transit work. *The transit is placed over the apex A, of the angle BAC, to be measured. Telescope is sighted to stake B (position M), and reading taken; then turned horizontally and sighted to stake C (dotted position S), and reading taken. The difference of these readings gives the angle BAC. Obviously C, may be located so that line AC will make a given angle with AB, by turning telescope until the scale reads the desired angle. The stake is then driven in the line of sight.*

or the error may be noted and applied as a correction to all measurements of vertical angles.

Sometimes it is necessary to adjust the compass; this is as follows:

First adjustment.—Straighten the needle. Examine to see if the ends of the needle set on opposite divisions; if not, fix pivot so that they will. Revolve the box by half a revolution; if the needle do not set on opposite divisions, bend both ends by half the difference.

Second Adjustment.—*Place pivot in center of the plate.* When sure that needle is straight, move pivot till the needle sets on opposite divisions at points such as 0°, 45° and 90°.

Instructions for Using the Transit.—The transit requires various adjustments as explained in the preceding section. To

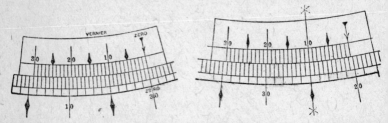

FIGS. 1,395 and 1,396.—The vernier. Fig. 1,395, zero setting; fig. 1,396, set to read 20°10′ from the zero mark. *In the illustrations,* the lower scale represents a portion of the graduations upon the limb, and the upper scale, the graduations upon the vernier. In fig. 1,396, the vernier plate has been revolved through a certain angle which it is desired to read. Looking at the pointer at the extreme right of the vernier, it will be seen that it stands between 20 and 20½ degrees on the lower scale. Next following along the vernier until a division is found which is exactly in line with one on the lower scale. This division is 10 on the vernier; therefore, the reading is 20 degrees and 10 minutes. A vernier reading to minutes is sufficiently accurate for ordinary work.

center the transit over a stake, rest one leg of the tripod upon the ground, then grasp the other legs and place the instrument as nearly over the stake as possible. Then attach the plumb-bob and center it accurately by means of the shifting head. Avoid having the plates too much out of level, as this will result in unnecessary straining of the leveling screws and plates. Having centered the instrument over the stake, level it up by the spirit levels upon the horizontal plate. To do this, turn the instrument upon its vertical axis until the bubble tubes are parallel to a pair of diagonally opposite plate screws. Then, stand facing the instrument and grasp the screws between the thumb and forefinger, and turn the thumb of the left hand in the direction the bubble must move.

When adjusting the screws, turn both thumbs in or out, never in the same direction. Adjusting one level will disturb the other but each must be adjusted alternately until both bubbles remain constant. The method of measuring a horizontal angle is shown in fig. 1,401.

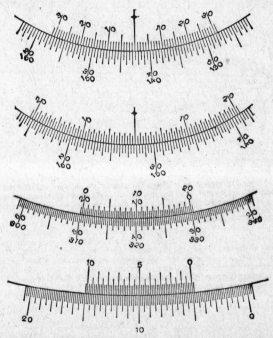

Figs. 1,397 to 1,400.—Various Dietzgen transit verniers made to read minutes 30, 20, or 10 seconds. Fig. 1,397, circle divided into half degrees, vernier reading single minutes; fig. 1,398, circle divided into 20 minute spaces, vernier reading to 30 seconds; fig. 1,399, circle divided to 20 minute spaces, vernier reading to 20 seconds; fig. 0,028, circle divided to 10 minute spaces, vernier reading to 10 seconds. On a building Y level the vernier usually reads to 5 minutes.

The process of laying off a given angle is similar to that of measuring an angle. The transit is set up at the vertex of the angle, the vernier clamped at zero, and the telescope pointed at the target marking the direction of the fixed line. The limb is now clamped, the vernier unclamped, and the vernier plate turned through the desired angle and clamped. A stake should

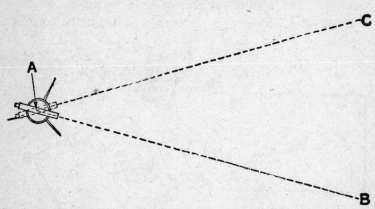

Fig. 1,401.—Method of measuring a horizontal angle. To measure an angle as between the lines AB and AC, set up and level the instrument at A, as already described and clamp one of the verniers at the zero mark on the circle. Turn the telescope upon the target at B, and clamp the limb. Unclamp the vernier plate, and turn the telescope upon the other target at C. Read the vernier which had been set at zero, and the reading will be the horizontal angle through which the telescope turned from B to C. It is not necessary to set the vernier at zero before pointing at the first target. The result will be the same if the vernier be read when pointed at the first target, and then again, when pointed at the second. The difference between the two readings will be the angle required. Care must be taken in this method to note if the vernier pass the 180 degree mark, and, if so, to make the proper calculations. For simple work, where there are but few angles to be measured, it is less confusing to set the vernier at zero each time, especially for those not experienced in the work.

now be driven in line with the vertical wire in the telescope, thus establishing the two sides of the angle. In laying out the foundations of buildings, a corner stake is first located by measurement, then the direction of one of the walls is laid out by driving a second stake. This direction may be determined by local conditions, such as the shape of the lot, or the relation to other buildings. If the building is to be an extension to, or in line with, another building, the direction can be obtained by sighting along the building wall and driving two stakes in line with it. If it be to make a given angle with another building, this angle can be laid off as shown in fig. 1,402.

Gradienter.—Some transits carry, attached to the horizontal

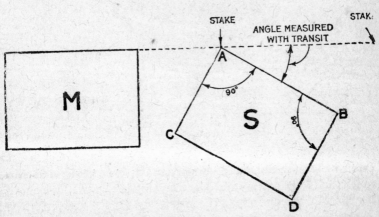

Fıg. 1,402.—Method of laying out a new building S, at a given angle with an old building M. After the corner and the direction of one wall are determined, a right angle may be laid off (if the building be rectangular), thus locating two of the sides, as AB and AC. The length of the side AB, is now measured, locating the corner B. The transit is set up at B, and the line BD, laid off at right angles to AB. AC, and BD, are then laid off the proper length, and thus the four corners of the building located. If the building had not been rectangular the proper angles could have been laid off instead of right angles. It is often desirable to make a block plan or map of the grounds and buildings of a plant.

axis by means of a clamp screw and inside of the right hand support, an attachment called gradienter, **Y** for the determination of grades and distances. It consists of an arm of the shape of an inverted **Y** with curved branches, to the extremities of which are attached an encased spiral spring and a nut through which moves a micrometer screw with a graduated head revolving in front of a scaled index Z, also carried by the arm. The ends of the screw and of the spring about on opposite sides of a shoulder

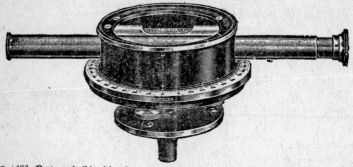

FIG. 1403.—Bostrom builders' level especially adapted for the use of builders, carpenters and stone masons. It can be used for any kind of foundation work and for obtaining angles. It is made of brass, oxidized and has a silvered circle graduated to vial. A plumb bob, tripod and graduated rod, 5 ft. extending to 9½ ft. completes the outfit. The rod is equipped with a target.

carried by the right hand support. The head is divided into tenths and hundredths, and every revolution moves it in front of the scale by one division of the latter; so that the scale gives the

NOTE.—*Care of Instruments.* With proper care the usefulness of an instrument can be preserved for many years; accordingly, the following suggestions on the care of instruments should be noted. The lenses of the telescope, particularly the object glass, should not be removed, as this will disturb the adjustment. If necessary to clean them, great care should be taken and only soft, clean linen should be used. To retain the sensibility of the compass needle, the delicate point on which it swings must be carefully guarded, and the instrument should not be carried without the needle being locked. When the needle is lowered it should be brought gently upon the center pin. The object slide seldom needs to be removed; but when removing is necessary, the slide should be carefully protected from dust. Do not grease or oil the slide too freely, as only a thin film is necessary. Any surplus of oil should be removed with a clean wiper. The centers, subject to considerable wear, require more frequent lubrication. After thoroughly cleaning, they should be carefully oiled with a fine watch oil. All of the adjusting screws should be brought to a firm bearing; but should never be tightened to such a degree that a strain is applied to the different parts, as, if this is done, the adjustment will be very unreliable. When the instrument is carried on the tripod all clamps should be tightened to prevent unnecessary wear on the centers.

number of turns of the screw, and the graduated head the fraction of a turn.

In grading, if one revolution of the screw move the cross hair a space of one foot on a rod held 100 feet away, the slope indicated by the telescope is 1 per cent. To establish a grade, level up the telescope, clamp the arm of the gradienter and turn the micrometer screw as many divisions as required in the grade. For instance: 2.35. Move the head two complete turns plus 35 sub-divisions. Measure height of telescope from ground; set rod at that height; then hold the rod at any point of line, raising it till the target is bisected by the cross hairs; the foot of the rod will then be on the grade.

The Stadia.—This is a device *for measuring distances*, and consists essentially of *two extra parallel hairs in addition to the ordinary cross hairs* of the telescope of a transit or a level as shown in fig. 1,404.

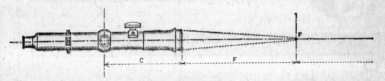

FIG. 1,404.—Principle of the stadia or *device for measuring distances*. The fixed stadia hairs are so set that *they will intercept one foot on a rod at a distance of* 100 *feet*. Since the image of the cross hairs is projected to a point beyond the telescope objective equal to its focal length, the rays of light converge at that point and measurements must begin from there; therefore, a constant is to be added to all stadia readings equal to the focal length of the object glass plus the distance from the face of objective to the center of the instrument. This constant is termed "F + C", and for transit telescopes is equal to about one foot. The stadia hairs are superior to any other appliances for measuring distances.

The stadia hairs may be adjustable or they may be fixed permanently on the diaphragm.

In using the stadia distances are measured by observing through the telescope of a transit the space, on a graduated rod, included between two horizontal hairs called stadia hairs. If the rod be held at different distances from the instrument, different intervals on the rod are included between the stadia

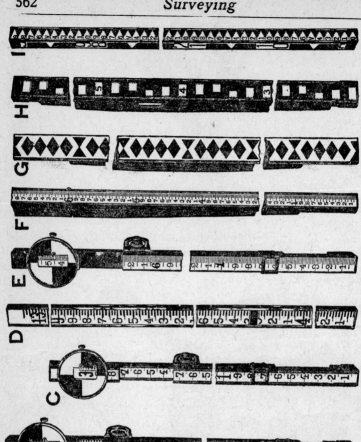

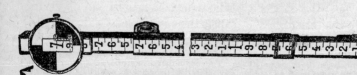

Figs. 1,406 to 1,413.—Various Dietzgen leveling rods. A, heavy Philadelphia rod; B, light Philadelphia rod; C, Philadelphia pattern mining rod; D, Chicago rod, sectional; E, New York rod; F, stadia rod; G, stadia rod; H, Florida rod; I, Illinois rod.

Fig. 1,414.—Measuring Chains. Made in various units as feet, surveyor's links, and in lengths 33, 50, 60 and 100 ft.

Figs. 1,415 and 1,416.—Steel chain tape and detachable handle. *In construction*, the steel ribbon is ¼ in. wide and is plated with white metal. Divided and numbered on hand nickel silver bands (sleeves) which are clamped and soldered preventing corrosion as moisture cannot enter between the bands and ribbon. The ends of the bands are beveled to prevent their catching on under brush etc., or on each other when winding or unwinding the ribbon. Divisions begin about 6 ins. from ends of ribbon.

hairs, the spaces on the rod being proportional to the distances from the instrument to the rod, so that the intercepted space is a measure of the distance to the rod. This method furnishes a rapid means of measuring distances in filling in details of topographic and hydrographic surveys. It is used either with a transit or a plane table which is provided with the two additional horizontal cross hairs. It has the great advantage that the intervening country does not have to be traveled, provides a means of measuring inaccessible distances such as across water surfaces, the errors of measurements are compensating rather than cumulative, and it affords an accuracy sufficient for many kinds of work, being applicable even to surveying for area of such lands as wood lots or farms, for an accuracy of one part in 500 may be attained with the stadia. The rod used may be of any desired pattern of self reading rod, the Philadelphia rod being a good type for short distances. It is well to use a rod with the graduations represented by some diagram which can be seen distinctly a long distance, 1,000 to 2,000 feet away. Portions of two of these rods are shown in figs. 1,405 and 1,406, with the reading of the three cross hairs marked in the figure.

CHAPTER 28

Strength of Timbers

The various mechanical properties of woods have been determined by many tests. In the shop the fitness of any kind of wood for a given purpose depends not on one, but a combination of several properties, such as strength, hardness, stiffness, etc.

In treating of the strength of timbers, numerous technical terms are used the meaning of which should be thoroughly understood. Accordingly a few definitions are here given.

Definitions

Brittle.—Breaking easily and suddenly with a comparatively smooth fracture, *not* tough or tenacious. This property usually increases with hardness. The hardest and most highly tempered steel is the most brittle; white iron is more brittle than grey, and chilled iron more than other. The brittleness of castings and malleable work is reduced by annealing.

Bending stress.—In physics, a force acting upon some member of a structure tending to deform it by bending or flexure; the effect of this force causes bending *strain* on the fibers or molecules of the material of which the part is composed. An instance of pure bending stress is given by pulling on the end of a lever, which tends to deflect it while performing work.

Compression.—To press or push the particles of a member closer together, as, for instance, the action of the steam pressure in a boiler on the fire tubes.

Deformation.—Change of shape; disfigurement, as the *elongation* of a test piece under tension test.

Ductile.—Easily drawn out; flexible; pliable. Material, as iron. is "ductile" when it can be extended by pulling.

Elastic limit.—The greatest strain that a substance will endure and still completely spring back when the strain is released.

Factor of safety.—The ratio between the breaking load and what is selected as the *safe working load*. Thus, if the breaking load of a bolt be 60,000 *pounds per square inch*, and the working load be 6,000 *pounds per square inch*, then the factor of safety is 60,000 ÷ 6,000 = 10.

Force.—That which changes or tends to change the state of a body at rest. or which modifies or tends to modify the course of a body in motion, as a pull pressure or push; a force always implies the existence of a simultaneous equal and opposite force called the reaction.

Load.—The total pressure acting on a surface; thus, if an engine piston having an area of 200 square inches be subjected to a steam pressure of 150 pounds per square inch, then the load or total pressure on the piston is 200 × 150 = 30,000 pounds.

Member.—A part of a structure as a brace, rivet, tube, etc., subject to stresses.

Modulus (or Coefficient) of elasticity.—The load per unit of section divided by the elongation or contraction per unit of length. Within the elastic limit, when the deformations are proportional to the stresses, the modulus of elasticity is constant, but beyond the elastic limit it decreases rapidly. In wrought iron and steel there is a well defined elastic limit, and the modulus within that limit is nearly constant.

Modulus of rupture.—A value obtained by experiment upon a rectangular bar supported at the ends and loaded at the middle substituting results in the formula

$$R = \frac{3Pl}{2bd^2}$$

in which P = breaking load in pounds; l, b and d, = length, breadth and depth respectively in inches.

Permanent set.—When a metallic piece is stressed beyond its elastic limit, deformation occurs, the piece being either stretched, crushed, bent or twisted, according to the nature of the strain. This alteration in form is known as permanent set.

Resilience.—The property of springing back or recoiling upon removal of a pressure, as with a spring. Without special qualifications the term is understood to mean the work given out by a spring, or piece strained similarly to a spring, after being strained to the extreme limit within which it may be strained again and again, without rupture or receiving *permanent* set.

Shear.—The effect of external forces acting so as to cause adjacent sections of a member to slip past each other. When so acted upon the member is said to be in shear.

Strain.—According to Wood it is a name given to the kind of alteration produced by the stresses. The distinction between stress and strain is not always observed, there being much confusion among writers as to these terms.

Strength.—Power to resist force; solidity or toughness; the quality of bodies by which they may endure the application of force without breaking or yielding.

Stress.—1. An internal action or internal force set up between the adjacent molecules of a body when acted upon by forces. 2. The force, or combination of forces, which produces a strain.

Tenacity.—The attraction which the molecules of a material have for each other, giving them the power to resist tearing apart. The strength with which any material opposes rupture, or its *tensile strength*.

Tensile strength.—The cohesive power by which a material resists an attempt to pull it apart in the direction of its fibers, this bears no relation to its capacity to resist compression.

Tension.—The stress or force by which a member is pulled; when thus pulled, the member is said to be in tension.

Tough.—1. Having the quality of flexibility without brittleness; capable of resisting strain, able to sustain hard usage; not easily separated or cut.

Ultimate strength.—The maximum unit of stress developed at any time before rupture.

Yield point.—The point at which the stresses and the strains become equal, so that deformation or permanent set occurs. The point at which the stresses equal the elasticity of a test piece.

The tie rod of a roof truss resists being pulled apart because of its *tensile strength*. The *stress* thus applied *strains* the tie rod, causing a *deformation* or change in the shape of the rod, that is, it is *stretched* (*elongated*) and a *contraction of area* in cross section takes place. If the *load* be not heavy enough to stretch the rod beyond its *elastic limit*, it will, when the load is removed return to its original form due to its *elasticity*.

If the load be heavy enough to stretch the rod beyond its elastic limit, it will not on the removal of the load return to its original form but remain *permanently set*. The elastic limit is reached when, in increasing the load a small increase in load will cause an unduly large contraction of area.

If the load be increased sufficiently to break the rod (overcome its *tenacity*), it is said to be *ruptured*. The rod itself considered as forming a part of the truss is called a *member* of

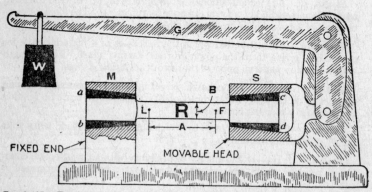

FIG. 1,417.—Tensile test. The specimen R, is placed in the wedge grips *a,b,c,d*, thus pulling it in tension between the fixed end and movable head of the machine. The latter is connected with the scale lever G, upon which slides the weight W, similar to an ordinary weighing scale. Two center marks L and F, are punched on the specimen at a standard distance A, apart. *In testing*, the pull on the specimen is gradually increased by moving W, to the left and the dimensions A and B, measured for each increase of load.

NOTE.—Ordinarily the carpenter, if called upon to specify the sizes of timber entering into the construction of a building, would size them according to his sense of proportion gained by observation of general practice. He knows, for instance, that 2 × 4 studs with the usual spacing are practically always used, but how can he determine if the ordinary floor frame be strong enough to support a heavy load of machinery, etc.? The carpenter should not be called upon to determine the size of timbers as that is the problem of the architect or designer of the building. However, the progressive carpenter will want to know how the architect proportions the timbers and such knowledge will in some instances be of use to him.

the truss, but a short portion of the rod cut off for testing in the laboratory is known as a *specimen*.

Tension.—A tension test is made as indicated in fig. 1,417. The specimen is placed in the machine and gripped at each end, then a tension stress is applied increasing in intensity until rupture, noting as the load is progressively increased, the elongation of the specimen, contraction of area, breaking load and elastic limit, the results being tabulated thus:

Tensile Test

Specimen length........ins. Cross section........sq. ins. Shape......

Load		Contraction of area in %	Elastic limit	Tensile strength (lbs. per sq. in.)
Total in lbs.	Lbs. per sq. in.			

Example.—A truss member is subjected to a load of 50,000 lbs. tensile stress. What size timber should be used if of long leaf yellow pine; if of spruce.

In the table of working stresses, the value given for yellow pine and spruce are 1,200, and 800 lbs. per sq. m. cross section respectively, hence

$$\text{cross section yellow pine timber} = \frac{50,000}{1,200} = 42 \text{ sq. in.}$$

$$\text{cross section spruce timber} = \frac{50,000}{800} = 62.5 \text{ sq. ins.}$$

Compression.—A column supporting the roof of a piazza is subjected to a stress tending to crush it and is said to be *in compression*.

Owing to their transverse position, the medullary rays (a large part of all woods) offer but one-tenth to one-twentieth as much resistance as the main body of fibres and also weaken the timber by disturbing the straight course of the fibres and the regularity of the entire structure. The resistance to compression is much affected by the position of the grain.

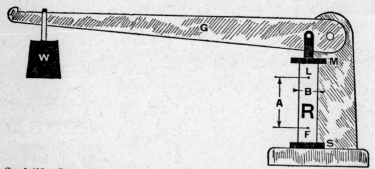

Fig. 1,418.—Compression test. The specimen R, is placed between the two plates M and S, and a compression stress of any intensity applied by moving the weight W, on the lever G. *In testing,* as the load is gradually increased, the changes in dimensions A and B, are noted and result calculated in a manner similar to that explained in the tension test fig. 1,417.

The perfectly cross grained piece sustains about one-tenth to one-twentieth of the load which is supported by the straight grained piece; the piece is also weakened by an oblique grain. When wood is compressed endwise, the fibres act as so many hollow columns firmly grown together. When the load becomes too great these small columns bend over and the piece "buckles." The oblique position of the fibres in cross grained and knotty timber tend to reduce the strength in compression.

In making a compression test, the specimen is placed between two plates as in fig. 1,418, and a compression stress applied gradually increasing in intensity until rupture takes place, noting its increase of cross section, decrease in length, for the various loads and its compression strength in lbs. per sq. in. of cross section of the specimen at rupture the results being tabulated in a similar manner as indicated under the tension test.

The following working stresses and loads from the New York Building Code will indicate limits of stress to which wood should be subjected in proportioning the parts.

Working Stresses for Timbers

(lbs. per sq, in. of cross section)

	Tension	Compression	
		with grain	across grain
Oak	1,200	1,400	1,000
Yellow pine, long leaf	1,200	1,600	1,000
Spruce and Douglas fir	800	1,200	800
Douglas fir	800	....	....
White pine, short leaf yellow pine, N. C. pine and fir	....	1,000	800
White pine	700	....	....
Locust	....	1,200	1,000
Hemlock	600	800	800

Working Stresses for Columns*

(for various length diameter ratios)

Lbs. per sq. in. cross section.

Length ÷ diameter, or least side	Long leaf yellow pine	Spruce
30	600	390
25	700	475
20	800	560
15	900	645
12	960	695
10	1,000	730

Builders in different sections of the country should compare the above with any local ordinances; and in the absence of such, they may be taken as safe working stresses.

Example.—A tank 10 ft. in diameter and 16 ft. high is to be supported by four rectangular posts. Find size of these posts for a working stress of 800 lbs per sq. in. neglecting weight of the structure.

Cubic feet of water contained in the tank when full

$$= \begin{Bmatrix} \text{area bottom} \\ .7854 \times 10^2 \end{Bmatrix} \times \begin{Bmatrix} \text{height} \\ 16 \end{Bmatrix} \; 1256.6 \text{ cu. ft.}$$

Taking weight of water at 62½ lbs. per cu. ft., then

weight of water = 1256.6 × 62.5 = 78,538 lbs.

For four posts and working stress of 800 lbs. per sq. in.

$$\text{cross area of each post} = \frac{78,538}{4 \times 800} = 24.6 \text{ ins.}$$

nearest rectangular post is 4 × 6

---

*NOTE.—For columns of short leaf yellow pine, N. C. pine or Douglas fir, the working stresses shall not exceed ¾ of the corresponding values given for long leaf yellow pine, for columns of white pine or fir, the working stresses shall be taken the same as for spruce; for columns of white oak, the working stresses shall be taken the same as for long leaf yellow pine.

If any of the wood be cut away for bolts, or by notches or mortises, the area should be proportionately increased, using the nearest *larger* size timber rather than nearest *smaller* size.

Example.—One side of a tower projecting from a building is to be supported by four long leaf yellow pine columns having a length of 25 times the diameter. If the total load to be supported be 75,000 lbs., what is the minimum cross section area of each column?

For four columns, the load to be carried on each column

$$= 75,000 \div 4 = 18,750 \text{ lbs.}$$

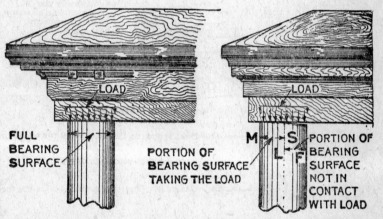

Figs. 1,419 and 1,420.—Good and poor bearing surfaces of columns showing the importance of squaring columns with precision in cutting. In fig. 1,419 the entire top of the column is in contact with the load member, hence the pressure per sq. in. of cross section coming on the column will correspond with the allowable working pressure for which the column was calculated. If the column be carelessly cut off (not square), or out of plumb, as in fig. 1,420, so that only part of the end as MS, is in contact (greatest at M), with the load member then there will be excess stress at this point. Suppose the portion MS, of the bearing surface in contact be only ½ of the entire surface then the stress coming on the top of the column will be twice that for full contact, as LF, shows the portion not in contact with the load member.

In the table of working stresses for columns, for 25 diameters ratio, 700 lbs. per sq. in. of cross section is allowed for a long leaf yellow pine column, hence

$$\text{cross section area} = 18,750 \div 700 = 26.8 \text{ sq. in.}$$

$$\text{diameter corresponding} = \sqrt{\frac{\text{area}}{7854}} = \sqrt{\frac{26.8}{.7854}} = 5.8, \text{ say } 5^{25}\!/_{32}$$

Taking nearest regular size larger would make the columns 6 ins. in diameter.

An important point with respect to timber in compression is that the ends should be cut exactly square so that there will be full bearing surface, otherwise the timber will be subjected at the ends to more than the working stress. This is illustrated in figs. 1,419 and 1,420.

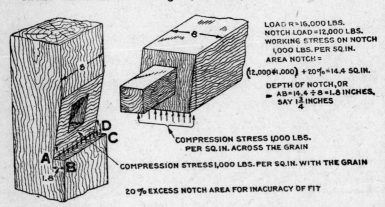

LOAD R=16,000 LBS.
NOTCH LOAD =12,000 LBS.
WORKING STRESS ON NOTCH
1,000 LBS. PER SQ.IN.
AREA NOTCH =

(12,000÷1,000) + 20% =14.4 SQ.IN.

DEPTH OF NOTCH, OR
AB=14.4 ÷ 8 =1.8 INCHES,
SAY $1\frac{3}{4}$ INCHES

COMPRESSION STRESS 1,000 LBS.
PER SQ. IN. ACROSS THE GRAIN

COMPRESSION STRESS 1,000 LBS. PER SQ. IN. WITH THE GRAIN

20% EXCESS NOTCH AREA FOR INACURACY OF FIT

FIGS. 1,421 and 1,422.—Notched mortise and tenon joint illustrating method of calculating the depth of the notch ABCD.

Example.—A load of 16,000 lbs. is to be carried at the end of an 8 × 8 girt. How deep a notch must be cut in the post so that the tenon will be relieved of ¾ of the load allowing 20% excess area for inaccuracy of fit, and working pressures of 1,600 lbs. per sq. in. with grain, and 1,000 lbs. across grain?

¾ of 16,000 = 12,000 lbs. load to be carried by notch

When the members are in position and loaded the end of the girt is subjected to a compression stress *across grain* and the notch, to a compression stress *with grain*. Since the bearing surface of girt and notch are necessarily equal, the joint must be calculated for the lower of the two compression working stresses or 1,000 lbs. per sq. in. Hence

area bearing surface = (12,000 ÷ 1,000) + 20%
$$= 12 \times 1.2 = 14.4 \text{ sq. ins.}$$

Since the girt is 8 ins. wide

depth of notch = 14.4 ÷ 8 = 1.8 ins. say 1¾ ins.

as illustrated in figs. 1,421 and 1,422. Ordinarily a dimension such as **1.8** would be increased to a workable value as 1⅞ or 2 ins., but since a liberal allowance was made for inaccuracy of fit, and it is not advisable to weaken

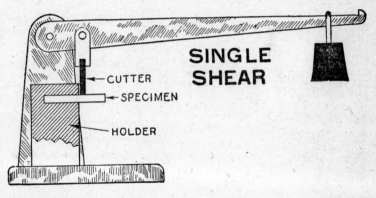

Figs. 1,423 and 1,424.—Single and double shear tests. The specimen is placed in the holder and the stress applied. The cutter shears the metal in a single plane for single shear **and in** two planes for double shear as clearly shown in the illustrations.

the post too much by cutting an unduly deep notch, the next regular dimension smaller is used—1¾ in.

Crushing Across the Grain.—Since timber is very weak in crushing across the grain, as compared to crushing endwise, this is found to be one of the most common methods of failure in

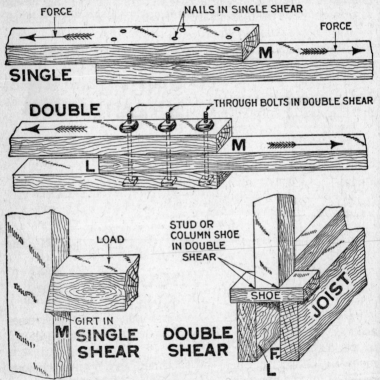

FIGS. 1,425 to 1,428.—Examples of single and double shear. In the lap joint fig. 1,425, the nails are in single shear in the plane of surface M. Evidently in fig. 1,426, there is a tendency to shear the through bolts both along the surfaces M and L, (double shear). In the case of a notched girt, loaded as shown, a shearing stress occurs in the plane M, or side of the post; the reason for the notch in heavy construction is to relieve the tenon of the shearing stress. Fig. 1,428 shows a stud shoe in double shear, the stresses being in the planes L, F.

practice. It is common to rest a timber column on a sill of the same wood, and to design the column for its maximum working load, paying no attention to the utter inability of the sill to carry this load without crushing. Many failures of timber structures are due to this cause alone. As there is no definite point of failure in crushing across the grain, two limits of deformation have been arbitrarily chosen at which the load has been recorded, namely: at *three per cent compression*, as a working limit allowable, and at *fifteen per cent compression*, as an extreme limit, or as failure.

The following values are given in *U. S. Forestry Circular* No. 15 for crushing strength across the grain of various timbers in lbs. per sq. in. (3% deformation):

Long leaf pine 1,000
Short leaf pine 900
White pine 700
Spruce 1,200
White cedar 700
Douglas spruce 800
White oak 2,200
Shagbark hickory 2,700
White elm 1,200
White ash 1,900

Shearing Stresses.—There are two kinds of shearing stresses according as the specimen is in *single* or *double* shear as shown in the tests figs. 1,425 and 1,426. In either case the test is made by cutting through the specimen and noting the load required for the operation. The difference between single and double shear is further illustrated in figs. 1,429 to 1,432, being examples in ordinary carpentry practice. The following table gives the safe working stresses for shearing:

Safe Shearing Stresses for Timbers

(lbs. per sq. in. of shearing surface)

	With grain	Across grain
Oak....................	200	1,000
Yellow pine, long leaf....................	150	1,000
Yellow pine, short leaf....................	150	1,000
N. C. pine, Douglas fir....................	100	1,000
White pine, spruce and fir....................	100	500
Hemlock.......	100	600

The distinction *across grain* and *with grain* should be carefully noted as shown in figs. 1,433 and 1,436. According to Johnson, "wet or green

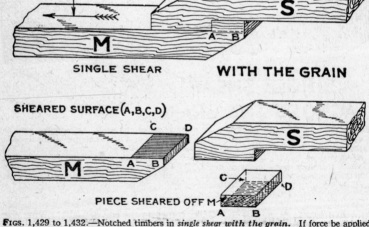

Figs. 1,429 to 1,432.—Notched timbers in *single shear with the grain.* If force be applied to the timbers M and S, tending to pull them apart as indicated by the arrows, a shearing stress is brought on the notches. The notch on M, being the weaker, will shear when sufficient force is applied, as indicated in figs. 1,431 and 1,432. Here the shaded surface ABCD, is the surface sheared. The total force applied divided by the area expressed in sq. ins. given the shearing load in lbs. per sq. in. *with the grain.* Fig. 1,432 shows the notch sheared off M.

wood in general shears about one-third more easily than dry wood; a surface parallel to the rings (tangent) shears more easily than one parallel to the medullary rays. The lighter conifers and hard woods offer less resistance than the heavier kinds, but the best of pine shears one-third to one-half more readily than oak or hickory, indicating that great shearing strength is characteristic of "tough woods."

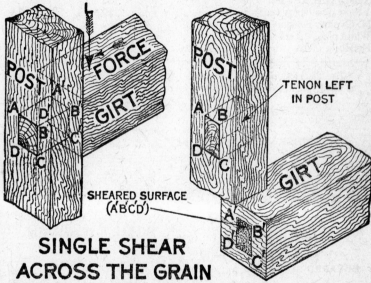

SINGLE SHEAR
ACROSS THE GRAIN

Figs. 1,433 to 1,435.—Mortised girt in *single shear across the grain*. If sufficient force be applied to the girt as indicated by the arrow L, it will force it down shearing off the tenon in the plane of its shoulder as indicated by the shaded surface A'B'C'D' in fig. 1,435. Fig. 1,433 shows girt and post in position before shearing; in fig. 1,434 the end of the tenon ABCD is visable. If the shearing load were, say, 2,000 lbs. per sq. in. (across the grain) and the area of the sheared surface A'B'C'D' were 6 ins., then the total force L, applied necessary to shear off the tenon is 2,000 × 6 = 12,000 lbs.

Example.—A load of 16,000 lbs. comes on the end of a girt. What size tenon must be cut to carry this load without notching, the girt being of yellow pine?

According to the table of safe shearing stress for timbers, yellow pine is allowed 1,000 lbs. per sq. in. across the grain. Hence sectional area of tenon = 16,000 ÷ 1,000 = 16 sq. in.

The relative dimensions of the tenon will depend on those of the girt and post. The tenon should be long and narrow rather than square, so that the cross sectional area of the post will not be unduly reduced.

Example.—If in figs. 1,436 to 1,439, the tenon of M, must carry a load of 16,000 lbs., how large should the tenon be and if S, be an 8 × 8 timber,

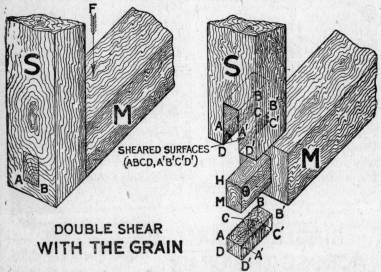

DOUBLE SHEAR
WITH THE GRAIN

SHEARED SURFACES
(ABCD,A'B'C'D')

Figs. 1,436 to 1,439.—Mortise and tenon joint *in double shear with the grain.* Similarly as in the preceding illustrations, if sufficient force be applied to the tenon member M, as indicated by the arrow F, and the tenon be stronger than the mortise of S, it will *double shear* the lower side of the mortise along the shaded surfaces ABCD, and A'B'C'D' as shown in fig. 1,437. If the shearing load were, say 200 lbs. per sq. in., *with the grain* and the area of the sheared surfaces ABCD, and A'B'C'D' were each 6 sq. ins., then the total force F, applied necessary to shear off the bottom of the mortise is (200 × 6) × 2 = 2,400 lbs. In a properly designed joint of this kind the distance AD (fig. 1,437) should be such that *shearing strength of tenon = shearing strength of bottom of mortise.*

determine dimension AD, for equal strength of tenon and mortise, assuming safe shearing stresses of 1,000 lbs. per sq. in. across the grain and 150 lbs. with the grain?

sectional area of tenon = 16,000 ÷ 1,000 = 16 sq. ins.

Take thickness of tenon OH (fig. 1,438) at approximately ⅛ thickness of S, or say 2½ ins., then breadth or

$$HM \text{ (fig. 1,438)} = 16 \div 2.5 = 6.4, \text{ say } 6½ \text{ ins.}$$

Now for equal strength the shearing surfaces ABCD, and A'B'C'D', for the mortise (fig. 1,438) should be proportioned for 150 lbs. per sq. in. Hence, for load of 16,000 lbs.

$$\text{mortise shearing surface} = 16,000 \div 150 = 107 \text{ sq. ins.}$$

or

$$107 \div 2 = 53.5 \text{ sq. ins. for each surface}$$

Since the length of each surface = length of tenon = 8 ins. then **height of** bottom of mortise from end of S, or distance

$$AD = 53.5 \div 8 = 6.6 \text{ ins., say } 6⅝ \text{ ins.}$$

Transverse or Bending Stress.—This is the kind of stress that comes on numerous timbers in buildings, such as girders, joists, rafters, etc., causing a deflection or bending between the points of support. What takes place when these or similar members are subjected to bending stress is considered under the subject of *beams* and it is a subject not easy to understand.

Stiffness.—By definition, stiffness is *that quality possessed by a beam or other timber of resisting the action of a bending force.*

The action of the bending force tends to change a beam from a straight to a curved form. That is a *deflection* takes place. When a load is applied the beam originally assumed to be straight and horizontal, sags or bends downward between the supports. The amount of downward movement measured at a point midway between the supports is the amount of deflection. The action of beams subjected to bending force is clearly described by Johnson as follows:

If 100 lbs. placed in the middle of a stick 2 × 2 ins. and 4 ft. long, supported at both ends, bend or "deflect" this stick one-eighth of an inch (in the middle) then 200 pounds will bend it about one-fourth inch, 300 pound three-eighths inch, the deflection varying directly as the load. Soon, however, a point is reached where an additional 100 pounds adds more than one-eighth inch to the deflection—the limit of elasticity has been reached. Taking another piece from the straight grained and perfectly clear plank of the same depth and width, but 8 feet long, the load of 100 pounds will cause it to bend not only one-eighth inch, but will deflect it by about 1 inch. Doubling the length reduces the stiffness eight-fold. Stiffness then decreases as the cube of the length.

If AB, in fig. 1,440, be a piece of wood, and d the deflection produced by a weight or load, the stiffness of the wood, as usually *stated* is found by the formula

$$E = \frac{Wl^3}{4bdh^3}$$

FIG. 1,440.—Simple beam loaded at middle and supported at ends, illustrating deflection and modulus of elasticity.

Wood. — Transverse and Thrusting Tests

	Tests.	Sizes abt. in square.	Span, inches.	Ultimate Stress	$S = \frac{LW}{4BD^2}$.	Thrusting Stress per sq in
Pitch pine............	10	11½ to 12½	144	45,856 to 80,520	1096 to 1403	3586 to 5438
Dantzic fir..........	12	12 to 13	144	37,946 to 54,152	657 to 790	2478 to 3423
English oak.........	3	4½ × 12	120	32,856 to 39,084	1505 to 1779	2473 to 4437
American white oak...	5	4½ × 12	120	23,624 to 26,952	1190 to 1372	2656 to 3899

Demerara greenheart, 9 tests (thrusting)............... 8169 to 10,785
Oregon pine, 2 tests.................................... 5888 and 7284
Honduras mahogany, 1 test 6769
Tobasco mahogany, 1 test............................... 5978
Norway spruce, 2 tests................................. 5259 and 5494
American yellow pine, 2 tests.......................... 3875 and 3993
English ash, 1 test.................................... 3025

in which

E = modulus of elasticity
W = weight or bending force in lbs.
l = length of beam in ft.
b = breadth and depth of beam in ins.
d = deflection of beam for load W.

In the table on page 585 the woods are grouped according to their stiffness. The figures are only rough approximations which are based on the data given in Vol. IX of the Tenth Census. The first column contains the above modulus, the

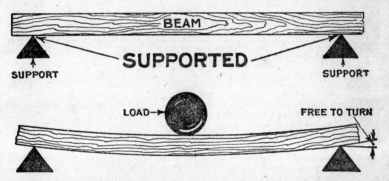

FIGS. 1,441 and 1,442.—Beam *supported at the ends*, showing (in fig. 1,442) how the ends of the beam are free to follow any deflection thus offering no resistance rendering the beam less stiff than when the ends are *fixed*, as in figs. 1,443 and 1,444.

second shows how many pounds will produce a deflection of 1 inch in a stick 1 by 1 by 12 inches, assuming that it could endure such bending within the limits of elasticity, and the third column gives the number of pounds which will bend a stick 2 by 2 inches and 10 feet long through 1 inch.

The stick is assumed to rest on both ends; if it be a cantilever, *i. e.*, fastened at one end and loaded at the other, it bears but half as much load as its end for the same deflection. From the third column it is easy to find how many pounds would bend a piece of the same kind of other dimensions. A 2 × 4 inch bears eight, a 2 × 6 inch, twenty-seven times as much as the 2 × 2 inch, a piece 8 feet long is about twice as stiff as a 10 foot piece; a piece 12 feet long only about three-fifths, 14 feet one third, 16 feet two-ninths, 18 feet one-sixth, and 20 feet one-eighth as stiff. The number of pounds which will bend any piece of sawed timber by 1 inch may be found by using the formula:

$$\text{Necessary weight} = \frac{4\,Ebh^3}{l^3}$$

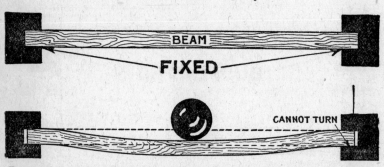

FIGS. 1,443 and 1,444.—Beam *fixed at the ends.* The term *fixed* means that the ends are gripped or embedded in an unyielding substance so that they cannot turn or follow the deflection of the beam under load. The beam then deflects in a compound curve adding greatly to its stiffness. That is, a beam with fixed ends will deflect *less* than one with *supported* ends.

where E, is the figure in the first column, and *b, h, l,* the breadth, depth and length of the timber in inches. If the deflection is not to exceed one-half inch, only one-half this load, and if one-fourth inch, only one-fourth this load is permissible: or in general

$$W = \frac{4Ebh^3}{dl^3} \text{ where } d, \text{ is the deflection in inches.}$$

The deepest beams are the strongest, stiffest and most economical.—The *strength* of a wooden or steel beam of rectangular cross-section varies as the *square of the depth*, directly as the breadth and inversely as the length, and the *stiffness* varies directly as the *cube of the depth*, directly as the breadth and inversely as the cube of its length; hence the deeper beam will have the greater strength and stiffness in proportion to its sectional area. With I beams these relations do not hold strictly, because of the variation in the forms of the cross-sections, but they are approximately true. It therefore follows that, for any given span, it is more economical in floors, where other conditions will permit, to use deep beams spaced farther apart or to use one deep beam in place of two shallower beams. Thus if a distributed load of 39 tons is to be supported over a span of 16 ft., one 20-in. 65-lb. beam, two 15-in. 42-lb. beams, or three 12-in. 40-lb. beams, could be used; but the 20-in. beam would weigh only 1105 lb., allowing for 6-in. bearings, as compared with 1428 lb. for the 15-in. beams and 2040 lb. for the 12-in. beams, and the bolts and separators would be saved.— *Kidder.*

Table of Stiffness (Modulus of Elasticity) of Dry Wood.
General Averages—Johnson

	Modulus of Elasticity per sq. in.	Approximate weight in lbs. which deflects a piece one inch	
		Piece 1″ × 1″ × 12″	Piece 2″ × 2″ × 10″
Live oak, good tamarack, long leaf, Cuban and short leaf pine, good Douglas spruce, Western hemlock, yellow and cherry birch, hard maple, beech, locust, and the best of oak and hickory..............	1,680,000	3,900	62
Birch, common oak, hickory, white and black spruce loblolly and red pine, cypress, best of ash, elm and poplar and black walnut........................	1,400,000	3,200	51
Maples, cherry, ash, elm, sycamore, sweet gum, butternut, poplar, basswood, white, sugar and bull pine, cedars, scrub pine, hemlock and fir................	1,100,000	2,500	40
Box-elder, horse-chestnut, a number of Western soft pines, inferior grades of hard woods..........................	1,000,000	2,300	37

Cutting out a piece 2 × 4 inches and 4 feet long, placing it flatwise so that it is double the width of the former stick, and loading it with 100 pounds, we find it bending only one-sixteenth inch: doubling the width doubles the stiffness.

Setting the same 2 × 4 inch piece on edge so that it is 2 inches wide and 4 inches deep, the load of 100 pounds bends it only about one sixty-fourth inch: doubling the thickness increases the stiffness about eightfold. It follows that if we double the length and wish to retain the same stiffness we must also double the thickness of the piece.

A piece of wood is usually stiffer with the annual rings set vertically than if the rings be placed horizontally to the load.

Cross grained and knotty wood, to be sure, is not as stiff as clear lumber; a knot on the upper side of a joist, which must resist in compression, is, however, not so detrimental as a knot on the lower side, where it is in tension.

Every large timber which comes from the central part of the tree contains knots, and much of its wood is cut more or less obliquely across the grain, both conditions rendering such material comparatively less stiff than small clear pieces.

The same stick of pine green or wet is only about two thirds as stiff as when dry. A heavy piece of long leaf pine is stiffer than a light piece;

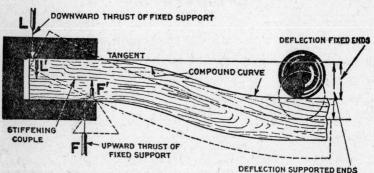

FIG. 1,445.—One end of loaded beam showing stiffening effect of *fixed ends* as compared with *supported ends*. Evidently when the ends are fixed the deflection of the beam will be resisted by an upward thrust indicated by the arrow F, and a downward thrust L, forming a resisting or stiffening couple which holds the portion of the beam embedded in the bearing in a horizontal position, causing the beam to deflect in a compound curve which increases its stiffness. The dotted outline shows the excess deflection for same load were the beam simply *supported* at the ends.

heavy pine in general is stiffer than light pine, but a piece of hickory, although heavier than the pine, may not be as stiff as the piece of long leaf pine, and a good piece of birch exceeds in stiffness any oak of the same weight.

In the same tree, stiffness varies with the weight, the heavier wood being the stiffer; thus the heavier wood of the butt log is stiffer than that of the top; timber with much of the heavy summer wood is stiffer than timber of the same kind with less summer wood. In old trees (of pine) the center of the tree and the sap are the least stiff; in thrifty young pine the center is the least stiff, but in young second-growth hard woods it is the stiffest.

Modulus of Elasticity.—Since it is desirable, and for many purposes essential, to know beforehand that a given piece with a given load will bend only a given amount, the stiffness of wood is usually stated in a uniform manner and under the terms "modulus" (measure) of elasticity.

BEAMS

By definition a beam is *a long horizontal piece of wood, metal or other material, or several such combined for supporting weight forming part of the frame of a building or other construction.*

With respect to the manner in which the load is carried, the ends of beams are said to be:

1. Supported.

2. Fixed.

It is important to carefully distinguish between these two classes, as it makes considerable difference in the strength whether a beam is "*supported* at the ends" or "*fixed* at the ends."

A beam is said to be

1. *Supported at the ends*, when it simply rests on supporting surfaces, being free to turn or follow the deflection caused by the load.

2. *Fixed at the ends*, when held rigid against turning.

These terms are illustrated in figs. 1,441 to 1,444.

A fixed beam is stiffer than a supported beam as shown in fig. 1,445.

Breaking Strength.—It has been found by experiment that a piece of wood one inch square *supported* on bearings one foot apart, will break under a certain weight. This weight varies

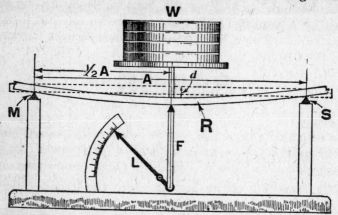

FIG. 1,446.—Transverse text. The specimen R, called a *unit beam* of dimensions 1 in. × 1 in. × 1 ft. is placed on two supports M and S, and a load W, applied at the mid-point as shown; this is called a "concentrated load," or "loaded at the middle." The deflection or amount of bending for any load is indicated with precision by the multiplying gear LF. *In testing,* the weight W, is gradually increased and deflections noted till the breaking load is reached, the results being tabulated thus:

Tensile Test

Specimen: length.........ins.   cross section.........ins.   shape.........

Load		Contraction of area in %	Elastic limit	Tensile strength
Total in lbs.	Lbs. per sq. in.			

with different woods and with different specimens of the same wood. Authorities, however, have agreed to regard the average results obtained from a large number of experiments as standard.

The following table gives the breaking loads for various woods for a beam one inch square, loaded in the middle and *supported* at the ends, the *span* or distance between supports being one foot.

Breaking Loads of Unit Beams

(unit beam 1 × 1 × 12)

Spruce	3,500 lbs.
Norway red pine	4,000 lbs.
Georgia pitch pine	5,000 lbs.
White oak	5,500 lbs.
Ash	7,000 lbs.
Teak	8,000 lbs.

FIG. 1,447.—Beam resting on knife edge supports, illustrating the terms *length l, breadth b* and *depth d.*

It has been further found by experiments that the strength of a beam

1. Is proportional to its breadth.
2. Is inversely proportional to its length.
3. Is proportional to the square of its depth.

Fig. 1,447 defines the dimensions of a beam giving the usual letters used in formulæ. The following examples illustrate the above three relations for beams supported at the ends and loaded at the middle.

Example.—What is the breaking load of a spruce beam *3 ins. wide*, 1 in. thick and 1 ft. long?

From table, the breaking load of the 1 × 1 × 12 or "unit" beam is 3,500 lbs. Hence, since the *strength is proportional to the breadth*, the breaking load of beam in the example = 3 × 3,500 = 10,500 lbs.

Example.—What is the breaking load of a spruce beam 1 in. square and *2 ft. long?*

From table, the figure for spruce is 3,500 lbs. and since the *strength is inversely proportional to the length*, the breaking load of beam in the example = 3,500 ÷ 2 = 1,750 lbs. That is, if the length of a beam be doubled, its strength is reduced one half.

Example.—What is the breaking load of a spruce beam where breadth = 1 in., *depth* = 2 ins., and length = 1 ft.?

Here it will be seen that increasing the depth will considerably increase the strength. For spruce strength of unit beam = 3,500 lbs. Since the *strength is proportional to the square of the depth*, the strength or breaking load of beam in the example = 3,500 × 2^2 = 3,500 × 2 × 2 = 14,000 lbs.

The relations just stated and illustrated in the examples for beams supported at the ends and loaded in the middle may be expressed as a formula thus:

$$\text{breaking load} = \frac{\text{breaking load unit beam} \times \text{breadth} \times \text{depth}^2}{\text{length}}$$

or using symbols

$$P_{cs} = \frac{Wbd^2}{l} \quad \ldots \ldots \ldots \ldots \ldots \ldots (1)$$

in which

P_{cs} = concentrated breaking load of given supported beam in lbs , loaded in middle.

W = breaking load of unit beam in lbs.

b = breadth of given beam in ins.

BREAKING LOADS

(various spruce beams)

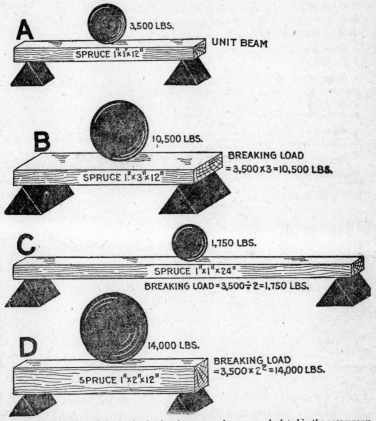

A 3,500 LBS. UNIT BEAM

SPRUCE 1"x1"x12"

B 10,500 LBS.

SPRUCE 1"x3"x12"

BREAKING LOAD = 3,500 x 3 = 10,500 LBS.

C 1,750 LBS.

SPRUCE 1"x1"x24"

BREAKING LOAD = 3,500 ÷ 2 = 1,750 LBS.

D 14,000 LBS.

SPRUCE 1"x2"x12"

BREAKING LOAD = 3,500 x 2² = 14,000 LBS.

FIGS. 1,448 to 1,451.—Breaking loads of various spruce beams as calculated in the accompanying examples. **A,** is the unit beam, (the dimension being $1'' \times 1'' \times 1$), the size used in testing. **B,** is equivalent to three unit beams. **C,** shows the inverse relation between strength and length. **D,** illustrates forcibly the importance of *depth* with respect to strength.

d = depth of given beam in ins.

l = length of beam or span, that is, distance between supports *in ft.*

In giving the dimensions of a beam, they are given in the order breadth, depth, length, the breadth and depth being given in inches and length in feet.

It is important not to confuse the terms breadth and depth,

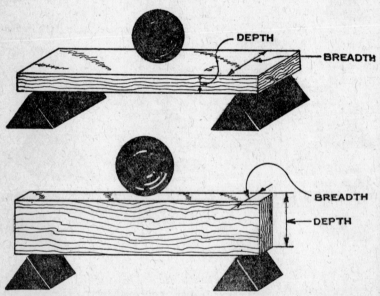

Figs. 1,452 and 1,453 —Breadth and depth of a beam. These terms depend upon the position of the beam. In fig. 1,452, the broad side is the *breadth* of the beam, whereas in fig. 1,453, which shows the same beam turned over 90°, the narrow side is the breadth of the beam.

as it is the position of the beam which determines this as shown in figs. 1,452 and 1,453. The application of the formula just given is illustrated in the example following:

Example.—What is the breaking load for a 2 × 10 × 16 white oak **beam** loaded at the middle and supported at the ends?

Substituting in formula (1), the given values $b = 2$, $d = 10$, and $l = 16$, and value from table for breaking load of unit white beam or W = 5,500, the breaking load of the given beam or

$$Pcs = \frac{5,500 \times 2 \times 10^2}{16} = 68,750$$

Example.—What would be the strength of the beam in the preceding example if it had been laid flat instead of on edge, that is, laid as in **fig. 1,452**, instead of as in fig. 1,453?

Here $b=10$ and $d=2$, the other values to be substituted in the formula remaining the same. Substituting

DISTRIBUTED LOAD

FIG. 1 454.—Distributed load as indicated by the iron balls equally spaced along the beam between supports.

$$Pcs = \frac{5,500 \times 10 \times 2^2}{16} = 13,750$$

Evidently by solving equation (1) for P, b, d, or l, the break-ing load, breadth, depth, or length of a beam may be calculated when the other values are given.

Distributed Load.—Instead of placing all the load in the middle of a beam, as in the examples just given it may be regarded as being *distributed*, that is, the beam is uniformly loaded as in fig. 1,454. It is important to get a correct idea c´

what constitutes a distributed load. This is shown in figs. 1,455 to 1,457. A distributed load is the kind of load usually considered in determining the size of girders, joists, etc., and is usually stated in lbs. per sq. ft. of floor surface.

Example.—A hay bay is 20 ft. wide, 40 ft. long and 12 ft. high. When filled with hay what is the load per sq. ft. of floor surface? If the joists be spaced 24 ins. on center, what is the distributed load coming on each joist?

The cubic contents of the bay or volume of hay = 20 × 40 × 12 = 9,600 cu. ft. At 512 cu. ft. to the ton of hay the bay will hold 9,600 ÷ 512 = 18¾ tons or 37,500 lbs. of hay. The floor area = 20 × 40 = 800 sq. ft. and load per sq. ft. of floor surface = 37,500 ÷ 800 = 47 lbs. per sq. ft.

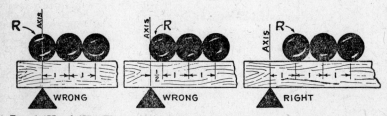

FIGS. 1,455 to 1,457.—Wrong and right conceptions of a distributed load. The distribution is assumed to be *uniform* as indicated by the iron balls of equal size equally placed as in fig. 1,457. They should not be placed so that the first unit of load as ball R, in fig. 1,455 will be in the axis of the support as it would not bring any pressure on the beam tending to flex it. Again if placed tangent to the axes as R, in fig. 1,456, the spacing would not be uniform. Fig. 1,457 shows uniform spacing which is the correct method of distributing the load.

For 24 ins. spacing of joist, loaded floor area to be supported by each joist = 2 × 20 = 40 sq. ft., for which distributed load per joist = 40 × 47 = 1,880 lbs.

A beam supported at the ends with a distributed load will carry twice as much as when all the load is placed at the middle.

Accordingly to find the breaking load when the load is distributed use formula (1) and multiply by 2.

Example.—What is the breaking distributed load for a 2 × 10 × 16 white oak beam supported at the ends, the strength of the unit white oak beam being 5,500 lbs.?

Substituting the values in formula and multiplying by 2

$$\text{breaking load} = \frac{5,500 \times 2 \times 10^2}{16} \times 2 = 137,500 \text{ lbs}$$

Safe Load; Factor of Safety.—The loads for beams thus far considered are the breaking loads. Evidently it would not do to load a beam up to its breaking point, hence in practice, a beam is made large enough so that it will require considerably more to break it than the *maximum load* to which it will be subjected. This maximum load is known as the *safe load* and the ratio between the safe load and breaking load is called the *factor of safety*, that is

$$\text{factor of safety} = \frac{\text{breaking load}}{\text{safe load}}$$

*The safe load tables of Profs. Lanza and Johnson are based on a factor of safety of 5 on green beams and of 8 on dry beams, when known to be either long leaf or Cuban yellow ("Georgia") pine. For white pine, cypress and Oregon fir 65% of the load given in the tables are to be taken; for short leaf yellow pine, for Norway pine, spruce, oak, elm and ash, 80%.

Example.—What is the safe distributed load on a 2 × 10 × 16 white oak joist taking factor of safety at 8?

$$\text{breaking load} = \frac{Wbd^2}{l} \times 2 = \frac{55,000 \times 2 \times 10^2}{16} \times 2 = 137,500 \text{ lbs.}$$

safe load 137,500 ÷ 8 = 17,188 lbs.

Strength of Joists.—The accompanying table has been calculated from the formula used in modern construction by F. E. Kidder and other noted engineers:

$$\text{safe load} = \frac{2 \times \text{breadth} \times \text{square of depth} \times A}{\text{length}} \quad \ldots\ldots\ldots\ldots(2)$$

*NOTE.—See The Materials of Construction by Johnson, page 681.

Safe Quiescent Loads
Uniformly Distributed
for
Long Leaf Yellow Pine

set on edge and supported at both ends. Multiply weight given by exact thickness of joists used.

1x4	1x6	1x7	1x8	1x9	Span in ft.	1x10	1x12	1x14	1x15	1x16
		SAFE LOAD POUNDS						SAFE LOAD POUNDS		
533	1200	1633	2133	2700	6	3333	4800	6533	7500	8533
400	900	1225	1600	2025	8	2500	3600	4900	5663	6400
320	720	980	1280	1620	10	2000	2880	3920	4500	5120
267	600	816	1066	1350	12	1666	2400	3266	3750	4256
228	514	700	914	1157	14	1428	2056	2800	3214	3658
213	480	653	853	1080	15	1333	1920	2613	3000	3412
200	450	612	800	1012	16	1250	1800	2450	2816	3200
188	423	576	753	953	17	1176	1694	2306	2653	3012
178	400	544	711	900	18	1111	1600	2177	2500	2844
160	360	490	640	810	20	1000	1440	1960	2250	2560
145	327	445	582	736	22	909	1309	1782	2045	2327
139	313	426	556	704	23	869	1252	1704	1956	2226
133	300	408	533	675	24	833	1200	1633	1875	2133
128	288	392	512	648	25	800	1152	1568	1800	2048
123	277	377	492	623	26	769	1107	1507	1730	1969
119	267	363	474	600	27	740	1066	1451	1665	1896
114	257	350	457	578	28	714	1028	1400	1607	1828
107	240	326	426	540	30	667	960	1306	1507	1706
100	225	306	400	506	32	625	900	1225	1406	1600
			376	476	34	588	847	1153	1323	1506
			355	450	36	555	800	1088	1250	1422
			337	426	38	526	757	1031	1184	1347
			320	405	40	500	720	980	1125	1280

☞ The safe loads above estimated are for *clear* pieces and *full* sizes. On account of scant sizes and more or less defective stock, an allowance of 20 per cent must be made. For example, the safe load for a 1 x 8-8 is 1600 pounds, and for a 2 x 8-8 two times this or 3200 pounds. But for reasons stated 20 per cent must be deducted, reducing the safe load of a 2 x 8-8 to 2560 pounds.

The safe load for fir is 90 per cent of above long leaf yellow pine; for white oak 75 per cent; for short leaf yellow pine and Norway pine 70 per cent; hemlock 65 per cent; white pine 60 per cent; spruce 70 per cent; cast iron 222 per cent; wrought iron 666 per cent, and medium steel 888 per cent.

I. When the load is concentrated midway between the supports, take only half of above loads.

II. For beams fixed at one end the other unsupported and the load uniformly distributed take one-fourth of above loads; if the load is concentrated on the unsupported end, then take only one-eighth of above.

III. In the above, the safe load includes the weight of the joists, which must be deducted to get the net or superimposed safe load.

IV. Joists longer than 12 times their width used without intermediate supports are apt to crack plastered ceilings.

NOTE.—*Nominal and actual sizes of beams.* Dressed beams and in many localities floor joists carried in stock, are more or less scant of the nominal dimensions and for such beams and joists a reduction in the safe load must be made to correspond with the reduction in size. The dressed sizes are generally ¼ in. scant up to 4 ins. in breadth, above which they are ½ in. scant, while in depth they are all generally ½ in. less than the nominal size. The safe loads may be obtained by multiplying the safe loads for the corresponding nominal sizes by the factors given in the above table.

the breadth and depth being taken in inches and the depth **in** feet.

In the formula, the letter *A* is a *constant* and denotes the safe load for **a** unit beam loaded at the middle. This is also $1/18$ of the allowable fibre stress in lbs. per sq. in. The following table gives the values of *A* obtained **by** dividing by 18, the recommended unit stresses for transverse bending **and** those given in the building laws of New York, Chicago, Baltimore **and** Boston.

Values of A

	New York	Chicago	Baltimore	Boston	*Recom- mended
Yellow pine ...	90	72	100	83	67
White pine....	67	44	56	56	39
Spruce........	67	44	75	56	39
Hemlock......	44	33	..	..	33
Chestnut......	..	..	..	..	44
Oak..........	67	67	83	56	67
Douglas fir....	67	72	..	..	56

Example.—In a certain hay bay, the hay load is 37,500 lbs. distributed on 21 joists spaced 24 in. centers. Determine if 2×10 joists using accompanying table of safe loads for long leaf yellow pine, will carry the load (the exact thickness of the joists being $1\frac{3}{4}$ ins.). Each joist will carry

$$1/21 \text{ of } 37,500 = 1,786 \text{ lbs.}$$

Referring to the table, the safe load for a $1 \times 10 \times 20$ joist is 1,000 lbs. This multiplied by $1\frac{3}{4}$ ins., the exact thickness of the joists, $= 1,750$ lbs., whereas provision must be made for 1,786 lbs. Hence, the joists must be spaced closer together or larger joists used.

The above table also shows the most economical sizes of joists to use. For instance, the safe load for a $4 \times 4 \times 16$ joist

---

*NOTE.—The recommended values of *A* for wooden beams may be increased from 30 to 40% for temporary structures and for commercially dry and protected timber, not subject to impact, or for ideal conditions.

Safe Loads for Long Leaf Yellow Pine and Fir Columns Standing Plumb, Supported at the Ends Only

8	10	12	14	SIZE OF POST — INCHES	16	18	20	22
POUNDS					POUNDS			
12160	11200	10240	9280	4x4	8320	7360	6400	5440
18200	16800	15360	12920	4x6	12480	11040	9600	8160
19500	18760	17550	16500	5½ diam. round	15460	14416	13395	12350
30200	28800	27400	25900	6x6	24500	23040	21600	20160
40300	38400	36500	34600	6x8	32600	30720	28800	26880
50400	48000	45600	43200	6x10	40800	38400	36000	33600
38540	37130	35710	34300	7½ diam. round	32890	31456	30035	28622
64000	54400	52560	50600	8x8	48600	46700	44800	42850
80000	68000	65600	63200	8x10	60800	58400	56000	53600
96000	81600	78700	76800	8x12	73000	70100	67200	64320
70900	61970	60190	58350	9½ diam. round	56585	54800	53018	51175
100000	100000	85600	83200	10x10	80900	78400	76000	73600
120000	120000	102700	99800	10x12	97000	94100	91200	88320
140000	140000	119800	116500	10x14	113100	109800	106400	103040
103900	103900	90912	88730	11½ diam. round	86350	84180	82290	79972
144000	144000	144000	123800	12x12	121000	118100	115200	109440
168000	168000	168000	145500	12x14	141100	137800	134400	127680
192000	192000	192000	165100	12x16	161300	157400	153600	145920
196000	196000	196000	196000	14x14	169100	165800	162400	155800
256000	256000	256000	256000	16x16	225300	221400	217600	209900
324000	324000	324000	324000	18x18	289400	285100	280800	272160
400000	400000	400000	400000	20x20	400000	356800	352000	342400

Above are results of full size columns tested at the United States arsenal at Watertown, Mass., by James H. Stanwood who is instructor in civil engineering at Massachusetts Institute of Technology, as quoted by Frank E. Kidder in his "Architect's Pocket-Book." Above table is based on the following formula:

Safe load per *square inch* of cross section $= 1000 - \left(10 \times \dfrac{\text{length in inches}}{\text{breadth in inches}}\right)$

Other woods gave the following, to-wit;

Short leaf yellow pine:

Safe load per *square inch* of cross section $= 850 - \left(8.5 \times \dfrac{\text{length in inches}}{\text{breadth in inches}}\right)$

Oak and Norway pine:

Safe load per *square inch* of cross section $= 750 - \left(7.5 \times \dfrac{\text{length in inches}}{\text{breadth in inches}}\right)$

White pine and spruce:

Safe load per *square inch* of cross section $= 625 - \left(6 \times \dfrac{\text{length in inches}}{\text{breadth in inches}}\right)$

For the breadth use shortest side, *i. e.*, in a 4 x 6 the breadth is 4 inches. The results from above equations multiplied by area of cross section give the safe load in pounds.

NOTE.—Structure and appearance of wood.—The structure of wood affords the only reliable means of distinguishing the different kinds. Color, weight, smell, and other appearances, which are often direct or indirect results of structure, may be helpful in this distinction, but cannot be relied upon entirely. In addition, structure underlies nearly all the technical properties of this important product and furnishes an explanation why one piece differs as to these properties from another. Structure explains why oak is heavier, stronger, and tougher than pine; why it is harder to saw and plane, and why it is so much more difficult to season without injury. From its less porous structure alone, 't is evident that a piece of a young and thrifty oak is stronger than the porous wood of an old or stunted tree; or that Georgia or long leaf pine excels white pine in weight and strength. Keeping especially in mind the arrangement and direction of the fibres of wood, it is clear at once why knots and "crossgrains" interfere with the strength of timber. It is due to structural peculiarities that "honeycombing" occurs in rapid seasoning, that "checks" or cracks extend radially and follow pith rays, that tangent or "bastard" boards shrink and warp more than quartered lumber. These same peculiarities enable cherry and oak to take a better finish than basswood or coarse grained pine. These same peculiarities enable cherry and oak to take a better finish than basswood or coarse grained pine. These same peculiarities structure, aided by color, determines the beauty of wood. All the pleasing figures, whether in a hardwood ceiling, a desk of quartered oak, or in the beautiful panels of "curly" or "birds eye" maple decorating the saloon of a ship or a palace car, are due to differences in the structure of the wood. Knowing this, the appearance of any particular section can be foretold, and almost unlimited choice and combination are thereby suggested. Thus a knowledge of structure not only enables us to distinguish the different woods, judge as to their qualities, and explain the causes of their beauty, but it also becomes an invaluable aid to the thoughtful worker, guiding him to a more careful selection and a more perfect use of his material.—*Johnson.*

Steel Joist Loading Tables Adopted by all Manufacturers

All values are for joists braced laterally as in standard floor construction. All sq. ft. loads include weight of floor construction. *To find safe live load deduct weight of floor and ceiling.* Average approximately 40 lbs. sq. ft. loads produce no deflections more than $1/300$ span per sq. in.

Total Safe Uniform Loads in Pounds Per Square Foot of Floor. Joists Spaced 19-inch Centers.

Span	B43	B53	B63	B73	B83½	B93½	B104	B114	B124
6	244								
7	179	241							
8	137	184	242						
9	97	145	196	266					
10	71	118	155	216					
11	53	89	128	178					
12	40	68	107	149	196				
13		54	85	127	168	211			
14		43	68	110	145	182			
15			55	90	126	159	199	252	
16			46	74	111	140	175	221	263
17				62	93	124	155	196	233
18				52	78	105	139	175	208
19					66	95	124	157	186
20					57	81	112	141	169
21					49	70	98	128	153
22						61	85	117	139
23						53	74	103	127
24							65	91	117
25							57	80	104
26							51	71	93

Total Safe Uniform Loads in Pounds Per Square Foot of Floor Joists Spaced 24-inch Centers.

Span	B43	B53	B63	B73	B83½	B93½	B104	B114	B124
6	193								
7	142	191							
8	108	146	192						
9	77	115	155	211					
10	56	94	123	171					
11	42	70	102	141					
12	32	54	85	119	156				
13		43	67	101	133	167			
14		34	54	87	115	144			
15			44	71	100	126	158	199	237
16			37	59	88	111	139	175	209
17				49	74	98	123	155	185
18				41	62	83	110	139	165
19					53	75	99	124	148
20					45	64	89	112	134
21					39	56	78	102	121
22						48	67	93	110
23						42	59	82	101
24							52	72	93
25							46	64	83
26							41	57	74

TRUSCON STEEL JOISTS

B124 .21 — B114 .11 — B104 .01
B93½ .6 — B83½ .9 — B73 .L
B63 .5 — B55 — B43

TRUSCON STEEL COMPANY, Youngstown, Ohio.

FIGS. 1,458 to 1,466.—Various steel joists.

NOTE.—To simplify the work of architects, engineers and designers, the manufacturers of steel joists have collaborated in establishing efficient section properties and uniform safe loading tables within the range of spans and loads for which steel joist floors are particularly adaptable. The attached tables are, therefore, standard, and the loads shown apply to the same size of joists over the same span, regardless of the manufacturer or detail of design or shape. This uniformity eliminates the necessity of considering alternates submitted on the basis of different section properties.

Steel Joist Loading Tables—Continued

Total Safe Uniform Loads in Pounds Per Square Foot of Floor. Joists Spaced 16-inch Centers.

16

Span	B43	B53	B63	B73	B83½	B93½	B104	B114	B124
6	289								
7	212	286							
8	163	219	287						
9	116	173	227	316					
10	84	140	184	256					
11	63	106	152	212					
12	48	82	128	178	234				
13		64	101	152	199	251			
14		51	81	130	172	216			
15			66	107	150	188			
16			54	88	131	166	236	299	356
17				74	110	147	208	262	313
18				62	93	131	184	232	277
19					79	113	164	208	247
20					68	96	147	186	221
21						83	133	168	200
22						72	116	152	182
23						63	101	139	165
24							88	123	151
25							77	108	139
26							68	95	124

Description and Properties Truscon Steel Joists.

Section Index	Wt. per ft.	Thickness Metal A	B	C	Mo. of Inertia	Sec. Mod.
B43	3.7	.072		.144	2.60	1.30
B53	4.2	.072		.144	4.38	1.75
B63	4.9	.072	.216	.216	6.90	2.30
B73	5.4	.072	.227	.227	11.20	3.20
B83½	5.9	.072	.227	.227	16.80	4.20
B93½	6.6	.072	.239	.239	23.85	5.30
B104	7.6	.072	.253	.253	33.25	6.65
B114	9.0	.083	.286	.286	46.20	8.40
B124	10.0	.083	.300	.300	60.00	10.0

Total Safe Uniform Loads in Pounds Per Square Foot of Floor. Joists Spaced 12-inch Centers.

12

Span	B43	B53	B63	B73	B83½	B93½	B104	B114	B124
6	385								
7	283	381							
8	217	292	383						
9	154	231	303	421					
10	112	187	245	341					
11	84	141	203	282					
12	64	109	170	237	311				
13		86	134	202	265	334			
14		68	108	174	229	288			
15			88	142	199	251	315	398	474
16			73	118	175	221	277	350	417
17				98	147	196	246	310	369
18				82	124	175	219	277	329
19					105	150	197	248	295
20					90	128	177	224	267
21						111	155	203	242
22						96	134	185	220
23						84	103	164	202
24							96	144	185
25							81	127	165
26								113	147

FIGS. 1,467 and 1,468.—Double chained joists.

is 800 lbs. (4 ∨ 200), while the safe load for a 2×6 is 900 (2×450), showing that while the 2×6 contains much less material, yet when used on edge it is ⅛ stronger than the 4 × 4.

In using the table the following instructions should be noted:

1. The values in the table apply to beams supported at the ends and subjected to distributed load

2. When the load is concentrated midway between supports, take only half the given loads.

3. For beams fixed at one end, unsupported at the other, and having a distributed load, take one fourth the given loads; if the load be concentrated on the unsupported end, take only one eighth of the given loads.

4. The safe load includes the weight of the joist which must be deducted from the given load to get the net load.

5. *Joists longer than 12 times their width used without intermediate supports are apt to crack plastered ceilings.*

6. The table loads are for *clear* pieces and *full* sizes. On account of scant sizes and more or less defective stock, an allowance of 20% must be made.

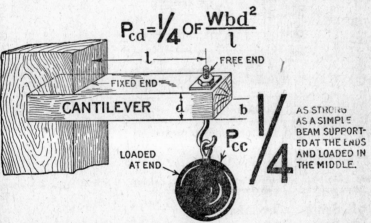

FIG. 1,469.—Simple cantilever beam or beam *fixed* at one end and supported at the other with *concentrated load*. It is ¼ as strong as a simple beam supported at the ends and loaded at the middle. A familiar example of the cantilever beam is on barn forming a projecting support for a hoisting tackle for hoisting hay into the loft.

7. The safe load for fir is 90% of the table load; for white oak, 75%; for short leaf yellow pine and Norway pine, 70%; hemlock, 65%; white pine, 60%; spruce 70%; cast iron, 222%, wrought iron 666%; medium steel, 888%.

Cantilever Beams.—By definition a cantilever beam is *a beam having one end fixed as in a wall and the other end free.*

The load may be either *concentrated* at the free end, as for instance, when a pulley is attached at that point for hoisting, or *distributed*, as for instance in a projecting loft loaded with goods and supported by cantilever beams. In this instance the cantilever beams may be extensions of simple beams beyond one of the supports. Such beams are virtually fixed as though cut off and the ends embedded in an unyielding substance.

Cantilever beams are frequently used for projecting galleries and projecting upper portions of buildings. They may be either:

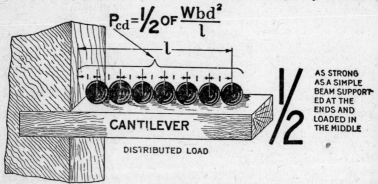

$$P_{cd} = \tfrac{1}{2} \text{ OF } \frac{Wbd^2}{l}$$

CANTILEVER

DISTRIBUTED LOAD

AS STRONG AS A SIMPLE BEAM SUPPORTED AT THE ENDS AND LOADED IN THE MIDDLE

Fig. 1,470 —Simple cantilever beam with *distributed load*. It is ½ as strong as a simple beam supported at the ends and loaded at the middle.

1. Simple (not reinforced) or
2. Braced.

It has been found by experiment that *the strength of a cantilever beam is ¼ that of a simple beam supported at both ends.* Hence to find the breaking load *divide the breaking load of a simple beam of same span and cross section by 4.*

Expressed as a formula, the breaking load of a cantilever beam loaded at the free end or

$$P_{cc} = \tfrac{1}{4} \text{ of } \frac{Wbd^2}{l} \dots\dots\dots\dots\dots\dots(2)$$

in which the sub letters placed after P indicate *cantilever beam* and *concentrated load*, the other letters in the formula being the same as in formula (1) on page 590.

Example.—What is the breaking load of a white oak 4 × 4 × 5 cantilever beam with load concentrated at the end? What is the safe load with a factor of safety of 8?

Referring to the table on page 589, the breaking load for a unit white oak beam is 5,500 lbs. Substituting this value for W, and $b = 4$, $d = 4$, $l = 5$ from the example in formula (2)

$$Pcc = \frac{1}{4} \text{ of } \frac{5,500 \times 4 \times 4^2}{5} = 17,600 \text{ lbs.}$$

With a factor of safety of 8,

safe load = $\frac{1}{8}$ of 17,600 = 2,200 lbs.

If the load be distributed instead of concentrated the beam will carry twice the load.

That is, in the example just given, the breaking load would be
17,600 × 2 = 35,200 lbs.

Now since a cantilever beam has $\frac{1}{4}$ the strength of a simple beam with the same kind of load, it follows that the cantilever with *distributed* load has half the strength of the simple beam loaded in the middle. Expressed as a formula, the breaking distributed load of a cantilever beam, or

$$Pcd = \frac{1}{2} \text{ of } \frac{Wbd^2}{l} \dots \dots \dots \dots \dots \dots \dots \dots (3)$$

in which the sub letters placed after P indicate cantilever beam, and distributed load, the other letters having the same meaning as in formula (1) page 589.

Example.—A gallery 6 × 20 must carry a distributed load of 150 lbs. per sq. ft. and is to be supported by white oak cantilever beams spaced

604 *Strength of Timbers*

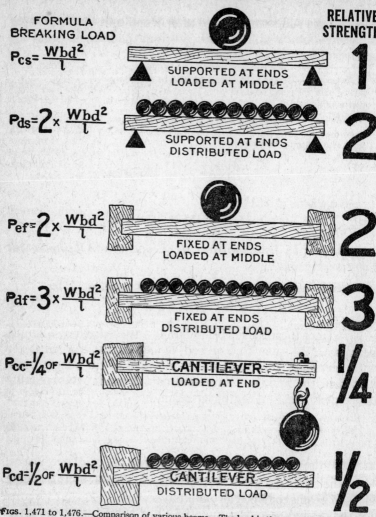

FORMULA BREAKING LOAD

RELATIVE STRENGTH

$P_{cs} = \dfrac{Wbd^2}{l}$ — SUPPORTED AT ENDS LOADED AT MIDDLE — **1**

$P_{ds} = 2 \times \dfrac{Wbd^2}{l}$ — SUPPORTED AT ENDS DISTRIBUTED LOAD — **2**

$P_{ef} = 2 \times \dfrac{Wbd^2}{l}$ — FIXED AT ENDS LOADED AT MIDDLE — **2**

$P_{df} = 3 \times \dfrac{Wbd^2}{l}$ — FIXED AT ENDS DISTRIBUTED LOAD — **3**

$P_{cc} = \frac{1}{4} \text{ OF } \dfrac{Wbd^2}{l}$ — CANTILEVER LOADED AT END — **¼**

$P_{cd} = \frac{1}{2} \text{ OF } \dfrac{Wbd^2}{l}$ — CANTILEVER DISTRIBUTED LOAD — **½**

FIGS. 1,471 to 1,476.—Comparison of various beams. The load is the same in each case, the relative strength when loaded in the middle and when the load is concentrated being given for each type of beam.

24 ins. centers. Determine the size of the beams (neglecting the weight of the structure).

Area floor surface = 6 × 20 = 120 sq. ft.

Loaded floor surface to be supported per beam = 2 × 6 = 12 sq. ft.

Distributed load per beam = 12 × 150 = 1,800 lbs.

Equivalent load for simple beam referred to table on page 596 (see *item* 3 of instructions for using this table) = 1,800 × 4 = 7,200 lbs.

According to *item* 6 (see page 601) 20% allowance must be made for defects in timber and scant size, and also, from *item* 7, the strength of white oak is 25% less than the long leaf yellow pine, hence a total allowance of 20 + 25 = 45% must be made. That is, increase the load of 7,200 lbs. calculated per beam 45%, giving equivalent table load of

$$7,200 \times 1.45 = 10,440 \text{ lbs.}$$

Referring to the table, look along the horizontal line for 6 ft. span and find sizes of joists to select from, thus

Depth of beam	Table load		Load per inch breadth		Required breadth
10	10,444	÷	3,333	=	3.13 ins.
12	10,444	÷	4,800	=	2.15 ins.
8	10,444	÷	2,133	=	4.9 ins.

These values for required breadth of course do not represent stock sizes. And in general the practice is to take the "nearest *larger* regular size."

In some cases, however, where the calculated value comes very near a regular size the next *smaller* regular size may be taken. For instance with selected timber 2 × 12 beams would answer. Again, for exposed construction where appearance is to be considered, special finished 5 × 8 beams may be used. In selecting a size it should be noted that the greater the depth of beam compared with breadth the less feet board measure of lumber are required.

In the absence of the special table on page 596, the dimensions of beams may be calculated by solving the given formulæ for the desired unknown quantities and substituting the given data. An example of cantilever beam will suffice to illustrate the process, similar calculation being made for the other beams using the proper formula in each case.

Example.—Determine the size of spruce beams to support the gallery under the conditions given in the preceding example, with factor of safety of 18, allowing 20% for imperfect stock.

The distributed load per beam was found to be 1,800 lbs. and the breaking load for factor of safety of 18 is

$$1,800 \times 18 = 32,400$$

allowing 20% for defective stock, the load must be increased to

$$32,400 \times 1.2 = 38,880$$

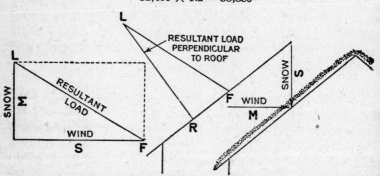

FIGS. 1,477 and 1,479.—Diagrams illustrating graphical methods of finding resultant load perpendicular to roof due to wind and snow loads.

In formula (3) page 589, solve the equation for one of the unknown beam dimensions and assume a trial value for the other, solving for *b* rather than *d*, to avoid extracting the square root. Solving for *b*, the equation becomes

$$b = \frac{2l\,P_{cd}}{Wd^2} \dots\dots\dots\dots\dots\dots\dots\dots\dots\dots\dots\dots(4)$$

Now, in table on page 589, the value for a spruce unit beam is W = 3,500 lbs. The given quantities are $l = 6$, $P_{cd} = 38,880$. Assume a depth of beam or $d = 10$ ins. and substituting in (4)

$$b = \frac{2 \times 6 \times 38,880}{3,500 \times 10^2} = 1.33, \text{ say } 1\frac{1}{2} \text{ in.}$$

CHAPTER 29

Practical Drawing

By definition the term mechanical drawing means *drawing executed mechanically by aid of drawing instruments as distinguished from that executed by the unguided hand*. Accordingly the first thing to consider is the drawing instruments, and secondly, how to use them.

Drawing Instruments.—A good draughtsman should have good instruments; in fact the best are none too good and are easily rendered unfit for use unless they be properly handled. The advice given by some instructors for beginners to buy a cheap set of instruments for use until he find out if he be gifted in the art of draughting, is rather questionable, for if an experienced draughtsman cannot do good work with poor instruments, how then can a beginner be expected to accomplish anything, or determine if he have any talent for drawing?

There are two general classes of drawing instruments, those of circular cross section friction joints of Riefler pattern, and those of angular cross section with set screw joints. The author very strongly recommends the purchase of the circular pattern instruments, as they are superior in every way to the other type.

The following is a list comprising everything needed for general draughting work:

1 drawing board
1 set of instruments
1 tee square
2 triangles, 30° and 45°
1 drawing scales
2 pencils 3H and 6H

1 bottle of drawing ink
1 box of thumb tacks (small)
1 ink and pencil eraser
1 sponge eraser
1 pen holder and lettering pens
1 irregular curve
1 protractor

In some cases involving enlarging or reducing the size of drawings propor tional dividers are necessary.

Drawing board.—The size of the board should be about 2 ins

Fig. 1,480.—Dietzgen white pine drawing board with dovetailed hardwood cleats or "ledges." This construction permits expansion and contraction. The dovetail grooves are sunk in ¼ the thickness of the board, thus securing a firm grip on the narrow wooden strips. *Stand-ard sizes:* 31 × 43; 37 × 55; 43 × 61; 49 × 73; 49 × 85 ins.

longer and 2 ins. wider than the size of paper to be used. The board should be made of well seasoned, straight grained pine, free from all knots; the grain should run lengthwise of the board.

The edges of the board should be square to each other and perfectly smooth in order to provide a good working edge for the head of the tee square to slide against.

A pair of hard wood cleats is screwed or dove tailed to the back of the board. The board should be about three-quarter inch in thickness. The cleats, fitted at the back of the board at right angles to its longest side, may be about two inches wide and one inch thick. Such cleats will keep the board from warp-ng through changes of temperature and moisture.

Fig. 1,480 shows a board of this type bottom side up. Another method of preventing warping is by two transverse end pieces into which the several pieces forming the board proper are secured by tongue and groove

FIG. 1,481.—Dietzgen white pine drawing board with tongue and groove end ledges. This board has two drawing surfaces. *Standard sizes:* 12 × 7; 16 × 22; 20 : 24½; 20 × 26; 23 × 31; 31 × 43 ins. A good size for the beginner and for ordinary use is the 16 × 22 ins.

FIG. 1,482.—Dietzgen Eureka adjustable drawing table. Hardwood frame, iron legs, pine wood board having hardwood ledges. Height adjustment 32 to 40 ins. The wheel clamp at right locks table when tilled to any desired angle.

joints as shown in fig. 1,481. The standard dimensions given in figs. 1,480 and 1,481 will indicate the ordinary sizes as regularly manufactured.

The paper is fastened to the board usually and most conveniently by *thumb tacks*. Under no circumstances should the large size tacks be used—get the smallest and thus increase the life of the board, as no board can be expected to remain in condition if jumbo tacks or railroad spikes be used to fasten down the paper.

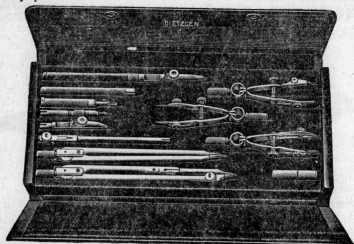

Fig. 1,483.—Dietzgen Riefler pattern or cylindrical set of drawing instruments, *comprising:* 5½ in. compass with detachable needle and pencil points; 5 in. hair spring dividers; 5½ and 4½ in. ruling pens; extension rod; 3 spring bows, pencil, pen, and point; box of leads; key. The extra or small size ruling pen is not necessary but can be used to advantage in some instances.

The board is sometimes mounted on legs and arranged to fold up when not in use, such device being called a drawing table. There are numerous kinds of these tables on the market. Most of these are too rickety to be satisfactory. Fig. 1,482 shows a rigid design of board having adjustments for height and inclination of board.

"Set" of Instruments.—Drawing instruments usually come

in sets, that is, several instruments in a case. For beginners, and for general use, a set containing the following instruments is all that is necessary.

1 compass   1 extension bar
1 hair spring dividers   1 ruling pen
3 spring bows (pencil, pen and points)

Fig. 1,483, shows a set comprising the above instruments of the Riefler pattern with exception that set contains an extra ruling pen.

Compasses.—This instrument is for describing arcs or circles

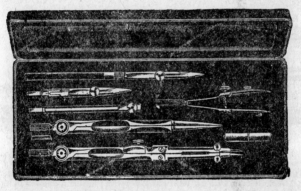

FIG. 1,484.—Set of angular pattern instruments shown to illustrate difference between these and the Riefler pattern or cylindrical instruments recommended by the author. In above figure note the set screws at joints and the shape of the instruments.

with either pencil or ink. It consists of two legs pivoted together so that they may be set to any desired radius. One leg carries an adjustable "needle point" or center, and the other has a joint in which may be secured the pencil or pen arms. Each leg has a pivoted joint permitting adjustment of the ends, so that the end arms which carry the center needle point and pen or pencil may be adjusted perpendicular to the paper for various radii. Figs. 1,485 to 1,487 show six inch compasses with pencil and pen arms and extension bar. The important requirement of good compasses is that the legs may be moved to any radius without any spring back; cheap instruments always spring back making it difficult to set them with precision. Figs. 1,488 to 1,493 show some construction details of compasses and dividers.

Hair Spring Dividers.—Compasses and dividers are very much alike but each has its special use.

Dividers consist of two legs pivoted at one end and provided with sharp needle points at the other, for use in spacing off dis-

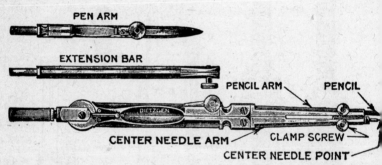

PEN ARM

EXTENSION BAR

PENCIL ARM   PENCIL

DIETZGEN

CENTER NEEDLE ARM   CLAMP SCREW

CENTER NEEDLE POINT

Fig. 1,485 to 1,487.—Compasses with pencil and pen arms and extension bar. Fig. 1,485, pen arm; fig. 1,486, extension bar; fig. 1,487 compasses with pencil arm clamped to leg.

tances, as shown in fig. 1,494. For precision, they are fitted with a "hair spring" device, consisting of an adjustable screw controlled by a steel spring in one leg, as shown in fig. 1,495. In operation the legs are set to the approximate desired position and brought to the exact position by turning the adjusting screw.

Spring Bows.—These small compasses and dividers made with two spring legs whose distance apart is regulated by a small through bolt and thumb screw. They usually come in sets of three: pen bow, pencil bow and dividers, as shown in figs.

1,496 to 1,498. Fig. 1,497 is the pencil bow shown without the lead. Spring bows are used for describing circles of small diameter, and for minute spacing.

Extension Bar.—In order to extend the range of compasses a lengthening or extension bar, as shown in fig. 1,486, is generally provided which greatly increases the diameters of circles which may be described.

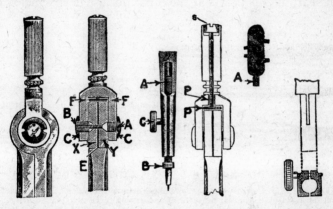

FIG. 1,488 and 1,489.—Main pivot as constructed for compasses and dividers. FF, on the pivot forks. The bolt AB, goes entirely through the legs and bolts the forks together. The conical parts of A and B, form the pivot joints which are securely held by lock nuts CC. E, is a steel disc which acts as an anti-friction bearing for the heads of the legs X, and Y. To apply tension in adjusting, loosen only one of the lock nuts CC.

FIGS. 1,490.—Screw thread needle point. *In construction,* the portion A, is threaded to the extremity of the arm. The portion B, is knurled to be more easily turned with the fingers. The thumb screw C, clamps the needle point rigidly.

FIGS. 1,491 and 1,492.—Clamping device. *In operation* by a turn of the key A, the screw S, is pressed down on pin P, which is fastened to the small plate P. The plate P, rests on the top of the legs of the compasses or dividers and when pressed down by turning the screw S, holds the legs firmly in the desired position. The device is useful when spacing or using the same opening of compasses or dividers repeatedly.

FIG. 1,493.—Shank and clamp socket. In the round form, the feathered shanks fit into side clamping spring sockets. By this construction the interchangeable parts of the compasses are firmly locked twice. First, by the steel feather of the shank, and secondly, by the clamping sockets being drawn together with the screw.

Drawing or Ruling Pens.—A special pen is used for drawing lines, as shown in figs. 1,499 and 1,500.   The points are made

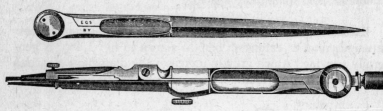

FIGS. 1,494 and 1,495.—Plain and hair spring dividers. Note the sharp pointed legs, and the adjusting screw of the hair spring in.

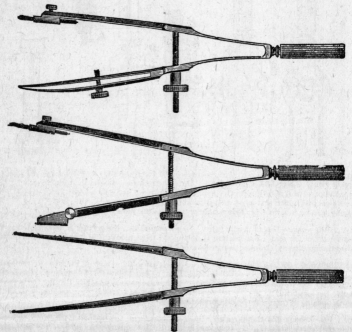

FIGS. 1,496 to 1,498.—Spring bows; fig. 1,496, bow pen; fig. 1,497, bow pencil (shown without lead); fig. 1,498, bow dividers.

of two steel blades which open and close as required for thickness of lines by a regulating screw.

A good drawing pen should be made of properly tempered steel, neither too soft nor hardened to brittleness. The nibs should be accurately set, both of the same length, and both equally firm when in contact with the drawing paper. The points should be so shaped that they are fine enough to admit of absolute control of the contact of the pen in starting and ending lines, but otherwise as broad and rounded as possible, in order to hold a convenient quantity of ink without dropping it. The lower (under) blade should be sufficiently firm to prevent the closing of the blades of the pen, when using the pen against a straight edge.

FIG. 1,499. — Dietzgen reservoir ruling pen.

FIGS. 1,500 and 1,501.—Dietzgen fountain ruling pen. In fig. 1,501, A is the metal top; B, the air escape; C, the cap; D, the pen socket; E, the plunger; F, the ink tube; G, the packing nut; H, the cap tension. The barrel is filled by unscrewing the metal top and dropping the ink into the barrel by means of an ink dropper which is furnished with each instrument. The ink is conveyed to the pen point by engaging the stud on the metal top in the longest slot in the cap and pressing the cap gently with the thumb or the forefinger. The intermediate slot is used when less ink is desired, and when the pen is not in use the stud is engaged in the smallest slot, thus preventing the cap being pressed down accidentally.

FIGS. 1,502 and 1,503. — Side views of ordinary ruling pen spring blade, polished ebony handle.

The spring of the pen, which separates the two blades, should be strong enough to hold the upper blade in its position, but not so strong that it would interfere with easy adjustment by the thumb screw. The thread of the thumb screw must be deeply and evenly cut so as not to strip. Figs. 1,499 and 1,500 are side and end views of an ordinary ruling pen.

Tee Square.—This instrument is used for drawing lines parallel to the lower edge of the board, and consists of two parts, the head and the blade, these being fastened at 90° to each other

Fig. 1,504.—Dietzgen fixed head T square; ash, maple lined, black walnut head.

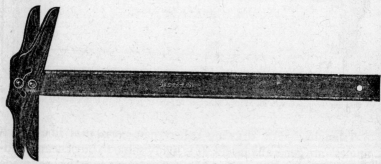

Fig. 1,505.—Dietzgen movable head T square; ash, maple lined blade, black walnut. This type of square has a fixed head on one side and movable head on the other. The movable head is pivoted so that it may be shifted to any angle with the blade, a clamp screw being provided to lock the head in any position.

as shown in fig. 1,504. This is the fixed head type of square. The square is sometimes fitted also with a movable head as shown in fig. 1,505, permitting drawing line inclined to the edge of the board. Fig. 1,506 shows the two types of square in position on the board.

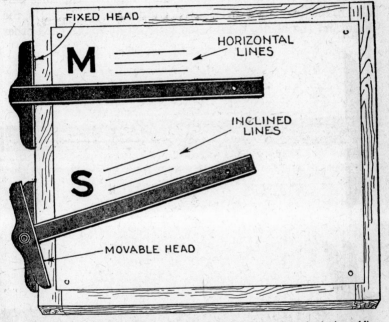

FIXED HEAD

M

HORIZONTAL LINES

INCLINED LINES

S

MOVABLE HEAD

FIG. 1,506.—Fixed and movable head **T** squares in position on board showing horizontal lines that may be drawn with the fixed head square **M**, and inclined lines with movable head square at **S**.

Triangles.—For drawing other than horizontal lines, "triangles" are generally used. It is inadvisable to buy cheap wooden triangles, as they soon warp out of true; get only the best made of transparent ambro. Two triangles will be ordinarily required —the 45° and the 30°. as shown in figs. 1,507 and 1,508. The first

one has two sides at right angles and the third at 45°; the second
two sides at right angles and the third making a 30° angle with

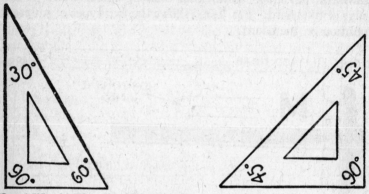

FIGS. 1,507 and 1,508.—45° and 30° triangles.

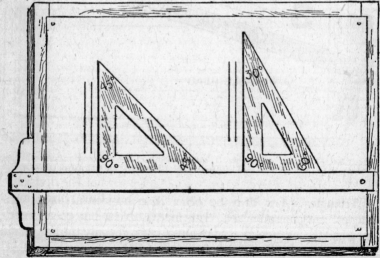

FIG. 1,509.—45° and 30° triangles in position on T square.

ne side and 60° with the other. By placing these triangles on the T square as in fig. 1,509, vertical, or inclined lines may be drawn.

Rule and Scales.—The rule is used for measuring and comparing dimensions the same as the ordinary carpenter's 2 ft. folding rule. For the drawing board however it is an instrument

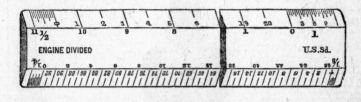

Figs. 1,510 and 1,511.—Flat and triangular draughtsmans' box wood scales. *An explanation* of the 1 in. and ½ in. scales will suffice for all. Where it is used as a scale of 1″ to one foot, each large space, as from 0 to 12 or 0 to 1, represents a foot, and is a foot at that scale. There being 12″ in one foot, the twelve long divisions at the left represent inches; each inch is divided into two equal parts, so from 0 to one division at the left of 9 is 9½″ and so on. The 1″ and ½″ scales being at opposite ends of the same edge, it is obvious that one foot on the 1″ scale is equal to two feet on the ½″ scale, and conversely, one foot on the ½″ scale is equal to six inches on the 1″ scale; and 1″ being equal to one foot, the total feet in length of scale will be 12; at ½″ to 1 foot the total feet will be 24.

of greater precision being usually 10 or 12 ins. long and divided into 32nds. The face is beveled to an edge so that the division lines will lie very close to the drawing paper, thus permitting distances to be marked off accurately.

When drawings are made the same size as the object that is "full size," a rule of the above description answers the purpose, however, when drawings are to be made smaller or larger than the actual size of the object to be drawn, *scales* are employed. For architectural drawing the various scales are divided into feet and inches with sub-divisions. The most convenient forms are the usual flat or triangular box wood scales as shown in figs. 1,510 and 1,511.

The triangular scale is the one generally used as it contains six different scales as shown. The usual scales are:

3	ins. = 1 ft.	¾ in.	= 1 ft.
1½	ins. = 1 ft.	⅜ in.	= 1 ft.
1	in. = 1 ft.	¼ in.	= 1 ft.

Fɪɢ. 1,512.—Dietzgen's India ink.

the scales being usually designated by the length of the foot division as for instance the 1½ or ¾ in. scale. On each scale, as can be seen, the first foot is divided into inches, and where the scale is large enough, into fractions of an inch.

Drawing Ink.—India ink, and not ordinary ink is used. It can be obtained either in the dry (stick) or liquid form.

Although the dry ink is considered the best, it is not generally used because of the time and skill required in mixing. The liquid India ink comes in small bottles having a quill attached to the cork, by means of which the pen is easily filled. Fig. 1,512 shows the type bottle used, and a brand that can be recommended. It can be had waterproof.

Pencils.—Drawings are generally made "*in pencil*" and then

FIGS. 1,513 to 1,517.—Chinese or India inks. Fig. 1,513 oval black; figs. 1,514 and 1,515, square black; fig. 1,516, oblong gilt; fig. 1,517 oblong black.

"*inked in.*" These are made in various degrees of "hardness," the hardest being designated 9H. The choice as to hardness depends upon the kind of drawing and precision. For ordinary work, as in laying out house frames on a large scale, a 3 or 4H would do. However, in drawing a roof stress diagram on. say,

FIG. 1,518.—Dixon's "Excello" drawing pencil. Note that the four H hardness is expressed "HHHH." On some pencils it would be expressed as "4H."

a scale of $1'' = 2,000$ lbs., a pencil no softer than 6H should be used, because a sharp point could not be maintained with a soft pencil, and precision could not be expected with a pencil having "*an acre of lead*" on its point.

Pencils are generally sharpened to a conical point, as in fig. 1,519, but some sharpen them so the lead is wedge-shape as in figs. 1,520 and 1,521.

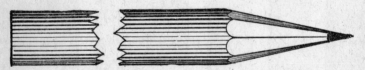

FIG. 1,519.—Pencil with conical point.

FIGS. 1,520 and 1,521.—End and side views of drawing pencil with lead sharpened "wedge shape."

Thumb Tacks.—As stated elsewhere, don't expect to get long service from a drawing board if "spikes" be used for holding down the paper. Thumb tacks are so called because they have a large head so that they may be easily pressed into the board by the thumb. Use the smallest tack that will hold the paper on the board; this will depend somewhat upon the size of the paper, its weight, backing, etc.

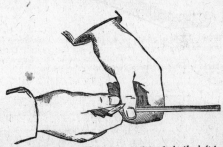

FIG. 1,522.—How to sharpen a pencil. Hold the pencil firmly in the left hand, as in the drawing, allowing about an inch to project beyond the fingers, and turn it gradually as the knife removes the wood. The knife should be held so that the blade alone projects beyond the fingers, and the part of it nearest the handle used for cutting. The pencil should be placed against the inside of the thumb of the right hand, as shown, and the wood removed by slight shaving. The lead should not be cut at the same time as the wood, but rested on the thumb and pared gently afterwards; by attention to these directions the pencil will be economized.

FIGS. 1,523 to 1,525.—Steel stamped thumb tacks. They come in cardboard boxes of 100.

FIGS. 1,526 to 1,537.—Gem union (solid head) thumb tacks.

The cheap steel stamped thumb tacks as shown in figs. 1,523 to 1,525 are preferable to the more expensive solid tacks shown in figs. 1,526 to 1,537. For large tacks they are conveniently removed with a tack lifter as in fig. 1,538, but this is not necessary with the small tacks as they are easily removed by aid of the finger nail.

FIG. 1,538.—Tack lifter. Made of metal, nickel-plated. Very convenient for pushing in or for extracting tacks from drawing boards, without injuring the points. The handle can be used as a paper cutter, and is also serviceable for pressing down the edges when stretching paper or for removing sheets which have been gummed to the board.

FIG. 1,539.—Ordinary form of pencil eraser.

FIG. 1,540.—Circular form of rubber ink eraser.

Erasers.—There should be three kinds of erasers included in the drawing outfit:

1. Pencil
2. Ink
3. Sponge

For erasing any portion of a line in pencil, a piece of prepared white vulcanized rubber is the best, small in size and of rectangular shape, as in fig. 1,539.

FIG. 1,541.—Steel ink eraser.

An ink eraser is made of a composition of rubber and ground glass, and it should be used as sparingly as possible on drawings, as it roughens the paper and removes the gloss from its surface. Fig. 1,540 shows an ink eraser. Steel ink erasers, as shown in fig. 1,541, are useful in removing defects, overrun lines, joint of lines if swollen, etc.; they have a fine point and can be used to advantage with a little practice; they are used with a scratching, not a cutting, motion.

FIG. 1,542.—Sponge rubber, made of soft cellular rubber. Ordinary sizes 1 × 1 × 1 to 4 × 2 × 1 ins.

After a drawing has been made in pencil and inked in it is in a more or less soiled condition. By means of a so called "sponge" rubber as shown in fig. 1,542, which is very soft, friable and entirely free of grit, the drawing may be cleaned of dirt and projecting pencil lines without disturbing the inked lines or marring the surface of the paper.

Lettering Pens.—Nearly all lettering is executed by a pen similar to a common writing pen, but having a fine or wide point. The width of the point depends upon the desired thickness of the letters. The pen must at all times be kept clean as otherwise no clean cut line can be obtained. Figs. 1,543 to 1,550 show usual styles of pen used for lettering.

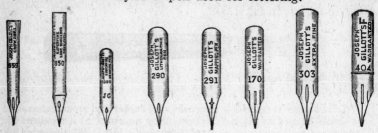

FIGS. 1,543 to 1,550.—Various lettering pens.

FIGS. 1,551 to 1,554.—Various irregular curves (sometimes called sweeps). They are useful when elliptical or parabolic curves are to be described.

Irregular Curves.—For describing curves other than circles, special cut forms called irregular curves are used to guide the pen. These may be obtained in great variety.

A set of two or three will be found frequently useful; several forms of these curves are shown in figs. 1,551 to 1,554.

Protractor.—This instrument is *for laying off or measuring angles*. Fig. 1,555 shows the ordinary form of protractor.

Its outer edge, as shown in the illustration, is a semi-circle with center at **O**, and for convenience is divided into 180 equal

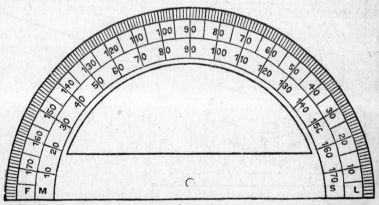

FIG. 1,555.—Protractor for laying out or measuring angles.

parts or degrees from **M** to **S**, and in reverse direction from **L** to **F**.

Protractors are often made of metal in which case the central part is cut away to allow the drawing under it to be seen.

A fine precision protractor is shown in fig. 1,556.

How to Draw

Preparing for Work.—The paper is first secured to the draw-ing board by means of *thumb tacks*, one at each corner of the sheet. It should be stretched flat and smooth; to obtain this result proceed as follows: press a thumb tack through one of

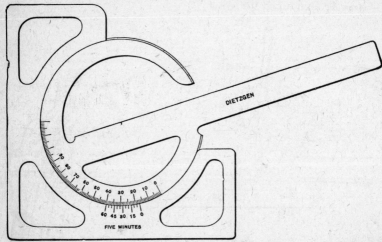

FIG. 1,556.—Dietzgen steel protractor. Blade 8½ ins. long and graduations reading to degrees, with vernier reading to 5 minutes. There are no projections on either face, and therefore it can be used on either edge of the blade or with either side up. This is an advantage when dividing circles, transferring angles, drawing oblique lines at right angles to each other, or laying off given angles each side of a vertical or a horizontal line without changing the setting.

the corners about ½ inch or ¼ inch from the edge. Place the tee square in position as in drawing a horizontal line, and straighten the paper so that its upper edge will be parallel to the edge of the tee square blade. Pull the corner diagonally oppo-site that in which the thumb tack was placed, so as to stretch the paper slightly and push in another thumb tack. Proceed in the same manner for the remaining two corners.

Another method consists in stretching the paper while it is damp. For stretching the paper in this way moisten the whole sheet on the under side, with the exception of a margin all around the sheet, of about half an inch and paste the dry border to the drawing board. To do this properly requires a certain amount of skill. The paper thus stretched gives undoubtedly a smoother surface than can be obtained when using thumb tacks, but there are objections to this process as the paper stretched in this way is under a certain strain and may have some effect on the various dimensions of the drawing when cut off the board.

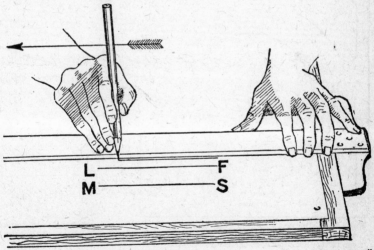

Fɪɢ. 1,557.—Parallel horizontal lines. These lines as MS, LF, are drawn by moving the pencil in the direction of the arrow, guided by the edge of the T square.

Straight Lines.—To draw a straight line use is made of the T square, or triangle, or both, depending upon the direction of the line. Horizontal lines are drawn by aid of the T square as in fig. 1,557 and sometimes vertical lines by applying the head of the square to the lower or horizontal edge of the board, as in fig. 1,558.

The usual method of drawing vertical lines is by aid of both the T square and one of the triangles as shown in fig. 1,561. Here one of the "legs" of the triangle is used to guide the pencil. By using the hypotenuse of the 45° triangle, oblique parallel lines may be drawn as in fig. 1,560, and by using the hypotenuse of the 30° triangle, oblique lines may be drawn at 30° or 60° as in fig. 1,559 and 1,562.

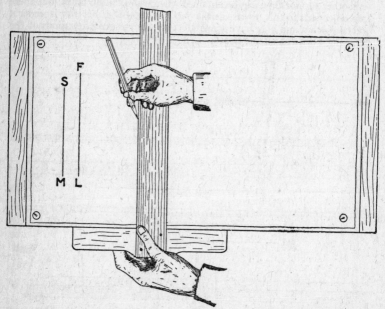

FIG. 1,558.—Parallel vertical lines with T square only. These lines as MS, LF, are drawn similarly as in fig. 1,557, but with the head of the T square in contact with the lower edge of the board.

By a combination of both triangles as in fig. 1,563, various other angles, such as 15°, 75°, 135°, may be obtained. Sometimes it is desired to draw a line parallel to another line which is not inclined at any of the angles obtained with the triangles. This is done by placing the edge of one triangle parallel with the given line and sliding it on the other triangle as in fig. 1,564.

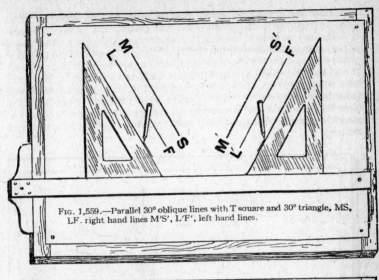

FIG. 1,559.—Parallel 30° oblique lines with T square and 30° triangle, MS, LF. right hand lines M'S', L'F', left hand lines.

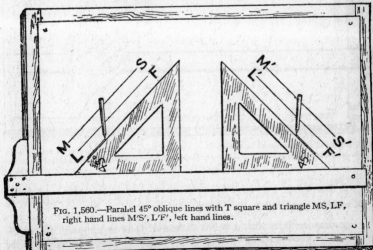

FIG. 1,560.—Parallel 45° oblique lines with T square and triangle MS, LF, right hand lines M'S', L'F', left hand lines.

In drawing a line it is important that the pencil be held correctly. Figs. 1,565 to 1,567 show the wrong ways and correct way to hold the pen. It should not be inclined laterally, but in drawing a line (with either pencil or pen) it should be held with its axis in a plane perpendicular to the plane of the paper, slightly inclined in the direction in which it is being moved. If held as in fig. 1,565, the inclination is likely to vary resulting in a wavy line; if held as in fig. 1,566, a reference point R, through which the line is to be drawn, may not be visible or only partially visible. When held for a Note here the right and wrong way to arrange the triangles. Always so place the triangles that the desired point may be reached without too much shifting.

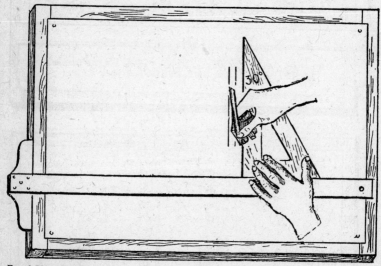

FIG. 1,561.—Parallel vertical lines with T square and triangle. The triangle in contact with the T square is shifted to any position at which it is desired to draw a vertical line.

perpendicular plane, as in fig. 1,567, the line comes very close to the lower edge, the reference point R, can be plainly seen, and there is least chance of drawing a wavy line.

In drawing lines with a pencil sharpened to a conical point the pencil should be given a slight twisting motion while the line is being drawn, as this tends to keep the point sharp.

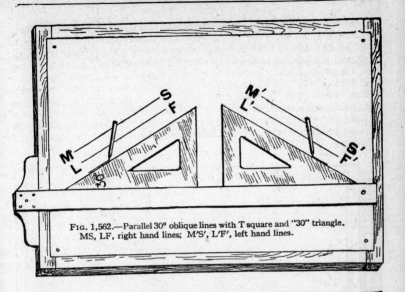

Fig. 1,562.—Parallel 30° oblique lines with T square and "30" triangle. MS, LF, right hand lines; M'S', L'F', left hand lines.

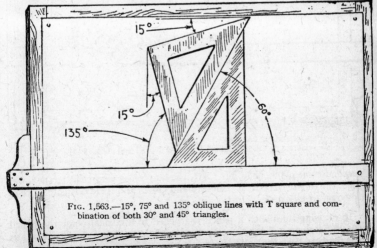

Fig. 1,563.—15°, 75° and 135° oblique lines with T square and combination of both 30° and 45° triangles.

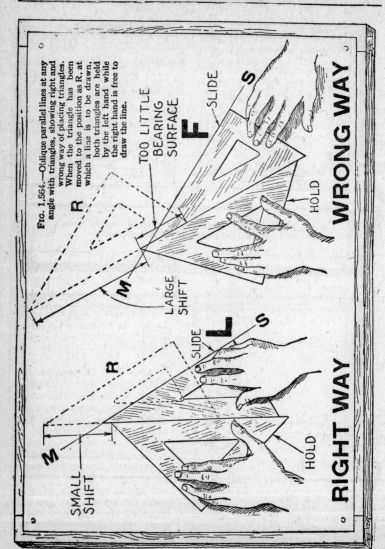

Fig. 1.564.—Oblique parallel lines at any angle with triangles, showing right and wrong way of placing triangles. When the triangle has been moved to the position as R, at which a line is to be drawn, both triangles are held by the left hand while the right hand is free to draw the line.

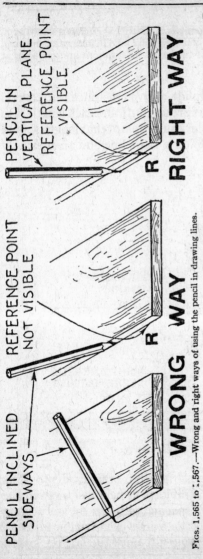

PENCIL IN VERTICAL PLANE

REFERENCE POINT VISIBLE

R

RIGHT WAY

REFERENCE POINT NOT VISIBLE

R

PENCIL INCLINED SIDEWAYS

WRONG WAY

Figs. 1,565 to 1,567.—Wrong and right ways of using the pencil in drawing lines.

Arcs and Circles.—These are "described" with the compass. The compass and proper positions for its use are shown in fig. 1,568. Both points should be nearly perpendicular to the paper—slightly inclined in the direction of movement.

The starting position should be such that the entire movement can be made in one continuous sweep by grasping the little handle at the pivot end by the thumb and forefinger, obtaining a twisting motion by moving the thumb forward without stopping to shift the hold on the compass.

Never hold the compass by the legs, even when the lengthening bar is used, as to do so will tend to move the legs to a different radius, as shown in fig. 1,569.

For very small circles a smaller compass called the bow compass is used; it is more convenient and having screw adjustment can be set with greater precision than the large compass. Particular attention is called to the result obtained by inclining the center point of a compass in describing circles as shown at S, fig. 1,570. Since these centers must be again used in inking in a drawing, accurate work cannot be done if the center indentations are spoiled as at S, by wrong use of the compass.

Spacing.—To accurately divide a given distance into several equal parts hair spring dividers are used. If an exact length is to be laid off with the dividers, a large multiple of that length should be first laid off with the scale on a right line and then exactly

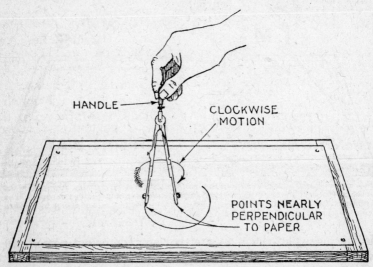

HANDLE

CLOCKWISE MOTION

POINTS NEARLY PERPENDICULAR TO PAPER

FIG 1,568.—Correct use of compass. Note method of holding compass grasping only the handle; also, upright positions of points, and clockwise motion.

sub-divided into the desired exact length by the dividers. This involves several trials. Set the dividers as near as can be to the desired length. Then test by spacing with the dividers along the line. The setting of the dividers after each trial is adjusted by turning slightly the hair spring nut until the correct length is obtained. For very fine divisions the bow dividers are more conveniently used. For precision the divisions L,A,R,F, should be marked off with a "pricker point."

Hints on Penciling.—The pencil drawing should look as nearly like the ink drawing as possible. A good draughtsman

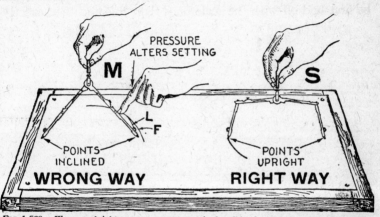

FIG. 1,569.—Wrong and right way to use compasses in describing large circles. **Always have the** points, especially the center point upright, otherwise the center indentation in paper will be enlarged and untrue. If both hands be used as at M, the setting may be altered by pressure on the leg, and part of the circle, as at L, will vary from the true part F.

leaves his work in such a state that any competent person can without difficulty ink in what he has drawn.

The pencil should always be *drawn, not pushed.* Lines are generally drawn from left to right and from the bottom to the top or upwards. Pencil lines should not be any longer than the proposed ink lines. By keeping a drawing in a neat, clean condition when penciling, the use of the rubber upon the finished inked drawing will be greatly diminished.

Inking.—A drawing should be *inked in* only after the penciling is entirely completed. Always begin at the top of the paper, first inking in all small circles and curves, then the larger circles and curves, next all horizontal lines, commencing again at the top of the drawing and working downward. Then ink in all vertical lines, starting on the left and moving toward the right; finally draw all oblique lines.

Irregular curves, small circles and arcs are inked in first,

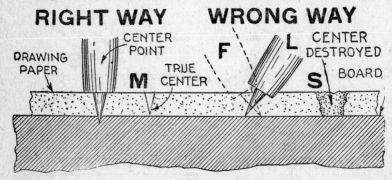

FIG. 1,570.—Right and wrong position of the compass center point (greatly enlarged for clearness). If the point be perpendicular to the paper in describing a circle as shown at the left, a clean cut indentation will be made in the paper as shown at M, with point removed, being in proper condition to use as a center. Again if the point be inclined in describing a circle the center point will rotate as indicated at L and F, the end of the point enlarging and tearing the indentation so that when the point is removed the indentation will be the condition shown at S, totally unfit to be again used as a center. The center point of a compass should be provided with a shoulder, as shown, instead of being simply conical—this limits the depth of indentation.

because it is easier to draw a straight line up to a curve than it is to take a curve up to a straight line.

In inking in lines the "ruling or lining" pen is used against the edge of the T square and triangles in making ink lines. The tool has two separate blades, or jaws, one of which is equipped with a spring to spread them apart. It is brought close to the other by a thumb screw or allowed to come away by turning the thumb screw. In the better class of drawing pens a hinge is wrought on one blade at the base, thus permitting the blade to open to a right angle, so that it can be cleaned of any ink which may cake or adhere to.

The drawing pen is applied by holding it perpendicular between the first and second fingers and thumb of the right hand, keeping the smooth blade close against the T square or triangle as required.

The ink is inserted between the jaws with a common writing pen or pen cork, which is now provided with every bottle of drafting ink sold, and any ink which remains outside must be cleaned off with a soft rag or piece of soft blotting paper. Similar directions must be followed when using the pen leg and point of compasses.

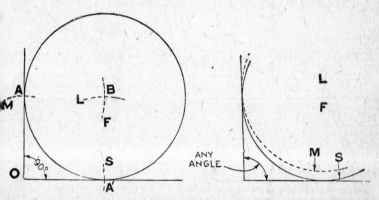

Figs. 1,571 and 1,572.—Two methods of describing a circle of given radius tangent to two lines meeting at a point. In fig. 1,571 let OA be the given radius. With O as center, describe arcs M, and S. With points A, A', where these arcs cut the lines describe arcs intersecting at B, then will a circle described with B, as center, and radius OA, be tangent to both lines. *In the second method,* set compass to given radius and describe a trial arc M, from a trial center L, selected with pencil resting on one of the lines. If trial arc be not tangent to the other line, bring compass back to initial position with pencil point resting on line, lift center point, by inclining compass a little and select another trial center as F. Continue the process until a center is obtained about which a circle described will be tangent to both lines. With little practice center can be quickly located by this method. The first method, fig. 1,571, holds when the lines are at 90° to each other, but the second method applies to any inclination.

The thicknesses of the lines are determined by the distance between the points of the blades, operated by the regulating screw. By separating or bringing together the blades a thick or thin line may be drawn, as desired.

Arcs, or circles, are inked in by removing the pencil end and inserting the pen end into the compass leg, or by using the bow compass.

Drawing to Scale.—The meaning of this is, that the drawing when done bears a definite proportion to the full size of the particular part, or, in other words, is precisely the same as it would appear if viewed through a diminishing glass.

When it is required to make a drawing to a reduced scale, that is, of a smaller size than the actual size of the object, say, for instance, ½ full size, every dimension of the object in the

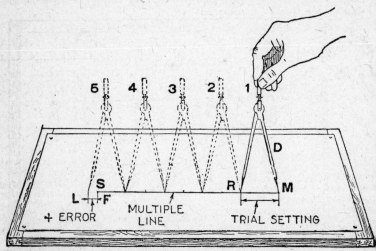

FIG. 1,573.—Spacing with the dividers. Suppose it be desired to divide the line MS, into 5 equal parts. Set dividers "by eye" to one-fifth the distance as MR. Space along the line by moving the dividers clockwise and counterclockwise to position 2, 3, 4, 5. As seen, MR, was taken too large. Adjust setting and respace until the correct setting has been obtained. Before setting the dividers "by eye," unloosen adjustment nut D, two or three turns, otherwise if the error LF, were negative (—), the hair spring could not be adjusted in the positive (+) direction.

drawing must be one-half the actual size; in this case one inch on the object would be represented by ½ inch. Such a reduced drawing could be made with an ordinary rule. This, however, would require every size of the object to be divided by the proportion of the scale, which would entail a very great loss of time in calculations. This can be avoided by simply dividing the rule itself by 2, from the beginning. Such a rule or *scale* as it is generally called, will be divided in ½ inches, each half inch representing one full inch divided into ½, ¼, ⅛, ¹⁄₁₆, each of these representing the same proportions of the actual sizes of the object to be drawn. From this contracted scale the dimensions and measurements are laid off on the drawing.

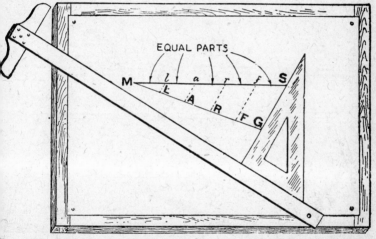

FIG. 1,574.—To divide a given line into any number of equal parts without use of dividers. Let MS, be the given line. From M, draw a diagonal line MG, of length in inches equal to the number of parts (say five) into which MS, is divided. Mark the inch divisions (L, A, R, F,) on MG, and join GS. With aid of T square and triangle, draw lines through L, A, R, F, parallel to GS, giving the points *larf* on MS. These points divide MS, into the desired number of equal parts. Note new use of T square by inclining it to any desired degree, the head not being in contact with the edge of the board.

A quarter size scale is made by taking three inches to represent one foot. Each of the three inches will be divided into 12 parts representing inches, each one of these again will be divided in ½, ⅛, ¹⁄₁₆, etc.; each one of these representing to a quarter size scale the actual sizes of ½, ¼, ⅛, ¹⁄₁₆ of an inch.

It must be mentioned that in several instances, in this work, distances in one figure are said to be equal to corresponding distances in the same object in another view, while by actual measurement they are somewhat different; this is owing to the use of different scales—each scale separate should be marked on the drawing.

It must be understood that the scale on a drawing is not given for a shopman to take his dimensions from; such dimensions must all be taken from the dimension figures; the scale is given for the chief draughtsman's use, or whoever may check the drawing, and also for the use of other draughtsmen who may

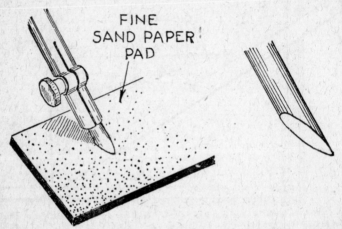

FINE
SAND PAPER
PAD

FIGS. 1,575 and 1,576.—Method of sharpening compass pencil by rubbing it over a pad of very fine sand paper (fig. 1,575), and appearance of pencil point after sharpening (greatly enlarged) fig. 1,576.

make at some future time alterations or additions to the drawing.

Dimensioning Drawings.—Every dimension necessary for the execution of the work indicated by the drawing should be clearly stated by figures on the drawing, *so that no measurements*

need to be taken in the shop by scale. All measurements should
be given with reference to the base or starting point from

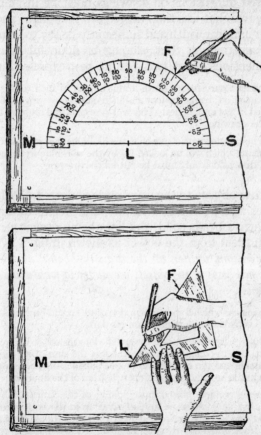

FIGS. 1,577 and 1,578.—Method of using the protractor to draw a line through a given point on a line and making a given angle with the line. Let MS and L, be respectively the given line and point on the line. Place protractor so that its center registers with point L, and its straight side with the line MS. Find angle on circular scale and mark same as at F. Remove protractor and join LF, by aid of triangle as in fig. 1,578, obtaining the required angle FLS.

which the work is laid out, and also *with reference to center lines*.

All figured dimensions on drawings must be in plain, round **v**ertical figures, not less than one-eighth inch high, and formed **b**y a line of uniform width and sufficiently heavy to insure print-**i**ng well, omitting all thin, sloping or doubtful figures. All **fi**gured dimensions below two feet are best expressed in inches.

It is not necessary to put down a multiplicity of inch marks (″)—these can well be left off, using the foot and inch marks only when the dimension is expressed in feet and inches. This will save time and improve the appearance of the drawing.

It may be put down as a rule that the draughtsman must anticipate the measurements which will be looked for by the workman in doing the work, and these dimensions only must be put on the drawing.

The author objects to the usual style of dotted dimension and **c**enter lines and weak arrow heads, and prefers to make these **l**ines and arrow heads solid, the lines being drawn very fine to **d**istinguish them from the object as shown in fig. 1,579.

The dimensions written on the drawing should always give the **a**ctual finished sizes of the object, no matter to what scale the object **m**ay be drawn.*

All dimensions which a shopman may require should be put on a drawing, so that no calculation be required on his part.

For instance, it is not enough to give the lengths of the different parts of the object, but the length over all, which is the sum of all these lengths, placed outside and the figures also be put outside, in which case an arrow should be put in to indicate the proper position of the figures.

The figure should be placed in the middle of the dimension line at right angles to that line, and so as to read either from the bottom, or from the right hand side of the drawing. The arrow heads should be put inside of the lines, from which the distance, as given in the dimension, is reckoned.

The dimension lines should also be put in the drawing, very near to the spaces or lines, to which they refer.

When "the view" is complicated, dimension lines drawn within it, might tend to make it still more obscure and difficult to understand; in such a case the dimension lines should be carried outside of the view and extension lines drawn from the arrow heads to the points, between which the dimension is given.

When the dimension includes a fraction, the numerator should be separated from the denominator preferably by a horizontal line instead of by an inclined line; care should also be taken to write the figures in a very clear and legible manner and crowding should be avoided.

Tracings.—Whenever it is desired to have more than one copy of a drawing, a "tracing" is made of it and from this as many blue prints can be obtained as are required.

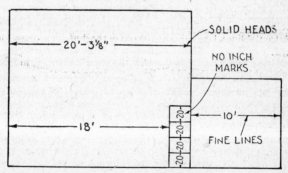

FIG. 1,579.—Method of dimensioning drawing as preferred by the author. Note, solid arrow heads that can be seen; fine dimension lines which by contrast are not confused with the lines of the drawing; no inch marks where dimension is in inches only.

When a tracing is needed for making blue prints, a piece of tracing paper or tracing cloth of the same size as the drawing is placed over the original drawing and fastened to the board. This tracing paper or cloth is almost transparent; the tracing is a mechanical copy of a drawing made by reproducing its lines as seen through a transparent medium such as has been described and the lines of the drawing can be seen through it.

The surfaces of the tracing cloth are called the "glazed side" and the "dull side," or "front" and "back"; the glazed side has a smooth polished surface and the dull side is like a piece of ordinary linen cloth.

Drawing on tracing paper or cloth is effected by pencil and drawing pen as in ordinary work.

The tracing cloth must be fastened to the board, over the drawing by pins or thumb tacks; moisture or dampness should be carefully avoided and the drawing done, preferably, on the smooth side of the cloth.

When tracing cloth will not take ink readily a small quantity of pounce may be applied to the surface of the cloth and distributed evenly with a piece of cotton waste, chamois, or similar material, but the pounce should be thoroughly removed before applying the ink.

In making tracings the order to be followed is as follows: 1, ink in the small circles and curves; 2, ink in the larger circles and curves; 3, then all the horizontal lines, beginning at the top of the drawing and working downward; 4, next ink in all the vertical lines, commencing at the left and moving back to the right; 5, draw in the oblique lines; 6, in finishing the figuring and lettering should be done with India ink, thoroughly black.

"Erasing," in case of mistakes or errors, should be done with an ink eraser or a sharp, round erasing knife; the surface of the tracing cloth must be made smooth in those places where lines have been erased; this is accomplished by rubbing the cloth with soapstone or powdered pumice stone, applied with a soft cloth or with the finger. When a mistake made is so serious that it cannot be corrected by erasing, a piece of the tracing cloth may be cut out and a new one inserted in its place.

A finished tracing should be provided with the title of the drawing, the date, scale and the initials of the draughtsman.

Lettering.—When the information necessary to the reading of a drawing cannot be expressed by lines and scale dimensions, it must be indicated in the form of printed explanations, remarks, etc.

NOTE.—Many concerns have rules of their own, directing their draughtsmen to use either the smooth or the rough side for all purposes; if there be no such rules, it is left to the judgment of the draughtsman. While it is immaterial which side of the cloth is used in tracing, however, if any mistakes be made and have to be corrected this can be done easier on the glazed side; on the contrary, if any *additions* must be made to the tracing, which have to be drawn in pencil first, the dull side will be found most convenient, as the pencil marks show plainer on the dull side.

To do good lettering is not an easy task, and unless the student be already experienced, he should devote much time to practicing the art, working slowly and bearing in mind that much time is required to make well finished letters.

The character and size of the letters on all working drawings

FIG. 1,580.—Winsor & Newton liquid Indian ink.

should be in harmony with the drawing on which they appear. It is desirable to have all lettering on a drawing made in the same style, only differing in size or finish of details.

Capital letters should always be sketched in pencil, especially by the beginner, and inked in afterwards; the lettering used on mechanical draw-is usually of the simplest character, the letters being composed of heavy and light strokes only; for headings, titles of large drawings, where comparatively large lettering is required, it will be most appropriate to use large letters.

The title should be conspicuous, but not too much so; sub-titles should be made smaller than the main-title.

The "scale" and general remarks placed in the margin of the drawing or near the title should come next in size. All explanations and remarks on the views should not be larger than one-eighth inch.

After deciding on the size of the letters, lightly draw two parallel lines at a distance apart equal to the height of the letters. Good lettering requires considerable practice. The beginner should first pencil in the letters before inking, but this is not necessary for the expert.

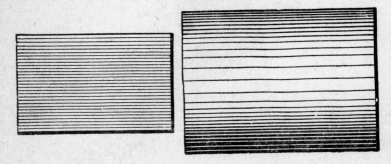

FIGS. 1,581 and 1,582.—Parallel line shading of flat and cylindrical surfaces.

Free hand lettering should only be taken up after the student is proficient in mechanical lettering; pencil guide lines for letters and words should be drawn; larger letters may first be penciled in very lightly, and an ordinary writing pen may be used for inking them in.

Letters should be so placed as not to interfere with the lines of the drawing and should clearly point out the part intended to be described. When single letters are used, they should be inked in before the shade or section lines are drawn; it is a good plan to start with the middle letter of the inscription and work in both directions.

Parallel Line Shading.—Plane surfaces are shaded by a number of parallel lines running parallel to the length of the plane which is to be shaded. If the plane is to be represented very light, it may be left blank or covered with very fine parallel lines, as shown in fig. 1,581.

A cylinder is shaded by a number of parallel lines, which are heaviest near to the side of the cylinder which does not receive

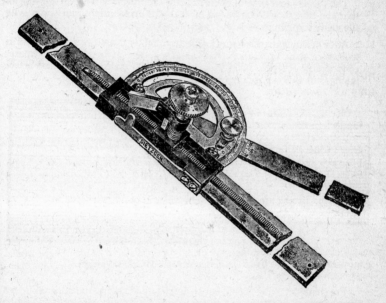

FIG. 1,583.—Dietzgen section liner and scale divider for drawing equally spaced parallel lines. *It consists of* a flat rack bar or base which carries a rack and carriage which slides on the rack bar. A semi-circular protractor with a ruler arm is attached to the carriage and by means of a simple mechanism from 4 to 200 parallel lines to the inch can be drawn. When the instrument is properly set, inch scales from ⅛ to 3 inches to the foot, decimal scales up to 1,000 to the foot can be produced.

any direct light, as in fig. 1,582. The heavy lines become lighter gradually and are drawn very fine near the middle of the cylinder: after this the lines are again drawn slightly heavier up to the side of the cylinder, which is nearest to the source of the light. The shading lines near the lighter side of the cylinder should never be as heavy as the heaviest lines on the dark side of the cylinder.

Section Lining is sometimes necessary to make use of a section, in order that certain details, which would otherwise be hidden, may be shown in a plain, clear manner. Such sections are usually indicated by drawing parallel oblique lines within the section, usually inclined 45°.

By changing the direction of these lines a clear distinction may be made between different pieces in the same view, which may be in contact.

Placing the lines too near together makes the work of sectioning much harder; the lines should not be drawn first in pencil, but only in ink, as the neat appearance of the drawing depends largely upon the uniformity of the lines in the section and these lines are to be spaced by the eye only. The process consists simply in ruling one line after another, sliding the triangle along the edge of the T square for an equal distance after drawing each section line.

Wooden beams are sectioned by a series of rings and radiating lines in imitation of the natural appearance of a cross section of the wood.

The side of a beam or board is represented by lines (drawn in free hand) running similarly to the grain of the wood. Sections of thin strips of metal as beam hanger straps, etc., are usually represented by filling in the whole sectional area solid black. In this case a white line must be left between adjoining sections.

CHAPTER 30

How to Read Plans

There are various ways of representing objects in drawings, and a knowledge of these different methods is essential in order to intelligently read a drawing or blue print.

The various methods of illustrating an object by a drawing are:

1. Perspective
2. Cabinet projection
3. Isometric projection
4. Orthographic projection
5. Development of surfaces

Of these methods, the first three may be classed as "pictorial" in that they show the entire visible portion of the object in one view, whereas the fourth requires several views to fully present the object and may be called "descriptive."

It is this latter method that is most generally used and which requires a little study to comprehend it.

A perspective drawing shows an object as it really appears to the eye, but presents so many difficulties of construction that the projection methods have been devised to overcome them. These projection methods will accordingly be considered first before taking up perspective.

Cabinet Projection.—In this system of drawing, the lines of an object are drawn parallel to three axes, one of which is horizontal, a second vertical, and the third, inclined 45° to the horizontal, as in fig. 1,584. The horizontal axis lie in the plane of the paper, and the vertical and inclined axes lie in a plane intended to appear to the eye as being at right angles to the plane of the paper.

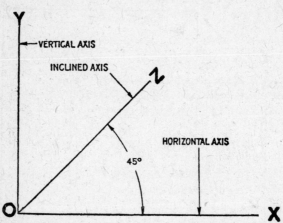

FIG. 1,584.—Cabinet projection axes.

These axes lie in planes at right angles to each other and known as the horizontal, vertical and profile planes.

In cabinet projection it is to be remembered that

1. All horizontal measurements, parallel to the length of the object must be laid off parallel to the horizontal axis, in their actual sizes.

2. All vertical measurements, parallel to the height of the object, must be drawn parallel to the vertical axis in their actual sizes.

3. All measurements parallel to the thickness of the object must be laid off on lines parallel to the 45° axis, in sizes of only one-half of the actual corresponding measurements.

It is not essential which side of the object should be considered its length and which side its thickness.

Problem 1.—To draw a cube in cabinet projection.

First draw the three axes, OX, OY, OZ, as in fig. 1,585. Lay off OA and OC, on OX and OY, equal to side of the given cube, and complete the side by drawing CB and AB. On OZ, lay off OG, equal to ½ OA. Through

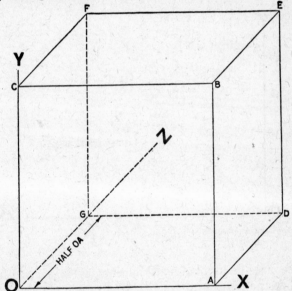

FIG. 1,585.—Cabinet projection of a cube.

C, draw a line parallel to OZ, and through G, a dotted line parallel to OY, giving the lines CF and GF. Similarly through points G,F,A and B, draw parallels to the axes, thus completing the cube.

In the drawing the face ABCO, is regarded as lying in the plane of the paper, the face DEFG, as parallel and the other faces ABED and OCFG, as perpendicular to the plane of the paper. The edges which would be invisible if the cube were made of opaque material such as wood, are represented by dotted lines.

Problem 2.—To draw a right cylinder with its bases in the XOY plane; length of cylinder 3 times the diameter.

This is the best position to draw a cylinder because the bases will be circles and the difficulty of describing ellipses avoided.

Draw the axes as usual. With O, as center and OA, equal to radius of cylinder, describe a circle. On OZ, lay off OM = 3 times OA (since length of cylinder = 3 times the diameter.)

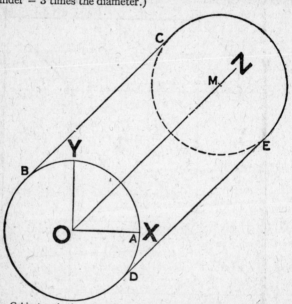

FIG. 1,586.—Cabinet projection of a cylinder with bases parallel to the plane of the paper.

With same radius describe a circle through M, and draw tangents BC, and DE, thus completing the outline of the cylinder.

The portion of the circle about M, between C and E, is shown by dotted lines because it would be invisible if the cylinder were made of opaque material.

Problem 3.—To draw a prism enclosing a cylinder with its bases parallel to the YOZ plane; length of cylinder 3 times the diameter.

Draw in the cube as directed in problem 1, making AD = ⅙ OA, as in fig. 1,587. Now, show half of the base ABED, in the plane of the paper as in fig. 1,588. Here, draw diagonals OB and OA, and describe the half circle tangent to the sides. Through the intersection of the circle with diagonals draw line 12.

In fig. 1,587 make B1 = ½ of B1 in fig. 1,588 and draw line 12, in fig.

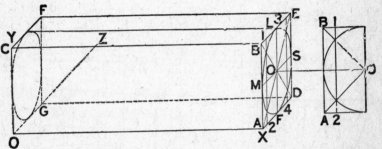

FIGS. 1,587 and 1,588.—Cabinet projection of a prism enclosing a right cylinder with its bases parallel to the YOZ plane.

1,587, and by similar construction line 34. Next draw diagonals AE and BD. The intersection of lines 12 and 34 with these diagonals will give four points together with points MLSF, through which to construct an ellipse representing the base of the cylinder as seen in profile constructing a similar ellipse at the other end and drawing the two tangents to the ellipses completes the outline of the cylinder.

Problem 4.—To draw a hexagonal prism inscribed in a right cylinder whose base equals twice diameter.

In construction fig. 1,589, describe a circle of diameter equal to diameter of the cylinder. Inscribe a hexagon. In fig. 1,590 lay off OF and OC, equal to *of* and *oc*.

Transfer points *m*, *s*, obtaining M, S, and through M and S, draw lines parallel to OZ, and on these lines lay off ME = ½ me; MA = ½ ma, etc. Through the points thus obtained draw in the ellipse ABCDEF.

Similarly construct upper ellipse A′B′C′D′E′F′ at elevation OO′ = ¾ FC, and draw tangents thus completing the cylinder. Join AB, A′B′, BC, B′C′, etc., and AA′, BB′, etc., thus completing outline of inscribed hexagonal prism.

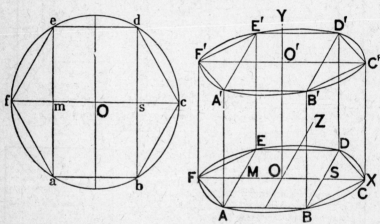

Figs. 1,589 and 1,590.—Cabinet projection of a hexagonal prism inscribed in a right cylinder.

Modified Cabinet Projection.—There are various ways in which the 45° one-half foreshortened profile cabinet projection just described can be modified for convenience to suit special conditions. For instance, instead of inclining the OZ, axis to the right, as in fig. 1,591, it may be pointed to the left as in fig. 1,592.

Instead of foreshortening the profile dimension one half, as in fig. 1,593, in some cases, where dimensions are to be taken from the drawing, the profile may be made full dimension as in fig. 1,594.

Sometimes, because of the limited space available, it is desirable to take the OZ, axis at some angle other than 45°. In such cases it is usually taken at 30° or 60°, because these angles are obtained directly with the T square

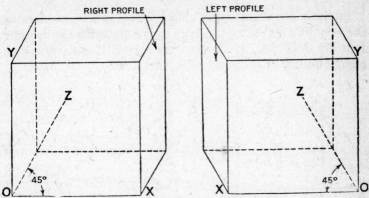

FIGS. 1,591 and 1,592.—45° cabinet projection with right and left profile.

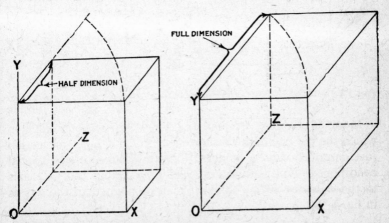

FIGS. 1,593 and 1,594.—Half and full profile dimension 45° cabinet projection. Evidently where all lines are drawn full dimension as in fig. 1,594, the drawing is made without calculating the profile dimensions, and especially in case of a complicated object time is saved.

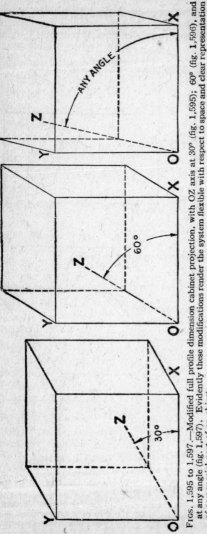

FIGS. 1,595 to 1,597.—Modified full profile dimension cabinet projection, with OZ axis at 30° (fig. 1,595); 60° (fig. 1,596), and at any angle (fig. 1,597). Evidently these modifications render the system flexible with respect to space and clear representation of any special part of an object.

and triangles—the object of the projection system being to use these instruments to conveniently and quickly execute drawings. In special cases, obviously any angle may be taken to suit the conditions.

These modifications of cabinet projection are shown in figs. 1,595 to 1,600. The first three figures show the object in full profile dimension for comparison. However, to save space and approach the natural appearance of the object, the following are the approved proportions for the profile.

OZ axis 45°, profile half dimension

OZ axis 30°, profile two-thirds dimension

OZ axis 60°, profile one-third dimension

The appearance of an object drawn to these proportions is shown in figs. 1,598 to 1,600.

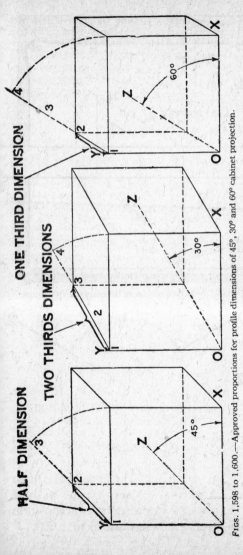

ONE THIRD DIMENSION

TWO THIRDS DIMENSIONS

HALF DIMENSION

FIGS. 1,598 to 1,600.—Approved proportions for profile dimensions of 45°, 30° and 60° cabinet projection.

Isometric Projection.—By definition the word *isometric* means *equal distances*, and as here applied, isometric projection is a system of drawing *with measurements on an equal scale in every one of three sets of lines 120° apart and representing the three planes of dimension.*

In other words, the axes are taken 120° apart and there is no profile foreshortening as in cabinet projection, all lines being drawn full length.

Isometric projection further differs from cabinet projection in that none of the three planes lie in the plane of the paper.

Fig. 1,601 shows method of laying out the isometric axes using T square and 30° triangle. Figs. 1,602 and 1,603 show comparison of axes of the cabinet and isometric systems.

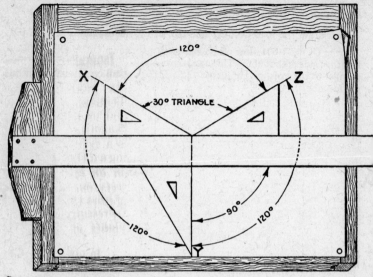

FIG. 1,601.—Isometric axes laid out at 120° to each other with 30° triangle and T square.

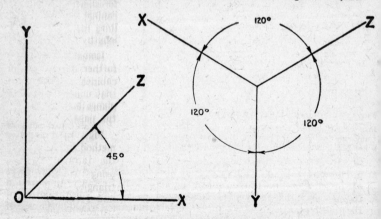

FIGS. 1,602 and 1,603.—Comparison of cabinet and isometric axes.

Problem 5.—To draw a prism in isometric projection.

First draw the axes OX, OY and OZ, at 120° as explained in fig. 1,601.

From O, fig. 1,604, lay off on the axes just drawn OA = OB = OC = length of side of the cube. Through points A,B,C, thus obtained, draw lines parallel to the axes, giving points D,E,F, thus completing visible outline of the cube.

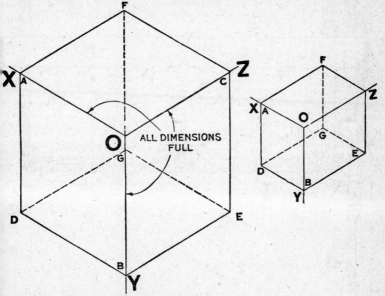

ALL DIMENSIONS FULL

Fɪɢ. 1,604.—Isometric projection of a cube.

Fɪɢ. 1,605.—Isometric projection of a parallelopipedon showing completed dotted outline of invisible portion as compared with that of the cube fig. 1,604 in which part of the dotted line FG, falls behind OB. The reference letters are the same in both figures.

Through D, E and F, draw dotted lines intersecting at G, which gives the invisible outlines of the cube, assuming it to be opaque. An objection to this view is that the point G, falls behind the line OB, thus the outline of the invisible portion does not appear so well defined as it would in the case of a parallelopipedon as in the little fig. 1,605 at the right.

An objection to isometric projection is that, since no projection plane lies in the plane of the paper, it is necessary to construct ellipses to represent circular portions of an object and this requires time and skill.

Problem 6.—Draw a horizontal prism with inscribed cylinder; length of cylinder two times the diameter.

Draw the prism as explained in fig. 1,604, and drawn in fig. 1,606, making its length twice its side. Now construct the half end view in plane of paper (fig. 1,607); describe circle, diagonals and intersecting line 12.

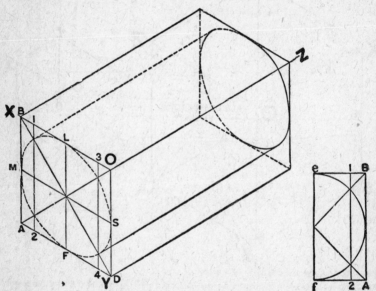

FIGS. 1,606 and 1,607.—Isometric projection of a horizontal prism with inscribed cylinder.

Transfer from fig. 1,607 line 12 to fig. 1,606 and draw symmetrical line 34 and diagonals. The intersections, together with points MS, and LF, of axial lines through the center, give eight points through which construct ellipse.

Construct also a similar ellipse at other end of prism and join two ellipses with tangents, thus completing outline of inscribed cylinder.

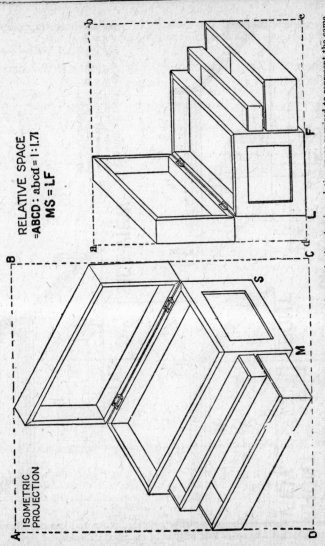

FIGS. 1,608 and 1,609.—Comparison of isometric and cabinet projection showing relative space required to represent the same object drawn to same scale. Note that dimension MS = LF. The saving in space by cabinet projection is due to the position of the axes and the fore shortening of the profile dimensions.

RELATIVE SPACE
=ABCD : abcd = 1:1.71
MS = LF

ISOMETRIC PROJECTION

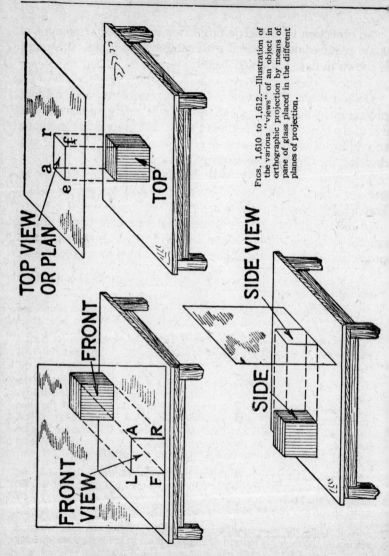

FIGS. 1,610 to 1,612.—Illustration of the various "views" of an object in orthographic projection by means of pane of glass placed in the different planes of projection.

An objection to isometric projection is the greater amount of space required as compared with cabinet projection; this point is shown in figs. 1,608 and 1,609.

Orthographic Projection.—Isometric drawing and cabinet projection, while showing the object as it really appears to the eye of the observer, are neither of them very convenient methods to employ where it is necessary to measure every part of the drawing for the purpose of reproducing it.

Drawings suitable for this purpose, generally known as *working drawings*, are made by the method known as *orthographic projection*.

In cabinet or isometric projections, three sides of the object are shown in one view, while in a drawing made in orthographic projection, but one side of the object is shown in a single view.

To illustrate this, a clear pane of glass may be placed in front of the object intended to be represented.

In fig. 1,610 a cube is shown on a table; in front of it, parallel to one face (the front face) of the cube, the pane of glass is placed.

Now, when the observer looks directly at the front of an object from a considerable distance, he will see only one side, in this case only the front side of the cube.

The rays of light falling upon the cube are reflected into the eyes of the observer, and in this manner he sees the cube. The pane of glass, evidently, is placed so that the rays of light from the object will pass through the glass in straight lines, to the eye of the observer. The front side of the object, by its outline, may be traced upon the glass, and in this manner a figure drawn on it (in this case a square) which is the view of the object as seen from the front which in this case is called the *front elevation*.

One view, however, is not sufficient to show the real form of a solid figure. In a single view two dimensions only can be shown, length and height; hence the thickness of an object will have to be shown by still another view of it, as the top view or *plan*.

Now, place the pane in a horizontal position above the cube which is resting on the table, as in fig. 1,611, and looking at it from above, directly over the top face of the cube, trace its outline upon the pane; as a result, a square figure is drawn upon the glass, which corresponds to the appearance of the cube, as seen from above. This square on the glass is the top view of the cube, or its *plan*.

Fig. 1,612 shows the manner in which a side view of the cube may be traced; the glass is placed on the side of the cube, which rests on the table

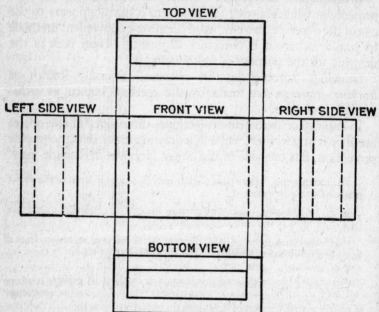

Figs. 1,613.—Five views of an object as drawn in orthographic projection.

as before, and the outline of the cube on the glass in this position, is called its *side elevation*.

Usually either two of the above mentioned views will suffice to show all dimensions and forms of the object, but to completely represent complicated objects, three or four views may be required.

In complicated pieces of machinery, however, more views, three and even more may be required to adequately represent the proportions and form of the different parts.

A drawing which represents the object as seen by an observer looking at it from the right side is called *the right side elevation* and a drawing showing the object as it appears to the observer looking at it from the left side is called *the left side elevation.*

In the case of a long object, a view at the end is called an *end view.*

A view of the object as seen from the rear is called the rear view or rear elevation, and a view from the bottom, the bottom view.

The different views of an object are always arranged on the drawing in a certain fixed and generally adopted manner, thus—

The front view is placed in the center; the right side view is placed to the right of the front view, and the left side view to the left; the top view is placed above the front view and the bottom view below it. The different views are placed directly opposite each other and are joined by dotted lines called *projection lines.*

By the aid of projection lines, leading from one view to the other, as in fig. 1,613, measurements of one kind may be transmitted from one view to the other; for instance, the height of different parts of an object may be transmitted from the front view to either one of the side views; in like manner the length of different parts of the object may be transmitted by the aid of projection lines, to the bottom view and top view.

It is often desirable to show lines belonging to an object, although they may not be directly visible. In fig. 1,613 the top view and the bottom view show plainly that the object is hollow; looking at the object from the front or from the sides, however, the observer could not see the inside edges of the object, except it were made of some transparent material.

In projection drawing it is assumed for convenience that all objects are made of such material, transparent enough to show all hidden lines, no matter from which side the object is observed; these hidden lines are represented in the drawing by dotted lines.

Problem 7.—Draw a plan, elevation and end view of the prism shown in fig. 1,614.

First draw the top view or plan as in fig. 1,615, by drawing the rectangle ABCD, to scale making AB, = 1 in. and AD, 4 ins. For the elevation, project the point AB, down to the parallel line obtaining line AB.

Lay off AE = 2 ins. and complete rectangle giving ABFE, or elevation. The end view BCGF, is drawn in a similar manner, side BF, being obtained by projection and BC, by measurement.

Problem 8.—Draw plan, end and front views of the barn shown in fig. 1,616.

The plan will consist simply of a rectangle CDFE (fig. 1,617), the length

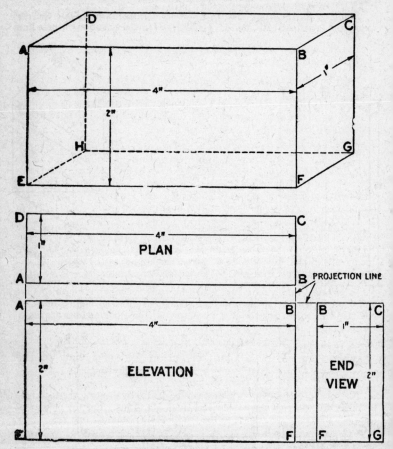

FIGS. 1,614 and 1,615.—Cabinet projection of a prism, and orthographic views of same, being shown in plan. elevation and end view.

of whose sides being obtained from the dimensions in the orthographic projections. The end view is projected down from points C,A,E, of the plan, being identical with the end in fig. 1,616, because it is here drawn in the "OX, plane" which is the plane of the paper and accordingly is seen in true size.

Similarly for the front view project over the points A,B,I, of the end view and lay off AB, EF, and IJ, equal to 40 ft., the elevation of these lines

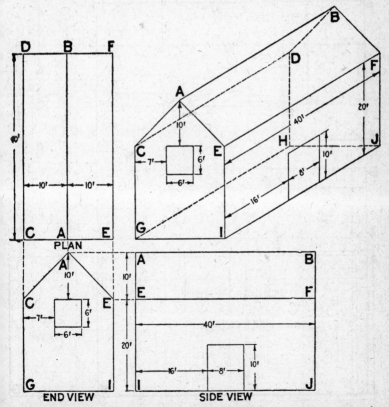

FIGS. 1,616 and 1,617.—Cabinet projection outline drawing of a barn and same drawn in orthographic projection.

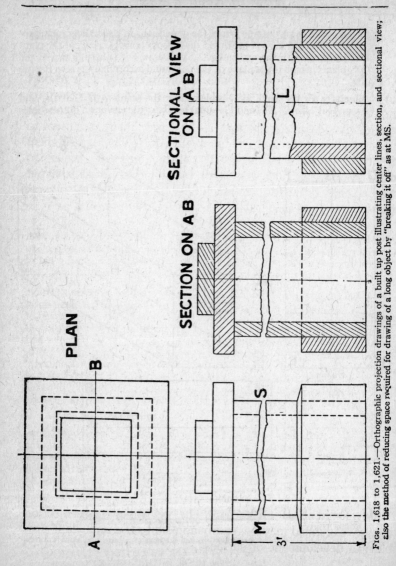

FIGS. 1,618 to 1,621.—Orthographic projection drawings of a built up post illustrating center lines, section, and sectional view; also the method of reducing space required for drawing of a long object by "breaking it off" as at MS.

PLAN

B

A

SECTION ON A B

SECTIONAL VIEW ON A B

L

S

M

3'

being obtained from the given dimensions. The door is laid out in a similar manner.

Center Lines.—Objects which are symmetrical with respect to some axis drawn through the center are most easily drawn by first drawing such axis or *center line* and then drawing the object so that its center coincides with the center line. It is usual to make such lines broken by dot and dash, to distinguish them from the lines of the object. The author, however, prefers to draw solid center lines, obtaining the proper contrast to avoid confusion by drawing them much finer than those of the object, the same method being used also for dimension lines.

Figs. 1,618 and 1,619 show a rectangular built-up post drawn with center lines. Evidently since the figure is symmetrical with respect to these lines, equidistances are conveniently spaced off each side by aid of dividers and the drawing made quickly and with precision.

Since to show the entire length of the post would require considerable space, it is usual to "break it off" as at MS, by two ragged free hand lines, which indicate that part of its length is not shown. The construction of the post may be more clearly shown by drawing it as though it were sawed through from end to end along the line AB; thus showing only the half back of AB; it would then have the appearance as shown in fig. 1,620, called a *section* on AB. The surface assumed to be sawed is "section lined." That is, covered with a series of parallel lines usually inclined 45°, 30° or 60°. It will be noted that the section lines in one plank run in a different direction from those in an adjacent plank so as to distinguish the separate parts.

To draw section lines consumes time, hence, time may be saved by showing in section not more than is sufficient for clearness, the rest of the drawing being seen "in full" as in fig. 1,621; this is called a sectional view. Here the post is shown in full down to the ragged line L, below this line the post is considered as being cut away to the axis AB.

Development of Surfaces.—The principles of projection already explained may be readily applied to the important problem of development of surfaces.

Whenever it is necessary to make an object of some thin material like sheet metal, as in the case of elbows or tees for leader or stove pipe, the surface of the desired object is laid out on sheet metal, in one or in several pieces; these are called the

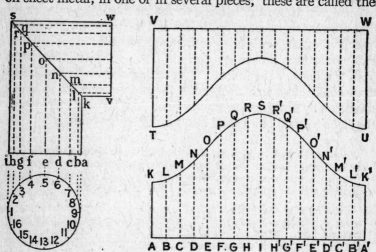

FIGS. 1,622 to 1,624.—Elevation and plan of 90° stove pipe elbow, and development of surfaces

Elbow Patterns.—In all elbow work the difficulty lies in obtaining the correct rise of the mitre line. By the use of a protractor this is overcome and thus the necessity of drawing a complete quadrant is avoided. Following the rule given in the illustration the rise can be easily found, when the throat and diameter of the pipe is known. The following table gives the rise of mitre line for elbows of various degrees and of various number of pieces.

ELBOW TABLE

No. of pieces	Divide by	Degree of elbow	Rise of mitre line
2	2	105	52½°
2	2	90	45°
2	2	70	35°
3	4	90	22½°
4	6	90	15°
6	10	90	9°

patterns of the object; the pattern being first laid out on the sheet metal and then cut out; when this is done the separate pieces are ready to be fitted together to form the required object.

The method by which the surface of an object is laid out on a plane is called *the development of the object*. A few exercises will sufficiently acquaint the student with the methods used in problems of this character.

Problem 9.—To draw the development of a right, or 90° stove pipe elbow.

A right elbow is made by joining two pieces of pipe for the purpose of forming a right angle. It is really *an intersection of two cylinders of equal diameters;* the center lines of the two cylinders meeting at one point, and as the joint is to be a right elbow, the center lines must be perpendicular to each other.

To develop the surfaces, divide the circumference of the cylinder into any number of equal parts, and through the points of division draw lines parallel to the center line of the cylinder.

On these parallel lines, mark the points which belong to the curve of intersection with another cylinder, or any other figure as happens to be the case, and then roll out the surface of the cylinder into a flat plate.

The rolled out surface will be equal in length to the circumference of the cylinder, and it will contain all parallel lines, which were drawn upon the cylinder, with spaces between them just equal to the actual space between the parallel lines which were drawn upon the surface of the cylinder.

By marking the points of intersection on the parallel lines in the rolled surface, the development of the cylinder or its part is obtained.

In fig. 1,622, the circle showing the circumference of the pipe is divided into any number of equal parts by the divisions 1, 2, 3, etc. Lines are drawn through these divisions parallel to the center line of the vertical portion of the joint. These lines are *ak, bl, cm, dn,* etc.

The points *k, l, m, n, o* are the points on the parallel lines designating the curve of intersection.

The development of the two branches of the right elbow are shown in figs. 1,623 and 1,624; the length of the development, VW (or AA′) is equal to the circumference of the figure shown in fig. 1,622. To obtain this

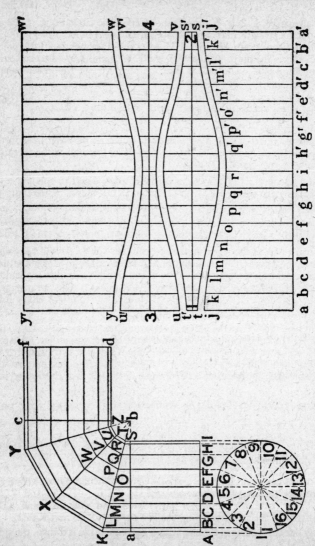

Fig. 1.625.—Elevation and plan of a four-part elbow, whose surfaces are developed as shown in fig. 1.626.

Fig. 1.626.—Development of surface of the four-part elbow, shown in elevation and plan in fig. 1.625.

length all spaces, 1, 2, 3, 4, etc., laid out upon the circle in fig. 1,622 are set off upon a straight line; these spaces are marked in fig. 1,624 by A, B, C, etc., perpendiculars AK, BL, CM, etc., are drawn through the points A, B, C, etc. The perpendicular AK and K'A' in fig. 1,624 are each equal to *ak* in fig. 1,622. The second lines on each side of the development, the lines BL and B'L' are equal to *bl*. Fig. 1,622.

The third lines on each side of the development, the lines CM and C'M', are equal to the third line cm, fig. 1,622.

The fourth lines in the development are made equal to the fourth parallel in the elevation, fig. 1,622, and in the same manner all other lines in the development are made equal to the corresponding parallels in the elevation of the pipe in fig. 1,622.

The middle line, SI in the development is made equal to the line *si*, in the elevation; the points KLMSM'L'K', etc.; thus found, define the position of the curve of intersection in the development of the cylinder.

The required curve is traced through these points; the development AA'K'K' is the pattern for the part *aksi* of the right elbow shown in fig. 1,622.

The other part of the elbow is developed in fig. 1,623. It will be readily seen that the figure TVWU is laid out in the manner in which the first development was obtained; in this figure the shortest parallels are laid off above the longest parallels in the first development. This arrangement gives the advantage of cutting out both branches of the right elbow from one square piece of sheet metal without any waste of material.

It will be noticed that the patterns shown in figs. 1,623 and 1,624 do not provide for the lap by which the two branches are held together. A lap of any desired width may be added to the pattern, after it is constructed by drawing an additional curve, parallel to the curve of the above pattern, the distance between the two curves being equal to the width of the desired lap.

Problem 10.—To draw the development of a 90° four part elbow.

A four part elbow is a pipe joint made up of four sections such as is used for stove pipes where it is desired to obtain an easier bend than with the abrupt turn in fig. 1,622.

Fig. 1,625 shows an elevation and plan of the four part elbow. Here the four sections forming the elbow are AKSI, KXTS, XYZT, and Y*fd*Z. Of these four parts, the two larger parts, AKSI and Y*fd*Z are equal. The same is true of the two remaining smaller parts, KXTS and XYZT.

To lay out these parts in the elevation a right angle *abc* is drawn, the sides of which intersect at right angles, the two largest branches of the joint. It is evident that the point b, must be equidistant from both pipes.

The right angle abc, is divided first into three equal parts and then each one of these parts is divided in turn into two equal parts; the right angle is thus divided into six equal parts, of which Kba, is one part, KbX, equals two parts, XbY equals two parts and Ybc one part. It will be noticed that this construction does not depend on the diameter of the pipe.

The problem of developing the four part elbow resolves itself into developing two only of its parts, one large branch and one smaller part of the elbow, the remaining parts being correspondingly equal to these.

The circumference of the pipe, fig. 1,625, is divided into sixteen equal parts by the points 1,2,3,4,5, etc.

Through these points are drawn lines parallel to the center line of the pipe which is to be developed.

In fig. 1,626, the vertical branch of the elbow, AKSI (of fig. 1,625), will be taken up for the purpose. The parallels upon the surface of this branch are AK, BL, CM, DN, EO, FP, GQ, HR, and IS. Through the points K,L,M,N,O,P,Q,R, and S, draw parallels for the part KXTS, which will be next developed; some of these parallels are ST, RU, QV, PW.

To develop the vertical branch of the four-part elbow set off, upon a straight line aa', fig. 1,626, sixteen equal parts, which altogether are equal to the circumference of the cylinder, which is to be developed

Let the division points, a,b,c,d,e,f, etc., correspond to the division points, 1,2,3,4, etc., upon the circle, fig. 1,625. Through the points, a,b, c,d,e, etc., draw vertical lines equal to the parallel lines drawn upon the surface of the vertical branch of the joint; thus aj, is made equal to AK (fig. 1,626), bk, equal to BL; cl, equal to CM and so on until ri is made equal to SI (fig. 1,626).

The part laid out so far is $ajklmnopgri$. This is one-half of the development; the other half, $i'r'j'a'$ being exactly the same as the first one, may be laid out in the same way.

The part $tt'ss'$ is the development of the small part of the elbow. It is evident that its length, ts, must be equal to the circumference of the pipe in the elbow. The lines in the pattern, $tt'ss'$ drawn at right angles to the center line of it, and bisected by it, are made equal to the parallel lines, ST, RU, QV, PW, etc., drawn upon the surface of the part, KXTS, fig. 1,626.

It is plain that the part, $uu'vv'$ is equal to the part $tt'ss'$, with the difference that the small parallels in it are laid out above the large parallels in the other part; in the same manner, the part $yy'ww'$ is equal to the part $aja'j'$.

Laying out the pattern in this manner makes it possible to cut out the complete elbow from one square piece of metal, $ay'w'a'$. The spaces between the patterns are left for laps, which are necessary for joining all parts.

Problem 11.—To draw the development of a tee pipe in which all branches are of equal diameter.

Front and side elevations of the tee are shown in fig. 1,627. As seen, it is made by the intersection of two cylinders of equal diameter. The section of the cylinders is represented in the front view by two 45-degree lines ad and dg.

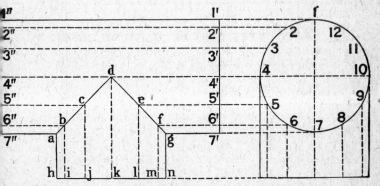

Fig. 1,627.—Side and end elevations of a tee pipe, where surfaces are developed as shown in fig. 1,628 to 1629; case, where diameter of all three outlets are the same.

To develop the pipes divide the circle in the end view of fig. 1,627, into any number of equal parts, in this case let it be twelve parts.

The greater the number of these divisions the more accurate will be the resultant pattern.

Through the divisions 1,2,3, etc., draw horizontal lines cutting the horizontal cylinder in the side view in the points $1''1'$, $2''2'$, $3''3'$, $4''4'$, $5''5'$, $6''6'$, $7''7'$; the line $4''4'$ just meets the lines of the section in the point d.

The line $5''5'$ cuts the lines of the section in the points e and c, the line

6"6' cuts the section lines in the points *f* and *b*, and the line 7"7' cuts th[e] lines of the section in the points *g* and *a*.

Draw vertical lines through the points *a,b,c,d,e,f,* and *g*. After a[ll] these lines are drawn we have all that is necessary to complete the develop[ment] of the cylindrical surfaces.

Fig. 1,628 shows the development of the horizontal cylinder; the re[c]tangle ABCD, is equal to the cylinder surface. The curve ODGL, is cu[r]

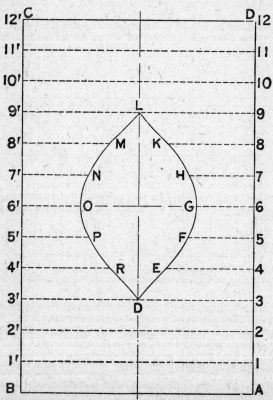

FIG. 1,628.—Development of run of tee pipe.

out within the rectangle for the joint which is the outline of the opening, into which the vertical cylinder will fit.

The rectangle ABCD, has one side AB, equal to the length of the horizontal cylinder, fig. 1,627; the other side AD, is equal to the circumference of the circle, show in the end view of the horizontal pipe, fig. 1,627 The twelve divisions marked on the circle are set off on the straight line AD, fig. 1,628, so that together they are equal to the circumference of the circle.

The outline of the opening for the intersection of the horizontal pipe with the vertical branch is laid out in the middle of the rectangle ABCD, in the following manner: On the middle line 6′6 are set off the distances 6′O and 6G each equal to g7′ (or a 7″) in fig. 1,627, on the lines 5′5 and 7′7 are set off the distances 5′P, 5F, 7′N and 7H each equal to the distance 6′f, fig. 1,627 (or b6″). The distances 4′R, 4E, 8K and 8′M are set off on the lines

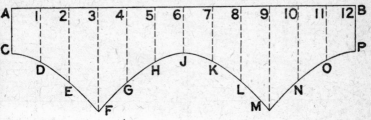

Fig. 1,629.—Development of outlet or branch of tee pipe.

8′8 and 4′4 to equal the distance e5′ (or c5″) of fig. 1,627. The lines 3′3 and 9′9 are touched by the curve of intersection in their center at points D and L.

There still remains to be drawn the development of the vertical branch of the tee-pipe; this is found in the same manner as the horizontal part, *i. e.*, by laying out the surface of the vertical cylinder; that is, by making it equal in length to the circumference of the circle showing the end view of the cylinder. The development is shown in fig. 1,629.

On the line AB, are set off the twelve parts of the circumference and in each one of these divisions is erected a perpendicular to the line AB; on these perpendiculars are laid off successively the length of the vertical lines drawn on the surface of the vertical branch; the lines AC, 1D, 2E, 3F, G4, 5H and 6J in fig. 1,629, are equal correspondingly to the lines *ah, bi, cj, dk, el, fm* and *gn*, in fig. 1,627.

Thus one-half of the development ACJ6 is constructed; the other 6JPB is exactly equal to the first part.

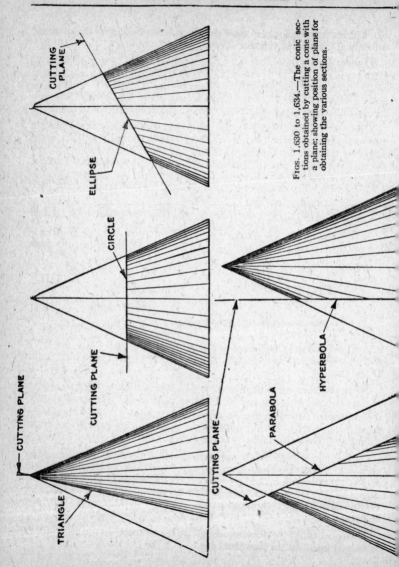

FIGS. 1,630 to 1,634.—The conic sections obtained by cutting a cone with a plane; showing position of plane for obtaining the various sections.

The method employed in these cases may be applied to nearly all developments of cylindrical surfaces; it consists in drawing on the surface of the cylinder, which is to be developed, any number of equidistant parallel lines. The cylindrical surface is then developed and all parallel lines drawn in it. *By setting off the exact lengths of the parallel lines a number of points are obtained, through which may be traced the outline of the desired development.*

It has been noted in fig. 1,627, that the intersection of two cylinders of equal diameters—their arcs intersecting each other—will always appear in the side view as straight lines at right angles to each other. If one cylinder be of a smaller diameter than the other then the intersection will be a curve.

Conic Sections.—By definition a conic section is *a section cut by a plane passing through a cone.*

These sections are bounded by well known curves, and the latter may be any of the following depending upon the inclination or position of the plane with the axis of the cone, as shown in figs. 1,630 to 1,634.

1. Triangle

     Plane passes through apex of cone

2. Circle

     Plane parallel to base of cone

3. Ellipse

     Plane inclined to axis of cone

4. Parabola

     Plain parallel to one element of cone

5. Hyperbola

     Plane parallel to axis of cone

These sections appear as straight lines in elevation, while in plan they appear (with exception of the triangle) as curves.

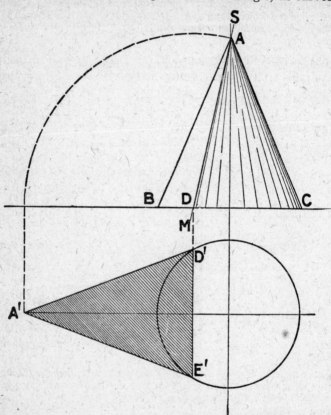

Fig. 1,635.—Surface cut by plane passing through apex of a cone—*triangle.*

Problem 12.—Find curve cut by a plane passing through apex of cone as in fig. 1,635.

Let ABC, be elevation of cone and MS, cutting plane passing through apex. Project point D, down to plan parallel to axis cutting base of cone **at** D' and E', obtaining line D' E', base of developed surface.

With D, as center and radius DA, equal to element of cone swing A, **around** to base line and project down to A'. Join A' with D' and E'. Then, A'D'E' is the developed surface or triangle cut by plane MS, with cone.

Problem 13.—Find surface cut by a plane passing through **a** cone parallel to its base as in fig. 1,636.

This may be found by simply projecting over to the plan. Where MS,

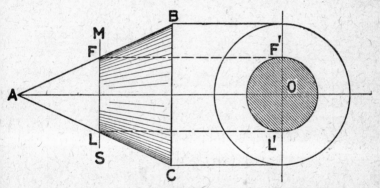

FIG. 1,636.—Surface cut by plane passing through a cone parallel to its base—*circle*.

cuts the element AB, as at F, project over to the axis of the plane and obtain point F'.

Similarly point L' may be found. These points are equidistant from **the** center O, hence with radius = OF' = OL', describe a circle which is the curve cut by plane MS, when parallel to base of cone.

Problem 14.—Find the curve cut by a plane passing **through a** cone inclined to its axis as in fig. 1,637.

In fig. 1,637 let the plane cut the elements OA and OB, of the **curve** at M and S, respectively. Project S, down to s', in plan giving one point on the curve. With S, as center swing M, around and project down **to**

m', in plan giving a second point on the curve, $m's'$, being the major axis of the curve.

To find the minor axis of curve, bisect MS, at R, and swing R, around to horizontal with S, as center and project down to plan. Through R, draw radius 3, and describe arc with radius 3, about O' as center. Where this cuts projection of R at r', project over to plan, intersecting the vertical plan projection of R at r'. $O''\ r'$, is half the minor axis.

To find the projection of any other point as L, or F, proceed in similar manner as indicated, obtaining l', or f'. The curve joining these points and symmetrical points below the major axis is an ellipse.

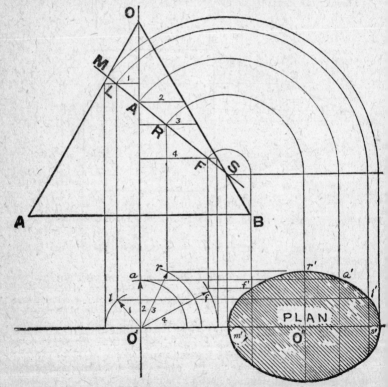

Fig. 1,637.—Surface cut by plane passing through a cone inclined to its axis—*Ellipse.*

Problem 15.—Find the curve cut by a plane passing through a cone parallel to an element of the cone as in fig. 1,638.

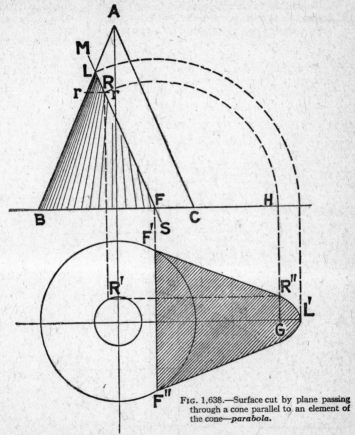

FIG. 1,638.—Surface cut by plane passing through a cone parallel to an element of the cone—*parabola.*

Let the plane MS, cut element AB, at L, and base at F. Project F, down to plan cutting base at F' and F", which are two points in the curve.

With F, as center and radius LF, swing point L, around and project down to axis of plan, obtaining point L' in the curve.

Now any other point as R, may be obtained as follows: swing R around with F as center and project down to plan with line HG.

Describe a circle in plan with a radius (= radius *rr* of cone at elevation of point R), and where such cuts the projection of R at R'; project R' over to line HG, and obtain point R", which is a point in the curve.

Other points may be obtained in a similar manner. The curve is traced

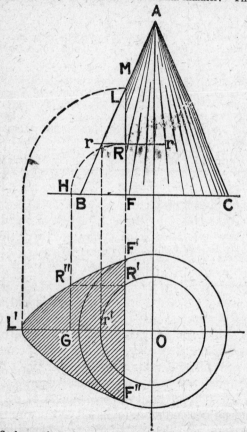

Fig. 1,639.—Surface cut by a plane passing through a cone parallel to the axes of the cone— *hyperbola.*

through points F′,R″,L′, and similar points on the other side of the axis, ending at F″. Such curve is called a *parabola*.

Problem 16.—Find the curve cut by a plane passing through a cone parallel to the axis of the cone, as in fig. 1,639.

Let plane MS, cut element AB, at L, and base at F. Project F, down to plan cutting base at F′ and F″, which are two points in the curve. With F, as center and radius FL, swing point L, around and project down to axis of plan obtaining point L′, in the curve.

Now any other point as R, may be obtained as follows: Swing R, around with F, as center and project down to plan with line HG. Describe a circle in plan with radius *rr′* (= radius of cone at elevation of point R) and where this circle cuts the projection of R at R′, project over to line HG, and obtain point R″, which is a point in the curve. Other points may be obtained in a similar manner.

The curve is traced through points F′,R″,L′, and similar points on the other side of the axis ending at F″. Such curve is called a *hyperbola*.

It will be noted that problems 1,638 and 1,639 are virtually worked out in the same way. In fact the text of one will apply to the other, the two cuts being symmetrically lettered, the only difference being the shape of the curve.

Perspective Drawing.—This is the art of representing objects as they appear to the eye at a *definite* distance from the object. In orthographic (perpendicular) projection the views represent the object as seen when the eye is *infinitely* distant. By the perspective method then the lines drawn from points on the object to the eye converge and intersect at the point of sight.

Before beginning the study of perspective projection it is well to consider some of nature's phenomena of perspective. These phenomena become more apparent when we attempt to sketch from nature. We notice that the size of an object diminishes as the distance between the object and the eye increases.

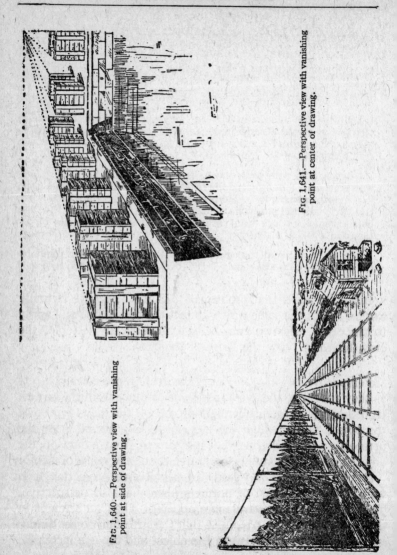

FIG. 1,640.—Perspective view with vanishing
point at side of drawing.

FIG. 1,641.—Perspective view with vanishing
point at center of drawing.

If several objects of the same size be situated at different distances from the eye, the nearest one appears to be the largest and the others appear to be smaller as they are further and further away.

At last the distance between the lines becomes zero and the lines appear to meet in a single point. This point is called the *vanishing point* of the lines, as shown in figs. 1,640 and 1,641.

By closer investigation of a perspective drawing it is found that

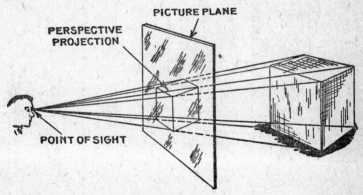

PICTURE PLANE

PERSPECTIVE PROJECTION

POINT OF SIGHT

FIG. 1,642.—Picture plane illustrating principles of perspective.

1. The limit of vision is a horizontal line called the *horizon,* situated at the height of the eye.

2. Objects of equal size appear smaller with increasing distance.

3. Parallel lines converge into one point, called *vanishing point.* For horizontal lines this point is situated at the height of the eye, that is, it lies in the horizon.

4. Vertical lines appear vertical.

5. The location of the observer's eye is called the *point of sight* and is located in the horizon.

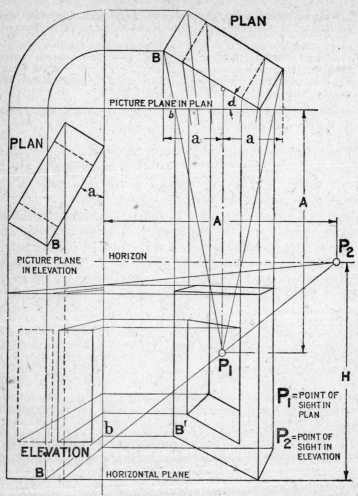

PLAN

PLAN

PICTURE PLANE IN PLAN

b

d

a

a

PICTURE PLANE
IN ELEVATION

HORIZON

A

A

P_2

P_1

H

b

B'

ELEVATION

P_1 = POINT OF
SIGHT IN
PLAN

P_2 = POINT OF
SIGHT IN
ELEVATION

B

HORIZONTAL PLANE

FIG. 1,643.—Perspective of a prism by means of plan and elevation. *To obtain the perspective* of any point of the object, for instance B, draw the visual ray in both plan and elevation to P_1 and P_2, respectively. From the point of intersection b, in the picture plane (in plan and

When an object in space is being viewed, rays of light, called *visual rays*, are reflected from all points of its visible surface to the eye of the observers.

If a transparent plane, fig. 1,642, be placed between the object and the eye, the intersection of the visual rays will be a projection of the object upon the plane. Such projection is called the *perspective projection* of the object. The plane on which the projection is made is called the *picture plane*. The position of the observer's eye is the *point of sight*.

This principle is illustrated by models where red strings represent the rays, piercing a glass plate.

Perspective by Means of Plan and Elevation.—This method of perspective can be put to practical use if we obtain a perspective projection in plan and elevation and then proceed by orthographic projection to obtain the perspective.

Fig. 1,643 shows in plan and elevation, a prism, its front face making an angle with the picture plane. As a general rule, the object is placed behind the picture plane with one of its principal vertical lines lying in the picture plane. P, is the point of sight (the observer's eye). Its distance A, from the picture plane in plan depends a great deal on the size of the object and it is important that the best viewpoint is obtained.

If a house about 40′ high is to be sketched, the point of sight should be taken about 80′ from the picture plane. A good rule to follow is to make this distance about twice the greatest dimension. When large objects are to be represented the best results are obtained when the point is taken nearly in front of the object.

The distance of the horizon from the horizontal plane equals the height of the eye above ground and may be taken $= 5′ — 3″$. For high objects this distance may be increased and for low objects decreased. In our case it is shown slightly above the object. P_1 is assumed on a vertical line half way between two lines dropped from the extreme edges of the diagram. This is not necessary, but it usually insures a more pleasing perspective projection.

Fig. 1,643.— *Text continued*

elevation) project perpendicularly and thus obtain the point B_1, as perspective picture of the point B of the object, In this manner all the other points of the perspective are obtained. This method of construction requires no further explanation and may be applied wherever plan and elevation is obtainable.

The method of obtaining the perspective is explained under the illustration.

Perspective by Means of Two Vanishing Points.—An example of this method of perspective is shown in fig. 1,644, which illustrates a rectangular prism in plan and elevation resting upon

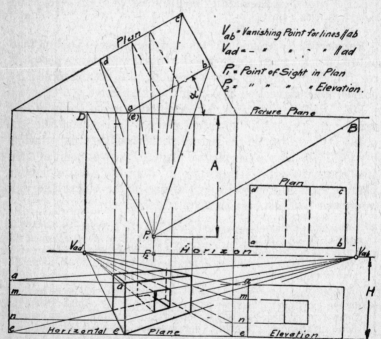

FIG. 1,644.—Perspective of rectangular prism by means of two vanishing points.

a horizontal plane.

The first step will be to redraw the plan, same as with the first method, behind the picture plane in plan, with the vertical line *ae*, lying in the picture plane and turned so that its long side makes an angle *a* (30°) with the picture

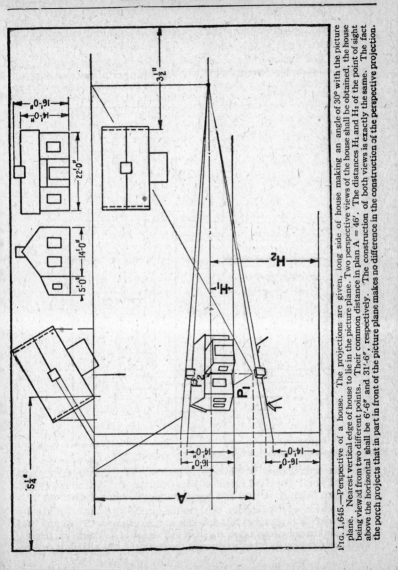

Fig. 1,645.—Perspective of a house. The projections are given, long side of house making an angle of 30° with the picture plane. Nearest vertical edge of house to lie in the picture plane. Two perspective views of the house shall be obtained, the house being viewed from two different points. Their common distance in plan A = 46′. The distances H₁ and H₂ of the point of sight above the horizontal shall be 6′-6″ and 31′-6″, respectively. The construction of both views is exactly the same. The fact that the porch projects that in part in front of the picture plane makes no difference in the construction of the perspective projection.

plane. The point of sight P_2 is at a distance H, above the floor and is located at the same height as the horizon.

Next, find the vanishing points for the different systems of lines in the object. There are three systems of lines in the prism. Vab and Vad, are found by drawing lines P_1B and P_1D, through P_1 parallel to ab and ad of the diagram and dropping vertical lines from the intersection of these lines

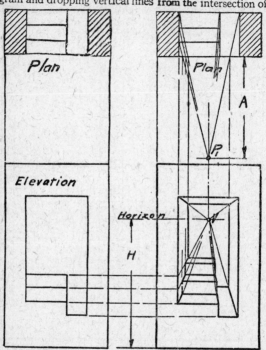

Fig. 1,646.—Perspective of a prism by means of one vanishing point.

with the picture plane (B and D) to the horizon, giving the vanishing points Vab and Vad. The third system of lines embraces the vertical lines which are drawn actually vertical and not converging towards one another.

The edge ae of the diagram, being in the picture plane, is called the *line of measures*, as it appears in its true size in the perspective view, and from a and e in the perspective view the lines will vanish at Vab and Vad, respectively, establishing by intersection with the vertical edges all points desired.

Besides this principal line of measures other lines of measures may easily be established by extending any vertical plane in the object until it intersects the picture plane. This intersection, since it lies in the picture plane, will show in its true size and all points in it will show at their true height above the horizontal plane.

If no line in the object should lie in the picture plane there would not be any principal line of measures, and some vertical plane in the prism must be extended until it intersects the picture plane.

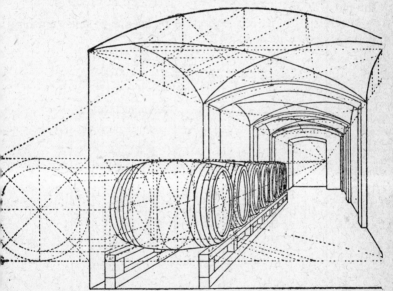

Fig. 1,647.—Perspective of a row of barrels by means of one vanishing point.

Instead of being some distance behind the picture plane, the prism might have been wholly or partly in front of the picture plane. In any case, find the intersection with the picture plane of some vertical face of the prism. This intersection will show the true vertical height of the prism.

Perspective by Means of One Vanishing Point.—In this method the plan is placed with one of its principal systems of horizontal lines parallel to the picture plane. This system there-fore has no vanishing point, and as the vertical system has no vanishing point, only the third system of lines will have a vanishing point.

In fig. 1,646, the vertical face of the prism lies in the picture plane and shows in its true size. Its edges are lines of measures.

The construction of the perspective is easily apparent from the illustration.

Another example of perspective by means of one vanishing point is shown in fig. 1,647.

CHAPTER 31

Architectural Drawing

The instruments and materials used in architectural drawing are practically the same as for machine drawing. There are, however, a few additional materials needed in architectural work, as a tinting brush, water glass, color saucer, colors, stick of India ink, slate, ink well, and white drawing paper suitable for water colors.

Architectural draughtsmen as a rule, use pencils of a much softer grade than those used by machine draughtsmen, but this practice is not to be recommended.

Architectural Practice.—At the first interview between an architect and his client, the general scheme of the proposed building, its location, size, cost, etc., are discussed.

The client has in mind the general arrangement of the house and his endeavor to illustrate it by a free-hand drawing will look something like the crude effort shown in figs. 1,648 and 1,649. It is for the architect to obtain from this and from questioning, a general idea of what is wanted. The sketch will serve as a memorandum and during the interview the architect will add a few principal dimensions, as given by clients. From the information thus gained, the architect will prepare for the next interview a reproduction of the client's rough sketch drawn to say "$^1/_8$" scale," and add a perspective free-hand sketch giving an idea of the appearance of the building. The client can then get a better idea of how the building will look. These preliminary sketches are then talked over, and being drawn in pencil, are easily altered until something satisfactory to the client is obtained. After the client accepts these rough sketches as

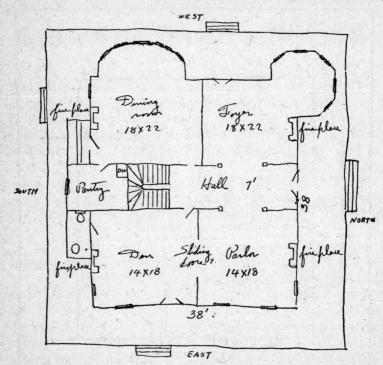

Fig. 1,648.—Owner's single line free hand sketch of proposed building. *First floor plan.* With this rough sketch and list of requirements the architect is ready to make preliminary pencil sketches, which are subject to revision before the final drawings are begun.

representing what he wants, the architect then prepares *working drawings* usually made on ¼″ scale.

Working drawings are drawings made to scale giving all

dimensions and information necessary to the builder. These
working drawings will consist of a plan of each flow and one or
more elevations as may be necessary to indicate the vertical
dimensions. The practice of calling these working **drawings**

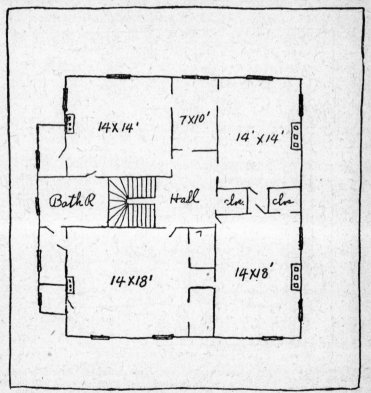

Fig. 1,649.—Owner's single line free hand sketch of proposed building. *Second floor plan.*

"plans" is ridiculous and should not be encouraged, because **a**
complete set of drawings consists not only of plans but also

of elevations, and the building could not be built from the plans alone but both plans and elevations are necessary.

Plans.—In drawing a plan, the essential parts are the outside wall lines and the positions of the interior partitions, irrespective of doors, windows, etc. After the walls and partitions are indicated, the windows and doors, chimneys, stairs, closets,

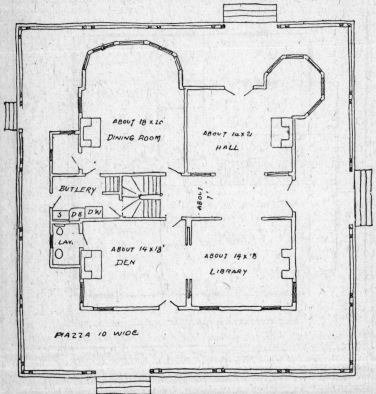

ABOUT 18 x 20'
DINING ROOM

ABOUT 14 x 21
HALL

BUTLERY

S DB DW

LAV.

ABOUT 14 x 18'
DEN

ABOUT 14 x 8
LIBRARY

ABOUT 7'

PIAZZA 10 WIDE

FIG. 1,650.—Architect's preliminary free hand sketch conforming to owner's ideas indicated in fig. 1,648. *First floor plan.*

fixtures, porches and other details may be shown in their correct location.

In both plans and elevation always work to center lines of windows, doors and like details, instead of working to the sides of them. By this method the work may be done more rapidly.

Hints on Interior Arrangements.—The architect is usually

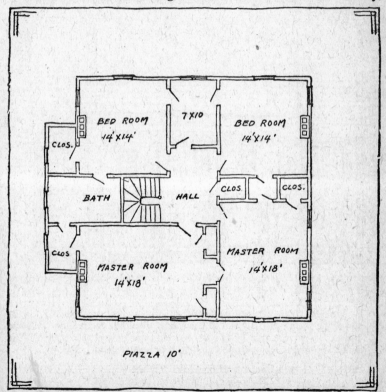

FIG. 1,651.—Architect's preliminary free hand sketch conforming to owner's ideas indicated in fig. 1.649. *Second floor plan.*

hampered in designing the interior by the suggestions of his client, which he must follow more or less.

In general, the sizes of rooms and their location will be determined by the requirements and the direction in which the building is to face. The service for which the room is intended and the furniture.

For instance the kitchen requires space for range, boiler, sink with drain board, table, etc.

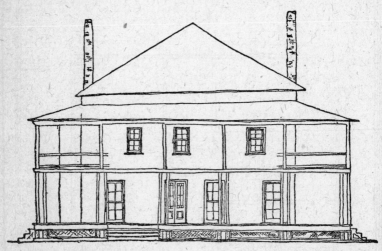

Fig. 1,652.—Architect's preliminary free hand elevation conforming with owner's sketches, and showing tentative outline of roof.

The bath room, if possible, should be located most conveniently for the plumbing installation. Most of the rooms should be rectangular in shape rather than square; the living room is often twice as long as it is wide. The following proportions will be found to represent general practice:

> Entrance hall at least 7′ wide
> Living room   14′ × 16′ to 18′ × 30′
> Dining room   14′ × 14′ or 13′ × 15′ to 16′
> Pantry at least 6′ wide

Kitchen	10′ × 12′ to 14′ × 16′
Bed rooms	10′ × 12′ to 14′ × 18′
Bath rooms	7′ × 10′ or more
Passage halls	3′ wide or more

Walls.—As usually constructed, outside walls of brick houses are 9″ or 13″ thick with 2″ inside for furring and plastering, or

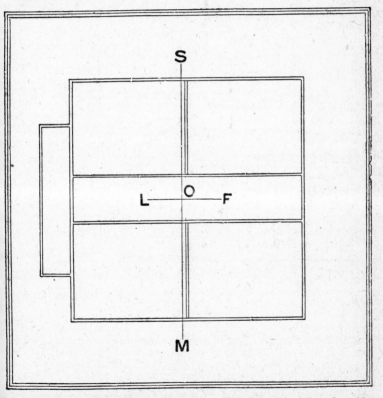

FIG. 1,653.—Development of plan of first floor. *1.* First draw main walls and partition showing them by two lines spaced to given thickness, extending them entire length irrespective to doors. etc. Similarly draw extension at the left, also, piazza, showing thickness of rail.

they may be 9″ brick and 4″ hollow tile. Eight to 12″ hollow tile walls are also used. The thickness of a frame building is made up as follows:

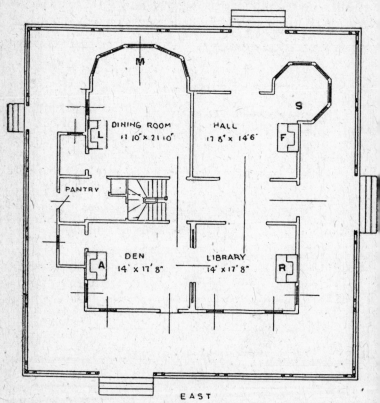

EAST

Fig. 1,654.—Development of plan of first floor. **2.** Draw extensions for bay windows at M and S, erasing the wall lines previously drawn between the limits of the bay windows. Indicate the positions and correct widths of all doors and windows, locating them by center lines when coming on the axes of rooms or halls. Locate outline of chimneys as at L,A,R,F. Show stairs to second floor. These must be figured out and drawn according to the height of ceiling for risers and number of steps.

studding	4 ins.
sheathing	1 in.
outside finish	1 in. to 1⅛ ins. trim
inside finish	1 in.

thickness of wall 7 ins.

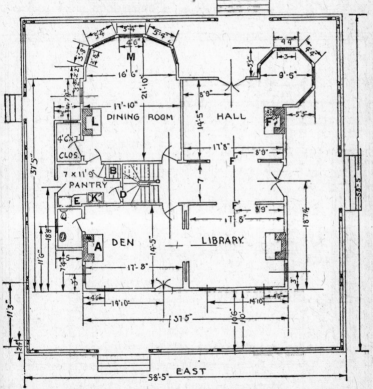

FIG. 1,655.—Development of plan of first floor. *3.* The drawing shown in fig. 1,654, is completed by sketching in all the details, of windows, doors, showing the way they swing, etc., and putting in all the dimensions necessary for the builder, indication of materials, etc., the drawing after this is done, having the appearance as here shown. K, dumb waiter; B, cellar stairs L,ARF, fire places; D, pantry to hall; EE, sink and drain board; F, porteir openings; G, sliding doors; H, lavatory.

Interior partitions are 6 ins. thick for main partitions and 4 or 6 ins. thick for closet partitions.

Doors and Windows.—These should be made to conform to standard sizes, which in widths are 2′ 8″, 2′ 10″, or 3′ for main rooms; 2′ 4″, or 2′ 6″ for closets.   Double doors are 4′ to 5′ 6″.

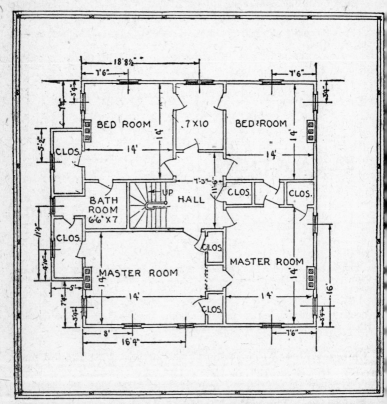

Fig. 1,656.—Finished plan of second story.   This is drawn similarly as explained in figs. 1,653 to 1,655.

Interior doors are 6′ 10″, 7′ or 7′ 6″ high.   Outside doors are 3′ or 3′ 2″ wide, and 6′ 10″ to 7′ 6″ high.

Stairs should be at least 3′ wide, treads 10″ and risers 7½″ or slightly less.

Rear, cellar and attic stairs may have 9″ treads and 8″ or 8½″ risers.

Chimney flues may be 8″ × 8″, 8″ × 12″, or 12″ × 12″, according to the amount of draught required.

Windows should be approximately 3′ 2″ wide, 3′ 6″ to 4′ high if an outside architrave be used.

Provide plenty of windows and have them large, as nothing will make a

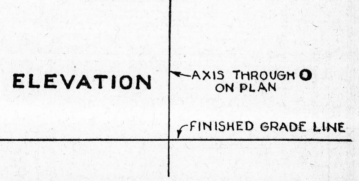

ELEVATION ←AXIS THROUGH O ON PLAN

⌐FINISHED GRADE LINE

FIG. 1,657.—Development of east elevation. *1.* Draw finished grade line and vertical axis through center of house as obtained from fig. 1,653 being there represented in plan as the intersection O, of MS. with LF.

house more attractive than plenty of light.   In some states the law requires that school rooms have 20% of light area.

Chimney Flues.—The general proportions for chimney flues are 8″ × 8″, 8″ × 12″, or 12″ × 12″.

Elevations.—The general heights for ceilings are: first story, 9′ or 9′ 6″; second story, 8′ 6″ to 9′; cellar 7′.

Floor joists are usually 2″ × 10″ and are covered with 1″ rough flooring and 1″ finished flooring.

The lath and plaster on the ceiling is 1″ thick, making a total of 13″ taken up by plaster, joists and flooring.

Attic floor joists may be 2″ × 8″. All floor joists are set 16″ on centers so that 4′ lath joists will break properly. Rafters are 2″ × 8″ or 2″ × 10″

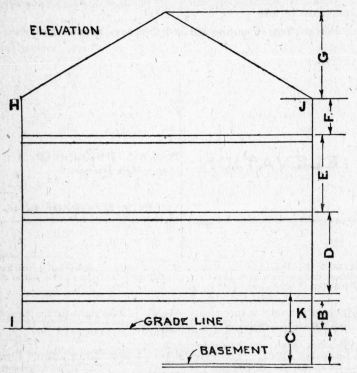

Fig. 1,658.—Development of east elevation. **2.** Lay off at the side of the drawing the principal vertical dimensions A,B,C,D,E,F,G. These show distances between floors, depth of basement, height of first floor joists above grade line, and height of roof. Draw vertical lines HI, and JK, indicating sides of building and block in roof outline. Indicate space taken up by flooring joists and ceiling for each story by light horizontal parallel lines. Note that the dimensions extend to floor levels, hence draw ceiling lines below with the proper spacing.

set 16, 20, or 24 ins. centers. If they are to be plastered they must be cross furred with strips set 16″ centers.

Exterior Details.—The dimensions from the floor lines to window sills (top of outside masonry sill) should be approximately 2′ 3″.

The usual lengths of window panes for the first story are 28″ or 32″, making the openings 5′ 6″, 5′ 10″, or 6′ 2″ in height be a 2″ reveal of frame be used, and higher if an especially wide architrave is used.

The second story windows usually have 26″ or 28″ glass, making the total height of the openings 5′ 2″ or 5′ 6″.

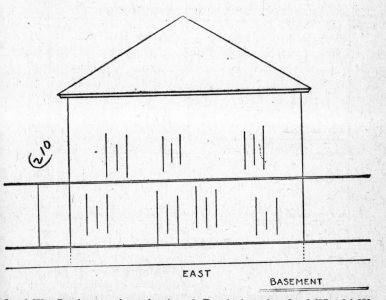

EAST

BASEMENT

Fɪɢ. 1,659.—Development of east elevation. *3.* Transfer from plans figs. 1,655 and 1,656, measurements for vertical line of windows, doors, etc., by marking them off on a strip of paper and reproducing them in the elevation above by line of indefinite length. Draw in the center lines lightly, as they will be found useful in working out the details of the windows and doors. Draw piazza floor and piazza roof lines.

Kitchen, pantry and bathroom window openings are usually less than stated above in order to have the sills set at a higher level.

These dimensions are given as a guide for laying out work, and of course may vary slightly with peculiarities of design.

Kitchen window sills are usually 3′ 0″ to 3′ 6″ above the floor line. This distance is to the top of the outside masonry sill.

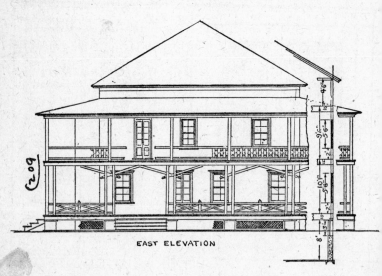

EAST ELEVATION

FIG 1,660.—Development of east elevation. *4.* Work up details of windows, door, piazza, railing steps, basement lattice work, etc. Indicate principal dimensions, construction notes, etc., thus completing the elevation.

The widths of windows and doors was noted previously under the head of Plans.

The usual heights of outside door openings are 6′ 10″, 7′ 0″ and 7′ 6″. In public buildings these may be made higher.

The window sills of masonry buildings are made of 5″ or 7½″ stone, or 4″ brick set on edge, with a cement wash. Heads are 7½″, 10″, or 12″ stone;

or brick ground to the proper radius; or 8″ and 4″ brick set on edge; or they are made of 8″ or 12″ brick segmental arches. All may have brick or stone key stones and skew blocks, according to design. These should project 2½″ or 5″ above the top of a flat arch, and if the cornice bed mould come directly over the second story arches, either one or two courses of brick stretchers should show between the top of key block or arch and the bottom of the bed mould.

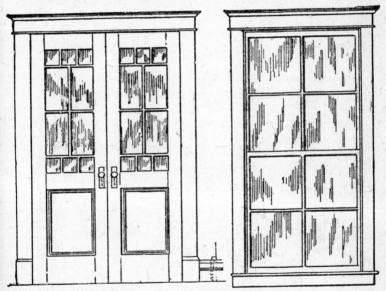

FIGS. 1,661 and 1,662.—Detail of double door east side, and windows.

Door openings have 5″ or 6″ stone sills.

Door and window openings of frame buildings usually have a 4″ or 4½″ plain or moulded outside architrave, and 2″ wood sills.

Slate and wood shingle roofs, to be free from leaks, should have at least 30 degrees pitch, but seldom more than 45 degrees. Tin and slag roofs are kept flat, but with a pitch of not more than ¼″ to the foot.

Show rafters or brackets are spaced approximately 24″ on centers. Porch floors should be 3″ to 6″ below the floor of the house. Porch rails are approximately 2′ 6″ high. Columns and steps have been previously noted under the head of Plans. The height of porches should be 8′ to .9′ 6″ from the floor of the under side of the plate or cornice soffit. Water tables are of stone, or brick on edge, about 8″ to 12″ in height. In frame structures they are of wood.

General Draughting Procedure.—With the small amount of data usually given by the client it can be readily seen that much depends on the ability of the architect to carry out his work rapidly and efficiently. He can only do this by having

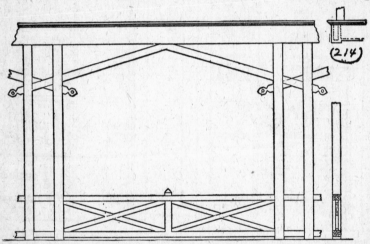

FIGS. 1,663 and 1,664.—Side and end view elevations, showing detail of piazza railing and column construction.

a thorough and broad understanding of the subject. Above all, he must follow a definite system of drawing, blocking out the important points first, and filling in details afterwards, as shown in the accompanying illustrations. This method is easier, quicker and more comprehensive than the method adopted by some student draughtsmen who early in the work labor over unimportant details, almost to the utter neglect of the more essential parts of the drawing.

In the accompanying illustrations (figs. 1,648 to 1,670), the student will proceed with the plans and elevations almost line for line the same as the professional draughtsman would do. This method should be used for working out all drawings

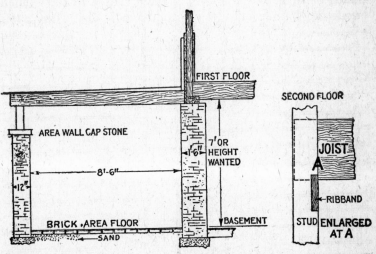

FIGS. 1,665 and 1,666.—Detail of construction. Fig. 1,665 elevation showing foundation, sill, piazza beams and surrounding brick area under piazza; fig. 1,666, second floor ribband joist support.

whether for small or large buildings. The only differences are in the size, the arrangement of the rooms, the location of partitions, etc. All drawings should of course, be first carefully drawn in lead pencil, and then just as carefully "inked in."

In drawing the elevations, usually each side of the house is shown on the drawings.

The front elevation is made the most elaborate because the owner wants to see how the building will look when completed, especially from the street. Accordingly in this elevation the materials are shown. If the walls be shingled, indicate by lines that there are shingles, not by covering the entire front, but with patches here and there over the entire front.

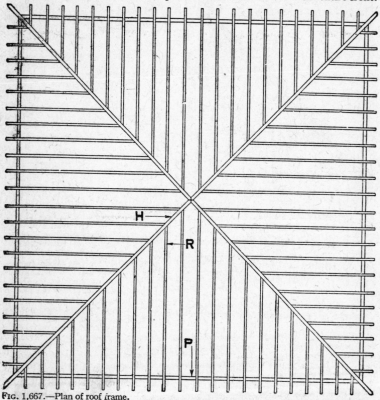

Fig. 1,667.—Plan of roof frame.

Indicate the brick or concrete of the foundation in the way just mentioned. Show type of windows and correct profile of cornice; the general design of the front door, porch and steps; indicate glass in door whether double strength, plate or beveled plate glass. By observing these suggestions the owner can see at once just what materials are used and the general appearance of the building from the front.

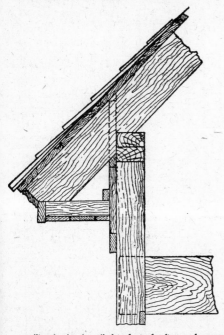

FIG. 1,668.—Detail of cornice. Cornices are made in great variety. In this detail is shown a strong simple method of construction. The rafters is continuous, notched over the 4 × 4 plate. Its end cut is of two angles, one at a right angle to its length or pitch for receiving the crown moulding and the other at right angle to side of building to receive the corona of cornice, which also is nailed to an outrigger. The section also shows how the outrigger or ceiling furring is nailed to foot of rafter, and secured to house by a cleat or piece of furring being nailed to sheathing at the point necessary to align the whoe to a level. To the under side of this furring is nailed the ceiling boards completing the plancher. The vertical dotted lines through rafter to roof boards show sheathing boards cut in tight between rafters. It is valuable for closing off draught, retarding spread of fire and mice travel. By reason of shrinkage of lumber leaving open joints, a large amount of cold air may be drawn into the house if this space is not closed, carrying cold air into the attice. By reason of gross errors or omissions such as inferior construction of floors and sills of many wooden houses an air duct is formed from the cellar to roof and with this space open is accelerated, carrying much cold air into the house, greatly increasing coal consumption, and endangering health by draughts. The 18″ to 24° breast or side wall above floor and the 45° pitch of rafter gives ample space for finishing top or attic story rooms.

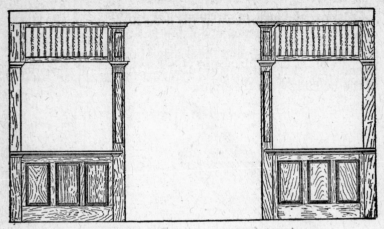

Fig. 1,669.—Interior wood work in main hall.

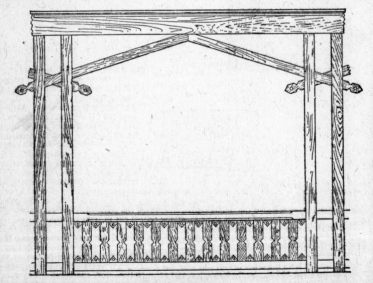

Fig. 1,670.—Detail of piazza construction, second floor.

Crossing of Lines in Architectural Drawing.—This almost universal practice among architectural draughtsmen does not represent carelessness due to haste, but is a studied effort on the part of the draughtsmen to produce what they call a "crisp, snappy" drawing. Some one originated the idea, then another

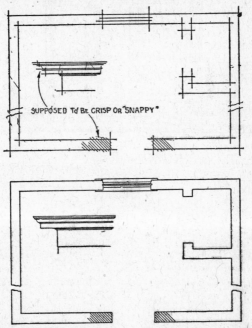

SUPPOSED TO BE CRISP OR "SNAPPY"

Figs. 1,671 and 1,672.—Comparison of the two styles of architectural drawings.

imitated it, and then they all thought it was the thing to do. The author fails to see anything "crisp" or "snappy" about this mode of drawing and does not recommend it.* Also, it has the appearance of a method to employ inexperienced labor.

---

*NOTE.—To be original is more commendable than being simply an imitator, and were it not for the fact that most of us are slaves to *the power of suggestion*, more progress would be made.

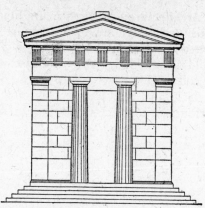

Fig. 1,673.—Temple of Diana Propylaea at Eleuses illustrating the characteristics of Greek architecture in its simplest and best form.

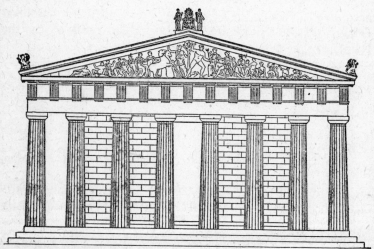

Fig. 1,674.—The Parthenon at Athens showing use of Greek Doric order and the relation of its various parts.

Orders of Architecture.—A great many fundamental principles of architectural design are due to the Greeks and Romans. They originated proportions for every part. Adopting some unit, the building was designed and erected according to this unit. They had certain arrangements of a cornice, a column, and a base which have been handed down for ages. All of the parts had certain relations to one another in size. This combination is known as an "order."

There are, in general, five of these so called "orders" of architecture.

1. Tuscan
2. Doric
3. Ionic
4. Corinthian
5. Composite

Strictly speaking, however, there are only three, because, according to Vignola the Tuscan may be regarded as a simplified Doric, and the Composite as a Corinthian modified by the Romans in an endeavor to surpass the Greeks.

Each order has three main divisions:

1. Entablature
2. Column
3. Pedestal

The entablature has three divisions: 1, cornice; 2, frieze; and 3. architrave.

The column is divided into cap, shaft and base; the pedestal into the cap, die and base.

The entablature varies from 1¾ to 2½ times the diameter of the column.

The cornice projects from the face of the column a distance equal to the height of the cornice in all cases except the Doric order.

The frieze is a flat band or surface, sometimes ornamented. The architrave may be made of a single band, or it may be divided into a number of bands. The column has a capital or top, varying from a plain cushion to the elaborate cap of the Corinthian and Composite orders.

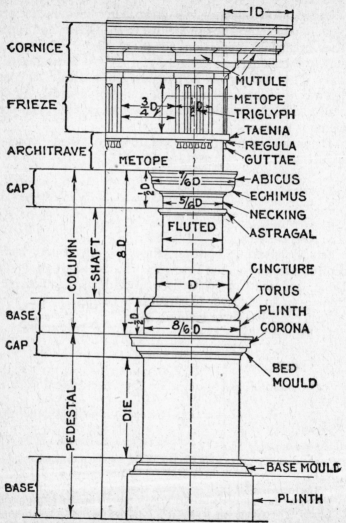

FIG. 1,675.—Doric order of architecture showing details.

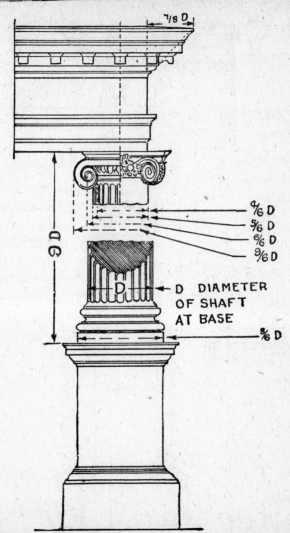

FIG. 1,676.—Ionic order of architecture showing details.

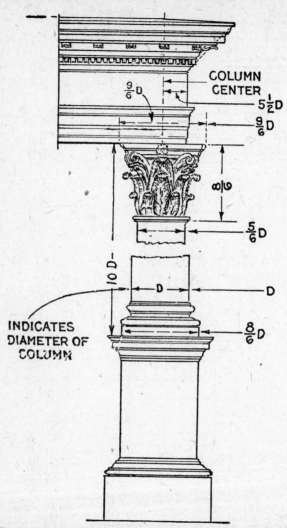

COLUMN
CENTER

$\frac{9}{6}$ D

$5\frac{1}{2}$ D

$\frac{9}{6}$ D

$\frac{8}{6}$

$\frac{5}{6}$ D

10 D

D   D

$\frac{8}{6}$ D

INDICATES
DIAMETER OF
COLUMN

FIG. 1,677.—Corinthian order of architecture showing details.

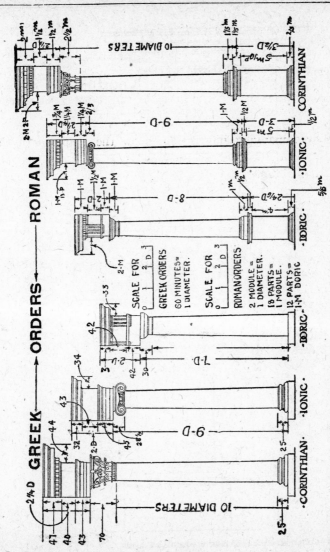

FIGS. 1,678 to 1,683.—Comparison of Greek and Roman orders showing proportions and relative dimensions.

The shaft in some orders is perfectly plain, while in others it is fluted. All columns have a taper at the top. The shaft is carried up straight for ⅛ of the height, and from this point it tapers.

This tapering is called *entasis*.

The shaft rests on a base which consists of a *torus* and a *plinth*, or a series of toruses called an attic base. *The diameter of the column at the straight portion is used as the* **unit of measurement** *for all other parts.*

The accompanying illustrations show the elements of the various orders.

CHAPTER 32

Specifications

By definition a specification is *a definite, particularized and complete statement, setting forth the nature and construction of a detail of the thing to which it relates,* and as applied to building, **specifications** *describe briefly, yet exactly, each item in a list of the things required to complete an architectural contract.*

Great care should be used in writing specifications to avoid misunderstandings and disputes. Each item entering into the construction should be defined and described with such precision that there can be no chance of misunderstanding or double interpretation. The language should be simple and brief. For the guidance of architects in writing specifications the American Institute of Architects has prepared a number of "Standard Documents," and these (reprinted in this chapter) should be carefully studied and consulted by the architect in writing specifications.

Specifications should refer to the form of contract of which they are to become a part. This saves repetition of statements as to liability of contractor, owner, etc.

The following is an example of specifications as ordinarily prepared by an architect.

Specifications
for
a frame dwelling

to be built for Mr. .... of ....
in the county of .... and state of ....
on lot number .... on the .... side of ....
street in the city or borough of ...., county of
................, state of .... These
specifications relating to a set of drawings attached consisting of:

1. Plan of foundation and basement
2. Plan of first floor
3. Plan of second floor
4. Plan of third floor
5. Plan of roof
6. Four elevations
(nine sheets in all)

Detailed working drawings to be furnished as required, all
of which are a part herewith, and are to be considered as such,
with any contract that may be made.

Height of Ceilings.—The following dimensions for these
heights are:

Cellar to be .... 8′ clear of finish.

First story to be .... 10′ between timbers.

Second story to be .... 9′ between timbers.

Third story to be .... 12″ on the breast at plate
to under side of rafter and 8′6″ on the level ceiling.

Interpretation of Drawings.—For arrangement of floors, general finish and measurements reference must be made to the
drawings. Should, however, any difference appear between the

scale measurements and the figures, or between the wording of the specifications and the lettering on the drawings, the figures shall in all cases take precedence of all.

Should there become apparent any error that is not explained either by reference to the drawings or specifications, the contractor shall refer them to the architect for correction before proceeding with the work.

Conditions.—The contractor must see that all the works of said building are performed in a thorough, workmanlike and substantial manner by competent mechanics, also to furnish all materials the best of their respective kinds, labor, implements, cartage, etc., if not otherwise specified.

The house is to be all enclosed, blinds hung and all shut in before any plastering is done unless the season will warrant it. All painted parts of exterior to have priming coat of paint as fast as ready. The succeeding coats must not be applied within 7 days of former, and then not in wet or freezing weather.

All the partitions are to be set, lathed and made ready for plastering which will not be done until after freezing weather unless suitable arrangements can be made to prevent its freezing, in which case no fires will be allowed that will smoke the walls, nor must the temperature rise above 70 degrees while the walls are wet.

Protect all work while the building is in his hands, remove all superfluous materials or rubbish and not obstruct the grounds around foundation so that teams can get near the same for grading and filling in as soon as foundation is up. Leave all clean and perfect at completion of contract, a copy of which is made a part herewith.

Figures are to take precedence of scale measurements.

Mason's Work.—Excavate to the length, breadth and depth required for the foundations as shown on drawings.

The top soil to be removed separate and placed in a separate pile from the other excavated materials, 25' away from the excavation where directed. And also for a septic tank and overflow 75' from foundation and near the bulkhead as will be directed, containing 28 cubic yards; to be built with concrete, with bumpers, drains, etc., all of which is set out in a special plan for same, including overflow tank.

The main tank must be waterproof. The overflow need not. It shows that the tank shall be connected to the house at a point below the lowest fixture and below frost line with a uniform declination of not less than 12" to 20; to have a runing U trap back-aired outside of it at a place to be designated, with back air protected.

Drain to be of 6" socket jointed salt glazed tile laid in tight cement joints. All other details with plan.

Foundation.—To be built as shown of good hard burned brick on 16" foot walls under 12" walls and 12" foot walls under 8" walls.

That part of foundations showing to be faced with cheapest gray pressed brick, either mottled or plain. Mortar in joints colored a deep brown.

Build proper foot walls under all partitions in basement Piers of sizes shown, gray brick on base of three step courses.

Chimneys.—Build two chimneys as shown, same size and shape. For all exposed parts of outside chimney and for topping out use Sayre & Fisher's No. 47 rock faced gray pressed brick.

The fireplaces in parlor, dining and bed rooms to be faced with same brick, smooth inside of fireplaces, revealing 8″ on sides and 24″ at top. Color joints, straight arches on strong angle irons unexposed.

Fire brick backs. Spring trimmer arches for hearths to be laid with same selected brick. All flues to have tile lining, proper chimney pots and clean outs, including two pots in bed rooms.

Mortar.—For all brick work the mortar must be mixed in a manner to make the best possible job. The following proportions are approved for lime mortar, 2 bushels of stone lime to 6 bushels of clean sharp sand, and for cement mortar by adding 1 bushel of Portland cement to above proportions. Use cement mortar in all brick work.

Lathing.—All walls, partitions, ceilings and all studded and furred places in all four stories and under all staircases to be lathed with best spruce lath set $\frac{3}{16}$″ apart and nailed to every stud, all laid horizontally and joints broken every 18″.

No lath allowed to pass from one room to another behind studding without corner nailing. The lather to call upon contractor who is required to furr and straighten all surfaces before lathing.

Plastering.—The walls and ceilings of all rooms, halls, closets and under stair runs to be plastered with two coats of King's Windsor cement, to true and sharp angles.

All rooms and halls in first and second stories to be finish coated in sand finish (or smooth at option of owner). All rooms in third story, kitchen and pantries, bath room above tiling and all closets throughout to be hard finish of King's Superfine plaster. Sand finish to be composed of 1 bbl. lime putty to 1 of white coarse sharp sand and 1 of King's Windsor.

All exposed corners to be protected with "Woods" steel corner or a like approved substitute.

Tiling.—The floors of bath rooms will be tiled with 3″ × 3″ octagonal and 1″ square N. Y. vitrified tiling, colors selected.

The side walls will be tiled 4′ high of plain white glazed 2½″ × 4″ moulded base and nosing, narrow tinted stripe at top of sanitary base and under nosing. The floors will be properly prepared by the carpenter by setting rough floor ½″ below top of floor beams. All tiling will be set in Keene's cement, and the floors finish flush with wood finish floors.

Other Floors.—There will be a concrete floor in furnace room in shop and in area from west end turning east end to cross wall. First there will be a concrete bed of gravel 2 parts, sharp sand 2 parts and one part hydraulic Portland cement, tamped to level and finished over with ⅝″ to ½″ with one part each of said clean sand and cement compound troweled to a smooth, true and level surface inside floors level with other floors. Kitchen hearth built in the same manner.

Coping.—There will be 4″ caps of blue stone on all piers showing them, edged on four sides, 3″ larger than piers. Cope area walls which are to be 8″ with 2″ × 10″ blue stone where circular, fitted to radius. Do all patching and pointing required to perfect the work after the carpenters are out.

Timber.—All timber to be thoroughly seasoned, merchantable, square and straight and free from imperfection that will impair its durability or strength. All to be hemlock unless otherwise specified.

Framing.—This to be balloon style, put up in the best manner. well anchored, braced and strapped.

Headers carrying more than one tail beam to be doubled. Girts to be let into studding, all floor joists notched over same and spiked to studding.

Where required, there will be trusses built according to architect's directions for supporting beams over wide openings. Header beams to be hung in iron joist hangers. Frame so that sheathing will be flush with foundation wall. All mouldings to be mitre-spliced and mitred at angles. No butt ends showing in finish.

Timber Sizes:

Sills	4″ × 6″
Girders	6″ × 8″
Posts	4″ × 6″ backed with 2″ × 4″ or built-up
Main plate	4″ × 4″ (2″ × 4″ doubled)
Rafter plate	4″ × 4″ (2″ × 4″ doubled)
Studding (general)	2″ × 4″
Closet studding	2″ × 3″
Girts	1¼″ × 6″ spruce
Main rafters	2″ × 6″
Dormer rafters	2″ × 4″
Ridge boards	1¼″ × 8″ spruce
Basement floor beams	2″ × 6″
First floor beams	2″ × 10″
Second floor beams	2″ × 10″
Third floor beams	2″ × 10″
Third story ceiling beams	2″ × 6″ and 2″ × 4″

Veranda

Sills	2″ × 8″ doubled
Cross sills	2″ × 8″
Floor joists	2″ × 6″
Rafters	2″ × 6″ and 2″ × 4″
Ceiling joists	2″ × 3″
Cornice plate framing	2″ × 4″

Spacing and Bridging.—Place all studding, floor and ceiling joists on 16″ centers, except basement floor and piazza floor joists. These will be on 24″ centers, also rafters. In every span of flooring exceeding 10′ there will be a row of 1 × 2 bridging or 2 × 3 doubled nailed each end.

Partitions.—All to be set plumb, well braced and nailed studs at all angles and openings to be doubled, extra block a door openings for base nailing.

All partitions not supported below to be firmly trussed and braced. Ceilings to all closets to be furred down to within 12″ of door head except in closets over 2′ deep. Trued grounds at top of base.

Relative Hardness of Woods

Shell Bark Hickory...... 100	Red Oak 69	Red Cedar............. 56
Pignut................. 96	White Beech........... 65	Wild Cherry.......... 55
White Oak 77	Black Walnut.......... 65	Yellow Pine ....,..... 54
Dog Wood 75	Black Birch............ 62	Chestnut............. 52
Scrub Oak............. 73	Yellow Oak........... 60	Yellow Poplar......... 51
White Hazel........... 72	White Elm 58	Butternut............. 43
Apple Tree........... 70	Hard Maple 56	White Birch........... 43
		White Pine... 30

Weight of Rough Lumber per 1,000 ft. B.M.

Kind of Wood	Green from Saw, lbs.	Dry lbs.	Well Seasoned lbs.	Kiln dried lbs.
Chestnut........................	4,600	.....	3,500	3,200
Hemlock........................	4,200	3,000	.....	.....
Hard Maple.....................	5,400	4,150	3,900	3,400
Red Oak........................	5,500	4,250	4,000	3,400
White Oak......................	5,700	4,500	4,100	3,600
Long Leaf Pine.................	4,500	3,500	.....	.....
White Pine......................	3,500	2,500	2,400	2,200
Spruce.........................	3,150	2,700	2,300	2,200
Sycamore.......................	4,750	3,200	3,000	.....
Black Walnut....................	4,900	4,000	3,800	.....

Lumber.—All lumber to be clear white pine unless otherwise specified. All exterior finish lumber to be the best second quality free from large or loose knots. All inside finishing lumber to be clear and thoroughly dry.

Sheathing and Sheathing Paper.—Cover all the exterior walls with ⅞″ matched hemlock, laid horizontally and well nailed to each stud, joints cut on studs or backed for end nailing, cover same as finish is set, with O. K. No. 3 mica building paper, well lapped and extending under all trim and around all corners to make a complete and tight job.

Exterior Finish.—Windows, door casings, cornices, corner boards, water table, piazzas, brackets, band courses, etc., to be made to detail furnished for same. Stock mouldings used must be approved by architect.

First story to be covered with best 6″ Washington cedar lap bevel siding laid 4½″ to the weather, gables shingled. Corner boards set out showing 1½″ × 7″ pilaster. Circles shingled same as second story. Window casings 2½″, front door frames and casement windows as per detail.

Shingling.—Cover second story exterior side walls with 5″ × 18″ No. 1 Jersey cedar shingles dipped ¾ of length in Cabot's No. 345 bleaching oil stain before laying.

Retouch any fitted parts showing after set. Lay 5½″ to the weather, with 2″ galvanized shingle nails. Cover all roofs with 8″ × 16″ Pennsylvania blue slate laid in lath set specially, 7″ to the weather. All hips and other parts requiring it to be made secure against leaks by proper use of slaters cement, and all proper flashings.

An ornamental galvanized iron ridge crest will be placed on main ridge and tower, detail for same.

Flashing.—Flash around chimneys, over all door and window heads exposed to wet and where roofs join walls with Taylor's old style charcoal iron redipped tin painted dark gray both sides before setting, same in all valleys and wherever required to secure perfectly tight job. Each side of valley to have water check turned up one inch, in the metal.

Piazzas.—Cross sills to be strongly secured to house with floor joists framed to them so that flooring will run at right angles to house with an inclination of $\frac{1}{8}''$ to the foot, joining house so that door sills will rest on floor which will be the best No. 2 $1\frac{1}{4}'' \times 3\frac{1}{2}''$ white pine or fir, well seasoned and free from sap, large or loose knots.

(The flooring on circles to be without T & G ripped to the radius and jointed.) Edges (ends) to finish with rounded nosing on top with $1\frac{1}{2}''$ bed moulding under, steps as shown. Treads of $1\frac{1}{4}''$, $12''$ wide, with nosing and $1\frac{1}{2}''$ moulding, nosing projecting $\frac{1}{2}''$ beyond ovolo. Risers $\frac{7}{8}''$, $10\frac{1}{2}''$ from face to face, all strongly built on $2''$ carriages not over $2'$ apart. Cover piazza ceilings, with $\frac{1}{2}'' \times 3\frac{1}{2}''$ T & G beaded and center beaded yellow pine of the best quality, laid parallel with house with no joints showing one board apart on same line or timber.

Staved columns to be patent staved turned as detailed; to be $10'$ and of white pine and primed before exposed to weather; to have the usual round and square caps and base, $2'' \times 8''$ nosed cap rails set over $3'' \times 4''$ rail, bottom rail $4'' \times 4''$. Balusters $\frac{15}{16}'' \times 2''$ set $1\frac{1}{2}''$ apart, as detailed. The $2''$ way is the depth. Ceil under over-hang of all roofs same as piazza ceilings, immediately filling same with white shellac, afterward to be finished with two coats of Vernosite Spar varnish. The false brackets to be set after this finish, and no paint of brackets to touch varnish finish. Prime before set.

Flooring.—First and second stories to have double floors, under floor of $\frac{7}{8}''$ matched hemlock laid diagonally.

First and second story finish flooring to be $\frac{5}{8}'' \times 2\frac{1}{2}''$ comb grain yellow pine thoroughly seasoned and blind nail laid over building paper. No joints in main hall and only one joint in run of boards in other rooms of parlor floor. The parlor, dining room and halls of first floor to have borders formed of cherry and ash, best quality strip next to base of cherry, Parquet designs. To average 20″ wide. basement floors and third floors to be ⅞″ × 3½″ N. C. pine. The first story floors to be cleaned and sand papered to a smooth finish for painter.

Set hard wood moulded thresholds to all doorways, carpet striping to all rooms, cherry, beveled, 2″ wide around hearths, and hard rubber tip door stops in base behind all doors opening against the wall.

Window Frames.—These are to be of seasoned white pine made in the customary way with jambs let into sill; to be for 1½″ sash, blind stop 5″, 2½″ casings, all fitted with invisible pockets, and 2″ steel wheel ball bearing pulleys.

Sash.—All sash to be of kiln dried white pine, made and moulded in the customary way and as shown, and primed with oil before glazed.

All to be hung and perfectly balanced, cast iron weights and hung with No. 8 Sampson spot cord. All sliding sash in first and second story to be fitted with Reading P. 668 bronze sash locks and 2 bronze flush lifts to match.

Screens.—All windows that open to be fitted with the Jesty metal wire window screen, bronzed copper wire, set on blind stop.

Glazing.—All sash and outside doors where indicated to be glazed with double thick selected American flint glass. All hall doors to be glazed with French plate, that in Dutch door beveled. Cellar sash not double hung on weights to be hinged and fastened as directed.

Blinds.—All windows to be provided with blinds 1¼″ with rolling slats, made of best seasoned white pine, all to move freely after painted; to be hung with best automatic blind hinges manufactured by R. P. Whipple & Co. Greenfield, Mass., or as approved.

Door Frames.—All inside door frames of finished parts of house, first and second stories, bed rooms and hall in attic to be of No. 1 clear white wood or fir, 1¼″ thick, with moulded stop bead ½″ × 2″.

Outside door frames to be rabbeted for doors. All frames to be flush with finish plaster and set so as to receive solid screw holds for all furniture.

Doors.—Unless otherwise specified, doors to be of clear dry kiln dried white birch, free from sap, well made, blind tenoned and sand papered smooth, one and two panelled as selected, all 1½″.

Outside doors to be 1¾″ thick. Front doors to be of design shown, mahogany and oak veneer, finishing 1⅞″ thick, bevel French plate glass, panel mouldings on both faces.

Hang all doors throughout with loose joint ball tip butts of sufficient size to throw them clear of architraves. All over 7′ high to have three (3) butts each. All inside doors of basement, second and third story, Japanned, ball tipped, dull finish iron. Those on first story and front doors to be 4½″ × 4½″ ball tipped bronze. Dwarf doors to have suitable butts and locks to match other furniture.

Knobs, Roses and Escutcheons.—The front doors and all outside doors to have plain bronze ball knobs, one piece roses and escutcheons. All inside doors, dressers, etc., to have suitable hard wood knobs, roses, escutcheons, etc.

Locks.—Front doors to have 6″ anti-friction lock with two keys, bronze front and striking plate and to each, two flush barrel bolts, coupling Dutch doors.

All other doors to have good steel mortise locks to match furniture.

Hang both double swing butlery doors on double acting Chicago brass spring hinges. Sliding doors to have astragal front locks and striking plate, brass flush fixtures complete, hung on Richards-Wilcox trolley parlor door hanger.

Furnish all nails galvanized and all such other hardware as shall be necessary to the true performance and completion of all the work.

Interior Trim.—For basement and attic the interior trim to be white wood or fir. To be selected cypress for first and second stories except in main halls, dining rooms, parlor and living room, which will be of white birch.

In the dining room and first hall and up stairway there will be a 4'6" panelled wainscoting, a 12" panel at top of long panel. A 5" cabinet plate shelf in dining room, the bottom member a picture moulding; to set and match with door head trim. Cabinet china closets shown to have leaded glass doors to a design, at a cost of 60 cents per square foot.

Picture mouldings furnished by the owner to be put up in 6 rooms where directed.

Stairs.—Main stair case all to be of Spanish mahogany except the treads, which will be of quartered white oak, strings and treads to be 1¼" thick.

Risers ⅞" thick. Risers and treads to be housed into wall string and return-nosed over outside string. Rails 3" × 3" moulded, with ramps as detailed. Balusters 1⅝" taper turned, three to a tread and proportionately more for increased widths.

Newels and column newels to details. Run on first flight to be 10¼" from face to face of rise cut (12" treads) second flight and basement stairs 9¾" run, (11½" tread) greater widths to shapes shown.

Other stairs from basement to third floor boxed in of cypress with yellow pine treads.

Mantels.—There will be three where indicated.

The contractor shall figure $100 each ($300) complete, including linings, face and hearth tile, which amount shall be allowed the owner to use at his, her or their option in the selection of same.

The whole cost to be figured in the contract price including the setting of the same by the contractor.

Butler's Pantry Dressers.—There will be a dresser where indicated with three glass doors above draining board, 10″ deep inside, three shelves.

The same in kitchen pantry. Below landing of dumb waiter build three drawers. Sink boards to be clear pine 1¼″, grooved with raised outer edge, apron under 4″, properly supported.

Closet Shelving.—Trim on inside of closets to be plain; to average 10′ of 12″ shelving to a closet, 6″ clothes strip and one dozen clothes hooks, Japanned.

Kitchen closet and closet under kitchen stairs to have suitable shelving and sufficient pot hooks and other fixtures, 25′ of shelving in shop closet. Suitable clothes hooks under basement front stairs.

Wainscoting.—Wainscote behind wash trays in laundry, in kitchen behind sink and draining board, butlery and pantry, 4′ high with ⅝″ matched beaded and center beaded Cypress, finish with neat nosed 1¼″ cap and ⅞″ cove moulding, this height may be varied at dressers and under windows.

Coal Bin.—Provide coal bin as shown of 2″ hemlock dressed on outside 5′ high sufficiently studded to be strong; to have a sliding door or slide that will admit of coal shovel, the same in bottom of laundry door with metal shod angle bottom edge so that it will close down.

Coal chute to be built of brick as shown from edge of coping to opening in cellar wall. Construct a door hung at top outside for closing, fastening with proper inside operative adjustment.

Do all cutting and fitting for and finishing after pipe fitters and any other work that the plans may seem to call for not specifically set forth here, such as shingling side walls of conservatory, etc.

Plumbing.—All necessary materials for completing the entire work as hereafter set forth, in a correct and sanitary manner are to be included in any contract made for the same.

The plumber to comply with the requirements of the architect and give his personal attention to important features, and sanitary code of requirements.

Gas Piping.—The entire house to be piped with sizes required for the correct distribution of acetylene gas.

Main to start from cellar where directed; to have center ceiling outlets in all the rooms of first and second floors and a No. 00 indicating number of lights. Basement, top floor and other side lights as shown. Furnish and set complete a 50 light 20th Century acetylene gas generator where directed in basement, connected with waste complete and guaranteed. Set fixtures supplied by owner.

Electric Light Wiring.—Wires to be installed with same outlets as gas, under and subject to the requirements of the National Board of Underwriters, using 3 point system switching all ceiling lights of first floor, halls and piazzas.

Water Pipes.—Water to be led from main in street to house through ⅞″ galvanized iron water pipe with level handle stop and waste cock within easy reach inside in cellar.

Galvanized iron water pipe to be used on all straight line work; place hose bib cock on the main at a point near or against house for hose purposes both front and rear with cut off below freezing. Do all digging necessary for the laying of sewer and water pipes to house, no trenches less than 30″ below grade at any point and to enter wall at a suitable point for intersecting with inside system. Earth to be well rammed as it is replaced.

The soil pipes to the sewer (see excavations) to be put in by the plumber and are to be perfect 5″ salt glazed socket jointed tile pipe with running (U) trap and capped vent clear of grade near outside of foundation. From drain inside of foundation wall there will be a 4″ cast iron calked and leaded joint drain and back air pipes with proper Y branches for other connections, including one for furnace connection and one for carbide waste. Where practical, no pipes will be run against outside wall; if necessary any such pipe or trap holding water liable to freeze must be cased in asbestos covering and packed with mineral wool to the satisfaction of the architect.

All water pipes must have a gradual fall from the fixtures which they supply and open at lowest point for purpose of blowing out.

All the cast iron pipe, both water and waste, must be perfect, tar coated and be put up in the strongest manner with iron hooks and stays and all necessary fittings.

All vertical lead pipes to be supported with hard metal tacks soldered to pipes and fastened with brass screws not over 2′ apart on finished pipe boards put up by carpenter. Horizontal lead pipes must be supported in a manner to prevent sagging and all of strength to carry 80 lbs. pressure. All joints between cast iron pipes must be properly calked with oakum and molten lead.

All joints between lead pipes to be neatly wiped, not soiled or painted. In place of wiped joints the star coupler may be used but no cup joints will be permitted. All joints between iron and lead pipes must be made with heavy brass ferrules same size as lead pipe and soldered to same. All pipes under floors to be installed and finished before floors are laid. There will be two lines of 4″ vent or back air pipes extending above any window openings in roof screened at top, carrying other bath rooms, with all proper branches required for the different back air connections and works. Where these pipes pass through roof, a water tight joint must be made by lead flange flashing and are to be placed in concealed positions as far as possible.

All other pipes to be concealed except in basement where carpenter will place 1″ beaded pipe boards upon which is to run all water and service pipes.

Boiler.—Finish and set on galvanized iron stand one extra heavy galvanized iron 65 gallon boiler testing to 200 lbs. per square inch, supplied with water through a ⅝″ lead pipe and connected with water back of range, which is to be furnished by the owner and set by the contractor, through ¾″ lead pipe and brass couplings.

Place shut off cock on supply pipe and a ¾″ sediment cock below connected by trapped pipe with nearest waste so as to empty and clean boiler.

Take hot water from boiler to and over sink in kitchen and to all other fixtures except toilets with ⅝″ pipe. Cold water to all fixtures through separate lines.

Boiler to have a combination safety and vacuum valve on top. There must also be a strong ½″ lead circulation pipe connected to hot water pipe at highest point and run down below boiler and there connected with sediment pipe inside of sediment cock for the purpose of circulation of hot water.

There must be no depressions in any pipe and hot water must be kept rising from head of boiler.

Kitchen Sink.—Fit up where indicated a galvanized iron pressed steel sink 18″ × 30″ set and supported in draining board as specified, same in pantry, boards of best 1¼″ pine grooved and outside edge raised and rounded half inch. Butlery sink to be the standard make complete as per plate P1230 Standard catalogue, all supplied with hot and cold water through ½″ brass faucets, those in butlery nickel plated, those for cold water to be hose bib. All to have 1½″ waste pipes to be trapped with 1½″ Dubois traps.

Wash Trays.—Provide and set where shown one three-part Alberine stone tub on galvanized iron legs, heavy ash rim and covers complete.

Supply with hot and cold water with ⅝″ pipe and brass tray bibs (faucets) one for cold water threaded 1½″ waste, Dubois traps, plugs and chains complete. All connected with soil pipe through 2″ iron pipe.

Bath Room Fixtures.—All fixtures of Standard Mfg. Co.'s make, as illustrated complete in their latest catalogue.

Basement bath room Paragon closet plate P851. Lavatory plate P558. Tub plate P141 Keystone. Bath tubs to be the Perfecto plate P103, 5′ 6″. Other three closets to be the Delecto plate P804. Lavatory for third floor bath to be the Everett plate P507, 22″ × 27″. The two in second story baths to be the Copley plate P502, 18″ × 27″.

Before plastering is done all supply pipes must be proven perfectly tight by a satisfactory test and all left perfect at completion.

Painting.—The whole exterior woodwork except shingles, to be painted three coats with Devoe's best ready mixed paints without adulteration. Should thinning become necessary in priming coat, only Luxeberry Calcutta oil shall be used. The colors, one for siding, trim, sash and blinds, not over five to be approved by the owner.

The shingles will be dipped or brush coated with Cabot's bleaching oil stain before they are laid and all cuts showing, stained after set. All painted work to be properly puttied after first coat. Under roof projections and piazza ceilings, as soon as laid, to be filled with white shellac and second coated with two coats of Vernosite Spar Varnish, full body.

For interior work, all mahogany trim to be filled with a paste stain filler to color desired and cabinet finished by a rubbed and second coat of Devoe's best interior cabinet varnish, all other finish to be with Devoe's stains in colors approved and two coats of their flat or Lacklustre finish, except in kitchen, pantry, laundry, furnace room and shop. These shall be varnished or painted at the option of the owner. All work must finish smooth and clean and all must be correctly color puttied before finishing.

All the floors to be filled, with or without color, as directed, those of first story, including stair platforms and treads, to be wax polished and all left clean and perfect at completion.

Condition of Bids.—The owner reserves the right to reject any or all bids.

THE STANDARD FORM OF AGREEMENT BETWEEN CONTRACTOR AND OWNER

ISSUED BY THE AMERICAN INSTITUTE OF ARCHITECTS FOR USE WHEN A STIPULATED SUM FORMS THE BASIS OF PAYMENT

The Standard Documents have received the approval of the National Association of Builders' Exchanges, the National Association of Master Plumbers, the National Association of Sheet Metal Contractors of the United States, the National Electrical Contractors' Association of the United States, the National Association of Marble Dealers, the Building Granite Quarries Association, the Building Trades Employers' Association of the City of New York, and the Heating and Piping Contractors' National Association.

THIRD EDITION, COPYRIGHT, 1915–1918, BY THE AMERICAN INSTITUTE OF ARCHITECTS, THE OCTAGON HOUSE, WASHINGTON, D. C.
THIS FORM IS TO BE USED ONLY WITH THE STANDARD GENERAL CONDITIONS OF THE CONTRACT

THIS AGREEMENT made the..

day of.........................in the year Nineteen Hundred and..............................

by and between...

....

hereinafter called the Contractor, and...

....

....hereinafter called the Owner,

WITNESSETH, that the Contractor and the Owner for the considerations hereinafter named agree as follows:

Article 1. The Contractor agrees to provide all the materials and to perform all the work shown on the Drawings and described in the Specifications entitled
(Here insert the caption descriptive of the work as used in the Proposal, General Conditions, Specifications, and upon the Drawings.)

....

....

....

....

prepared by...

....

acting as, and in these Contract Documents entitled the Architect, and to do everything required by the General Conditions of the Contract, the Specifications and the Drawings.

Article 2. The Contractor agrees that the work under this Contract shall be substantially completed..
<small>(Here insert the date or dates of completion, and stipulations as to liquidated damages, if any.)</small>

....

....

....

....

....

....

....

....

Article 3. The Owner agrees to pay the Contractor in current funds for the performance of the Contract

....

....($...........................) subject to additions and deductions as provided in the General Conditions of the Contract and to make payments on account thereof as provided therein, as follows: On or about the...........................day of each month...........................per cent of the value, proportionate to the amount of the Contract, of labor and materials incorporated in the work...
....up to the first day of that month as estimated by the Architect, less the aggregate of previous payments. On substantial completion of the entire work, a sum sufficient to increase the total payments to...........................per cent of the contract price, and...........................
...........................days thereafter, provided the work be fully completed and the Contract fully performed, the balance due under the Contract.

....

....

....

....

Article 4. The Contractor and the Owner agree that the General Conditions of the Contract, the Specifications and the Drawings, together with this Agreement, form the Contract, and that they are as fully a part of the Contract, as if hereto attached or herein repeated; and that the following is an exact enumeration of the Specifications and Drawings:

....

....

....

....

....

....

....

....

....

....

....

....

....

....

....

....

....

....

....

....

....

....

....

....

....

....

....

....

....

....

....

....

....

....

The Contractor and the Owner for themselves, their successors, executors, administrators and assigns, hereby agree to the full performance of the covenants herein contained.

IN WITNESS WHEREOF they have executed this agreement, the day and year first above written.

TITLE PAGE

TITLE AND LOCATION OF THE WORK.

NAME AND ADDRESS OF THE OWNER:

NAME AND ADDRESS OF THE ARCHITECT:

TITLES OF DOCUMENTS BOUND HEREWITH
AND ENUMERATION OF DRAWINGS:

THE GENERAL CONDITIONS OF THE CONTRACT

Standard Form of the American Institute of Architects

The Standard Documents have received the approval of the National Association of Builders' Exchanges, the National Association of Master Plumbers, the National Association of Sheet Metal Contractors of the United States, the National Electrical Contractors' Association of the United States, the National Association of Marble Dealers, the Building Granite Quarries Association, the Building Trades Employers Association of the City of New York, and the Heating and Piping Contractors National Association.

THIRD EDITION, COPYRIGHT 1915-1918 BY THE AMERICAN INSTITUTE OF ARCHITECTS

THE OCTAGON, WASHINGTON, D. C.

Index to the Articles of the General Conditions.

Article 1. Principles and Definitions.—

(a) The Contract Documents consist of the Agreement, the General Conditions of the Contract, the Drawings and Specifications, including all modifications thereof incorporated in the documents before their execution. These form the Contract.

(b) The Owner, the Contractor and the Architect are those named as such in the Agreement. They are treated throughout the Contract Documents as if each were of the singular number and masculine gender.

(c) The term Subcontractor, as employed herein, includes only those having a direct contract with the Contractor and it includes one who furnishes material worked to a special design according to the plans or specifications of this work, but does not include one who merely furnishes material not so worked.

(d) Written notice shall be deemed to have been duly served if delivered in person to the individual or to a member of the firm or to an officer of the corporation for whom it is intended, or if delivered at or sent by registered mail to the last business address known to him who gives the notice.

(e) The term "work" of the Contractor or Subcontractor includes labor or materials or both.

(f) All time limits stated in the Contract Documents are of the essence of the contract.

(g) The law of the place of building shall govern the construction of this contract.

Art. 2. Execution, Correlation and Intent of Documents.—

The Contract Documents shall be signed in duplicate by the Owner and Contractor. In case of failure to sign the General Conditions, Drawings or Specifications the Architect shall identify them.

The Contract Documents are complementary, and what is called for by any one shall be as binding as if called for by all. The intention of the documents is to include all labor and materials reasonably necessary for the proper execution of the work. It is not intended however, that materials or work not covered by or properly inferable from any heading, branch, class or trade of the specifications shall be supplied unless distinctly so noted on the drawings. Materials or work described in words which so applied have a well known technical or trade meaning shall be held to refer to such recognized standards.

Art. 3. Detail Drawings and Instructions.—

The Architect shall furnish, with reasonable promptness, additional instructions, by means of drawings or otherwise, necessary for the proper execution of the work. All such drawings and instructions shall be consistent with the Contract Documents, true developments thereof, and reasonably inferable therefrom. The work shall be executed in conformity therewith and the Contractor shall do no work without proper drawings and instructions. In giving such additional instructions, the Architect shall have authority to make minor changes in the work, not involving extra cost, and not inconsistent with the purposes of the building.

The Contractor and the Architect, if either so requests, shall jointly prepare a schedule, subject to change from time to time in accordance with the progress of the work, fixing the dates at which the various detail drawings will be required, and the Architect shall furnish them in accordance with that schedule. Under like conditions, a schedule shall be prepared, fixing the dates for the submission of shop drawings, for the beginning of manufacture and installation of materials and for the completion of the various parts of the work.

Art. 4. Copies Furnished.—Unless otherwise provided in the Contract Documents the Architect will furnish to the Contractor, free of charge, all copies of drawings and specifications reasonably necessary for the execution of the work.

Art. 5. Shop Drawings.—The Contractor shall submit, with such promptness as to cause no delay in his own work or in that of any other contractor, two copies of all shop or setting drawings and schedules required for the work of the various trades and the Architect shall pass upon them with reasonable promptness. The Contractor shall make any corrections required by the Architect, file with him two corrected copies and furnish such other copies as may be needed. The Architect's approval of such drawings or schedules shall not relieve the Contractor from responsibility for deviations from drawings or specifications, unless he has in writing called the Architect's attention to such deviations at the time of submission, nor shall it relieve him from responsibility for errors of any sort in shop drawings or schedules.

Art. 6. Drawings and Specifications on the Work.—The Contractor shall keep one copy of all drawings and specifications on the work, in good order, available to the Architect and to his representatives.

Art. 7. Ownership of Drawings and Models.—All drawings, specifications and copies thereof furnished by the Architect are his property. They are not to be used on other work and, with the exception of the signed contract set, are to be returned to him on request, at the completion of the work. All models are the property of the Owner.

Art. 8. Samples.—The Contractor shall furnish for approval all samples as directed. The work shall be in accordance with approved samples.

Art. 9. The Architect's Status.—The Architect shall have general supervision and direction of the work. He is the agent of the Owner only to the extent provided in the Contract Documents and when in special instances he is authorized by the Owner so to act, and in such instances he shall, upon request, show the Contractor written authority. He has authority to stop the work whenever such stoppage may be necessary to insure the proper execution of the Contract.

As the Architect is, in the first instance, the interpreter of the conditions of the Contract and the judge of its performance, he shall side neither with the Owner nor with the Contractor, but shall use his powers under the contract to enforce its faithful performance by both.

In case of the termination of the employment of the Architect, the Owner shall appoint a capable and reputable Architect, whose status under the contract shall be that of the former Architect.

Art. 10. The Architect's Decisions.—The Architect shall, within a reasonable time, make decisions on all claims of the Owner or Contractor and on all other matters relating to the execution and progress of the work or the interpretation of the Contract Documents.

The Architect's decisions, in matters relating to artistic effect, shall be final, if within the terms of the Contract Documents.

Except as above or as otherwise expressly provided in these General Conditions or in the specifications, all the Architect's decisions are subject to arbitration.

Art. 11. Foreman, Supervision.—The Contractor shall keep on his work, during its progress, a competent foreman and any necessary assistants, all satisfactory to the Architect. The foreman shall not be changed except with the consent of the Architect, unless the foreman proves to be unsatisfactory to the Contractor and ceases to be in his employ. The foreman shall represent the Contractor in his absence and all directions given to him shall be as binding as if given to the Contractor. Important directions shall be confirmed in writing to the Contractor. Other directions shall be so confirmed on written request in each case.

The Contractor shall give efficient supervision to the work, using his best skill and attention. He shall carefully study and compare all drawings, specifications and other instructions and shall at once report to the Architect any error, inconsistency or omission which he may discover.

Art. 12. Materials, Appliances, Employees.—Unless otherwise stipulated, the Contractor shall provide and pay for all materials, labor, water, tools, equipment, light and power necessary for the execution of the work.

Unless otherwise specified, all materials shall be new and both workmanship and materials shall be of good quality. The Contractor shall, if required, furnish satisfactory evidence as to the kind and quality of materials.

The Contractor shall not employ on the work any unfit person or anyone not skilled in the work assigned to him.

Art. 13. Inspection of Work.—The Owner, the Architect and their representatives shall at all times have access to the work wherever it is in preparation or progress and the Contractor shall provide proper facilities for such access and for inspection.

If the specifications, the Architect's instructions, laws, ordinances or any public authority require any work to be specially tested or approved, the Contractor shall give the Architect timely notice of its readiness for inspection, and if the inspection is by another authority than the Architect, of the date fixed for such inspection. Inspections by the Architect shall be promptly made. If any such work should be covered up without approval or consent of the Architect, it must, if required by the Architect, be uncovered for examination at the Contractor's expense.

Re-examination of questioned work may be ordered by the Architect. If such work be found in accordance with the contract, the Owner shall pay the cost of re-examination and replacement. If such work be found not in accordance with the contract, through the fault of the Contractor, the Contractor shall pay such cost, unless he shall show that the defect in the work was caused by another contractor, and in that event the Owner shall pay such cost.

Art. 14. Correction of Work Before Final Payment.—The Contractor shall promptly remove from the premises all materials condemned by the Architect as failing to conform to the Contract, whether incorporated in the work or not, and the Contractor shall promptly replace and re-execute his own work in accordance with the Contract and without expense to the Owner and shall bear the expense of making good all work of other contractors destroyed or damaged by such removal or replacement.

If the Contractor does not remove such condemned work and materials within a reasonable time, fixed by written notice, the Owner may remove them and may store the material at the expense of the Contractor. If the Contractor does not pay the expense of such removal within five days thereafter, the Owner may, upon ten days written notice, sell such materials at auction or at private sale and shall account for the net proceeds thereof, after deducting all the costs and expenses that should have been borne by the Contractor.

Art. 15. Deductions for Uncorrected Work.—If the Architect and Owner deem it inexpedient to correct work injured or done not in accordance with the Contract, the difference in value together with a fair allowance for damage shall be deducted.

Art. 16. Correction of Work After Final Payment.—Neither the final certificate nor payment nor any provision in the Contract Documents shall relieve the Contractor of responsibility for faulty materials or workmanship and he shall remedy any defects due thereto and pay for any damage to other work resulting therefrom, which shall appear within a period of two years from the time of installation. The Owner shall give notice of observed defects with reasonable promptness. All questions arising under this Article shall be decided under Articles 10 and 45.

Art. 17. Protection of Work and Property.—The Contractor shall continuously maintain adequate protection of all his work from damage and shall protect the Owner's property from injury arising in connection with this Contract. He shall make good any such damage or injury, except such as may be directly due to errors in the Contract Documents. He shall adequately protect adjacent property as provided by law and the Contract Documents.

Art. 18. Emergencies.—In an emergency affecting the safety of life or of the structure or of adjoining property, not considered by the Contractor as within the provisions of Article 17, then the Contractor, without special instruction or authorization from the Architect or Owner, is hereby permitted to act, at his discretion, to prevent such threatened loss or injury and he shall so act, without appeal, if so instructed or authorized. Any compensation claimed to be due to him therefor shall be determined under Articles 10 and 45 regardless of the limitations in Article 25 and in the second paragraph of Article 24.

Art. 19. Contractor's Liability Insurance.—The Contractor shall maintain such insurance as will protect him from claims under workmen's compensation acts and from any other claims for damages for personal injury, including death, which may arise from operations under this contract, whether such operations be by himself or by any subcontractor or anyone directly or indirectly employed by either of them. Certificates of such insurance shall be filed with the Owner, if he so require, and shall be subject to his approval for adequacy of protection.

Art. 20. Owner's Liability Insurance.—The Owner shall maintain such insurance as will protect him from his contingent liability for damages for personal injury, including death, which may arise from operations under this contract.

Art. 21. Fire Insurance.—The Owner shall effect and maintain fire insurance upon the entire structure on which the work of this contract is to be done and upon all materials, in or adjacent thereto and intended for use thereon, to at least eighty per cent of the insurable value thereof. The loss, if any, is to be made adjustable with and payable to the Owner as Trustee for whom it may concern.

All policies shall be open to inspection by the Contractor. If the Owner fails to show them on request or if he fails to effect or maintain insurance as above, the Contractor may insure his own interest and charge the cost thereof to the Owner. If the Contractor is damaged by failure of the Owner to maintain such insurance, he may recover under Art. 39.

If required in writing by any party in interest, the Owner as Trustee shall, upon the occurrence of loss, give bond for the proper performance of his duties. He shall deposit any money received from insurance in an account separate from all his other funds and he shall distribute it in accordance with such agreement as the parties in interest may reach, or under an award of arbitrators appointed, one by the Owner, another by joint action of the other parties in interest, all other procedure being in accordance with Art. 45. If after loss no special agreement is made, replacement of injured work shall be ordered under Art. 24.

The Trustee shall have power to adjust and settle any loss with the insurers unless one of the contractors interested shall object in writing within three working days of the occurrence of loss and thereupon arbitrators shall be chosen as above. The Trustee shall in that case make settlement with the insurers in accordance with the directions of such arbitrators, who shall also, if distribution by arbitration is required, direct such distribution.

Art. 22. Guaranty Bonds.—The Owner shall have the right to require the Contractor to furnish bond covering the faithful performance of the contract and the payment of all obligations arising thereunder, in such form as the Owner may prescribe and with such sureties as he may approve. If such bond is required by instructions given previous to the receipt of bids, the premium shall be paid by the Contractor; if subsequent thereto, it shall be paid by the Owner.

Art. 23. Cash Allowances.—The Contractor shall include in the contract sum all allowances named in the Contract Documents and shall cause the work so covered to be done by such contractors and for such sums as the Architect may direct, the contract sum being adjusted in conformity therewith. The Contractor declares that the contract sum includes such sums for expenses and profit on account of cash allowances as he deems proper. No demand for expenses or profit other than those included in the contract sum shall be allowed. The Contractor shall not be required to employ for any such work persons against whom he has a reasonable objection.

Art. 24. Changes in the Work.—The Owner, without invalidating the contract, may make changes by altering, adding to or deducting from the work, the contract sum being adjusted accordingly. All such work shall be executed under the conditions of the original contract except that any claim for extension of time caused thereby shall be adjusted at the time of ordering such change.

Except as provided in Articles 3, 9 and 18, no change shall be made unless in pursuance of a written order from the Owner signed or countersigned by the Architect, or a written order from the Architect stating that the Owner has authorized the change, and no claim for an addition to the contract sum shall be valid unless so ordered.

The value of any such change shall be determined in one or more of the following ways:

(a) By estimate and acceptance in a lump sum.
(b) By unit prices named in the contract or subsequently agreed upon.
(c) By cost and percentage or by cost and a fixed fee.
(d) If none of the above methods is agreed upon, the Contractor, provided he receive an order as above, shall proceed with the work, no appeal to arbitration being allowed from such order to proceed.

In cases (c) and (d), the Contractor shall keep and present in such form as the Architect may direct, a correct account of the net cost of labor and materials, together with vouchers. In any case, the Architect shall certify to the amount, including a reasonable profit, due to the Contractor. Pending final determination of value, payments on account of changes shall be made on the Architect's certificate.

Art. 25. Claims for Extras.—If the Contractor claims that any instructions, by drawings or otherwise, involve extra cost under this contract, he shall give the Architect written notice thereof before proceeding to execute the work and, in any event, within two weeks of receiving such instructions, and the procedure shall then be as provided in Art. 24. No such claim shall be valid unless so made.

Art. 26. Applications for Payments.—The Contractor shall submit to the Architect an application for each payment and, if required, receipts or other vouchers showing his payments for materials and labor, including payments to subcontractors as required by Article 44.

If payments are made on valuation of work done, such application shall be submitted at least ten days before each payment falls due, and, if required, the Contractor shall, before the first application, submit to the Architect a schedule of values of the various parts of the work, including quantities, aggregating the total sum of the contract, divided so as to facilitate payments to subcontractors in accordance with Article 44 (e), made out in such form and, if required, supported by such evidence as to its correctness, as the Architect may direct. This schedule, when approved by the Architect, shall be used as a basis for certificates of payment, unless it be found to be in error. In applying for payments, the Contractor shall submit a statement based upon this schedule and, if required, itemized in such form and supported by such evidence as the Architect may direct, showing his right to the payment claimed.

Art. 27. Certificates and Payments.—If the Contractor has made application as above, the Architect shall, not later than the date when each payment falls due, issue to the Contractor a certificate for such amount as he decides to be properly due.

No certificate issued nor payment made to the Contractor, nor partial or entire use or occupancy of the work by the Owner shall be an acceptance of any work or materials not in accordance with this contract. The making and acceptance of the final payment shall constitute a waiver of all claims by the Owner, otherwise than under Articles 16 and 29 of these conditions or under requirement of the specifications, and of all claims by the Contractor, except those previously made and still unsettled.

Should the Owner fail to pay the sum named in any certificate of the Architect or in any award by arbitration, upon demand when due, the Contractor shall receive, in addition to the sum named in the certificate, interest thereon at the legal rate in force at the place of building.

Art. 28. Payments Withheld.—The Architect may withhold or, on account of subsequently discovered evidence, nullify the whole or a part of any certificate for payment to such extent as may be necessary to protect the Owner from loss on account of:

(a) Defective work not remedied.
(b) Claims filed or reasonable evidence indicating probable filing of claims.
(c) Failure of the Contractor to make payments properly to subcontractors or for material or labor.
(d) A reasonable doubt that the contract can be completed for the balance then unpaid.
(e) Damage to another contractor under Article 40.

When all the above grounds are removed certificates shall at once be issued for amounts withheld because of them.

Art. 29. Liens.—Neither the final payment nor any part of the retained percentage shall become due until the Contractor, if required, shall deliver to the Owner a complete release of all liens arising out of this contract, or receipts in full in lieu thereof and, if required in either case, an affidavit that so far as he has knowledge or information the releases and receipts include all the labor and material for which a lien could be filed; but the Contractor may, if any subcontractor refuses to furnish a release or receipt in full, furnish a bond satisfactory to the Owner, to indemnify him against any claim by lien or otherwise. If any lien or claim remain unsatisfied after all payments are made, the Contractor shall refund to the Owner all moneys that the latter may be compelled to pay in discharging such lien or claim, including all costs and a reasonable attorney's fee.

Art. 30. Permits and Regulations.—The Contractor shall obtain and pay for all permits and licenses, but not permanent easements, and shall give all notices, pay all fees and comply with all laws, ordinances, rules and regulations bearing on the conduct of the work as drawn and specified. If the Contractor observes that the drawings and specifications are at variance therewith, he shall promptly notify the Architect in writing, and any necessary changes shall be adjusted under Article 24. If the Contractor performs any work knowing it to be contrary to such laws, ordinances, rules and regulations, and without such notice to the Architect, he shall bear all costs arising therefrom.

Art. 31. Royalties and Patents.—The Contractor shall pay all royalties and license fees. He shall defend all suits or claims for infringement of any patent rights and shall save the Owner harmless from loss on account thereof, except that the Owner shall be responsible for all such loss when the product of a particular manufacturer or manufacturers is specified, but if the Contractor has information that the article specified is an infringement of a patent he shall be responsible for such loss unless he promptly gives such information to the Architect or Owner.

Art. 32. Use of Premises.—The Contractor shall confine his apparatus, the storage of materials and the operations of his workmen to limits indicated by law, ordinances, permits or directions of the Architect and shall not unreasonably encumber the premises with his materials.

The Contractor shall not load or permit any part of the structure to be loaded with a weight that will endanger its safety.

The Contractor shall enforce the Architect's instructions regarding signs, advertisements, fires and smoking.

Art. 33. Cleaning Up.—The Contractor shall at all times keep the premises free from accumulations of waste material or rubbish caused by his employees or work and at the completion of the work he shall remove all his rubbish from and about the building and all his tools, scaffolding and surplus materials and shall leave his work "broom clean" or its equivalent, unless more exactly specified. In case of dispute the Owner may remove the rubbish and charge the cost to the several contractors as the Architect shall determine to be just.

Art. 34. Cutting, Patching and Digging.—The Contractor shall do all cutting, fitting or patching of his work that may be required to make its several parts come together properly and fit it to receive or be received by work of other contractors shown upon, or reasonably implied by, the Drawings and Specifications for the completed structure and he shall make good after them, as the Architect may direct.

Any cost caused by defective or ill-timed work shall be borne by the party responsible therefor.

The Contractor shall not endanger any work by cutting, digging or otherwise and shall not cut or alter the work of any other contractor save with the consent of the Architect.

Art. 35. Delays.—If the Contractor be delayed in the completion of the work by any act or neglect of the Owner or the Architect, or of any employee of either, or by any other contractor employed by the Owner, or by changes ordered in the work, or by strikes, lockouts, fire, unusual delay by common carriers, unavoidable casualties or any causes beyond the Contractor's control, or by delay authorized by the Architect pending arbitration, or by any cause which the Architect shall decide to justify the delay, then the time of completion shall be extended for such reasonable time as the Architect may decide.

No such extension shall be made for delay occurring more than seven days before claim therefor is made in writing to the Architect. In the case of a continuing cause of delay, only one claim is necessary.

If no schedule is made under Art. 3, no claim for delay shall be allowed on account of failure to furnish drawings until two weeks after demand for such drawings and not then unless such claim be reasonable.

This article does not exclude the recovery of damages for delay by either party under article 39 or other provisions in the contract documents.

Art. 36. Owner's Right to Do Work.—If the Contractor should neglect to prosecute the work properly or fail to perform any provision of this contract, the Owner, after three days' written notice to the Contractor, may, without prejudice to any other remedy he may have, make good such deficiencies and may deduct the cost thereof from the payment then or thereafter due the Contractor; provided, however, that the Architect shall approve both such action and the amount charged to the Contractor.

Art. 37. Owner's Right to Terminate Contract.—If the Contractor should be adjudged a bankrupt, or if he should make a general assignment for the benefit of his creditors, or if a receiver should be appointed on account of his insolvency, or if he should, except in cases recited in Article 35, persistently or repeatedly refuse or fail to supply enough properly skilled workmen or proper materials, or if he should fail to make prompt payment to subcontractors or for material or labor, or persistently disregard laws, ordinances or the instructions of the Architect, or otherwise be guilty of a substantial violation of any provision of the contract, then the Owner, upon the certificate of the Architect that sufficient cause exists to justify such action, may, without prejudice to any other right or remedy and after giving the Contractor seven days' written notice, terminate the employment of the Contractor and take possession of the premises and of all materials, tools and appliances thereon and finish the work by whatever method he may deem expedient. In such case the Contractor shall not be entitled to receive any further payment until the work is finished. If the unpaid balance of the contract price shall exceed the expense of finishing the work, including compensation to the Architect for his additional services, such excess shall be paid to the Contractor. If such expense shall exceed such unpaid balance, the Contractor shall pay the difference to the Owner. The expense incurred by the Owner as herein provided, and the damage incurred through the Contractor's default, shall be certified by the Architect.

Art. 38. Contractor's Right to Stop Work or Terminate Contract.—If the work should be stopped under an order of any court, or other public authority, for a period of three months, through no act or fault of the Contractor or of any one employed by him, or if the Owner should fail to pay to the Contractor, within seven days of its maturity and presentation, any sum certified by the Architect or awarded by arbitrators, then the Contractor may, upon three days' written notice to the Owner and the Architect, stop work or terminate this contract and recover from the Owner payment for all work executed and any loss sustained upon any plant or material and reasonable profit and damages.

Art. 39. Damages.—If either party to this contract should suffer damage in any manner because of any wrongful act or neglect of the other party or of any one employed by him, then he shall be reimbursed by the other party for such damage.

Claims under this clause shall be made in writing to the party liable within a reasonable time of the first observance of such damage and not later than the time of final payment, except in case of claims under Article 16, and shall be adjusted by agreement or arbitration.

Art. 40. Mutual Responsibility of Contractors.—Should the Contractor cause damage to any other contractor on the work, the Contractor agrees, upon due notice, to settle with such contractor by agreement or arbitration, if he will so settle. If such other contractor sues the Owner on account of any damage alleged to have been so sustained, the Owner shall notify the Contractor, who shall defend such proceedings at the Owner's expense and, if any judgment against the Owner arise therefrom, the Contractor shall pay or satisfy it and pay all costs incurred by the Owner.

Art. 41. Separate Contracts.—The Owner reserves the right to let other contracts in connection with this work. The Contractor shall afford other contractors reasonable opportunity for the introduction and storage of their materials and the execution of their work and shall properly connect and coordinate his work with theirs.

If any part of the Contractor's work depends for proper execution or results upon the work of any other contractor, the Contractor shall inspect and promptly report to the Architect any defects in such work that render it unsuitable for such proper execution and results. His failure so to inspect and report shall constitute an acceptance of the other contractor's work as fit and proper for the reception of his work, except as to defects which may develop in the other contractor's work after the execution of his work.

To insure the proper execution of his subsequent work the Contractor shall measure work already in place and shall at once report to the Architect any discrepancy between the executed work and the drawings.

Art. 42. Assignment.—Neither party to the Contract shall assign the contract without the written consent of the other, nor shall the Contractor assign any moneys due or to become due to him hereunder, without the previous written consent of the Owner.

Art. 43. Subcontracts.—The Contractor shall, as soon as practicable after the signature of the contract, notify the Architect in writing of the names of subcontractors proposed for the principal parts of the work and for such others as the Architect may direct and shall not employ any that the Architect may within a reasonable time object to as incompetent or unfit.

If the Contractor has submitted before signing the contract a list of subcontractors and the change of any name on such list is required or permitted after signature of agreement, the contract price shall be increased or diminished by the difference between the two bids.

The Architect shall, on request, furnish to any subcontractor, wherever practicable, evidence of the amounts certified to on his account.

The Contractor agrees that he is as fully responsible to the Owner for the acts and omissions of his subcontractors and of persons either directly or indirectly employed by them, as he is for the acts and omissions of persons directly employed by him.

Nothing contained in the contract documents shall create any contractual relation between any subcontractor and the Owner.

Art. 44. Relations of Contractor and Subcontractor.—The Contractor agrees to bind every subcontractor and every subcontractor agrees to be bound, by the terms of the General Conditions, Drawings and Specifications, as far as applicable to his work, including the following provisions of this Article, unless specifically noted to the contrary in a subcontract approved in writing as adequate by the Owner or Architect. This does not apply to minor subcontracts.

The Subcontractor agrees—

(a) To be bound to the Contractor by the terms of the General Conditions, Drawings and Specifications and to assume toward him all the obligations and responsibilities that he, by those documents, assumes toward the Owner.

(b) To submit to the Contractor applications for payment in such reasonable time as to enable the Contractor to apply for payment under Article 26 of the General Conditions.

(c) To make all claims for extras, for extensions of time and for damages for delays or otherwise, to the Contractor in the manner provided in the General Conditions for like claims by the Contractor upon the Owner, except that the time for making claims for extra cost as under Article 25 of the General Conditions is one week.

The Contractor agrees—

(d) To be bound to the Subcontractor by all the obligations that the Owner assumes to the Contractor under the General Conditions, Drawings and Specifications and by all the provisions thereof affording remedies and redress to the Contractor from the Owner.

(e) To pay the Subcontractor, upon the issuance of certificates, if issued under the schedule of values described in Article 26 of the General Conditions, the amount allowed to the Contractor on account of the Subcontractor's work to the extent of the Subcontractor's interest therein.

(f) To pay the Subcontractor, upon the issuance of certificates, if issued otherwise than as in (e), so that at all times his total payments shall be as large in proportion to the value of the work done by him as the total amount certified to the Contractor is to the value of the work done by him.

(g) To pay the Subcontractor to such extent as may be provided by the Contract Documents or the subcontract, if either of these provides for earlier or larger payments than the above.

(h) To pay the Subcontractor on demand for his work or materials as far as executed and fixed in place, less the retained percentage, at the time the certificate should issue, even though the Architect fails to issue it for any cause not the fault of the Subcontractor.

(j) To pay the Subcontractor a just share of any fire insurance money received by him, the Contractor, under Article 21 of the General Conditions.

(k) To make no demand for liquidated damages or penalty for delay in any sum in excess of such amount as may be specifically named in the subcontract.

(l) That no claim for services rendered or materials furnished by the Contractor to the Subcontractor shall be valid unless written notice thereof is given by the Contractor to the Subcontractor during the first ten days of the calendar month following that in which the claim originated.

(m) To give the Subcontractor an opportunity to be present and to submit evidence in any arbitration involving his rights.

(n) To name as arbitrator under Article 45 of the General Conditions the person nominated by the Subcontractor, if the sole cause of dispute is the work, materials, rights or responsibilities of the Subcontractor; or, if of the Subcontractor and any other subcontractor jointly, to name as such arbitrator the person upon whom they agree.

The Contractor and the Subcontractor agree that—

(o) In the matter of arbitration, their rights and obligations and all procedure shall be analogous to those set forth in Article 45 of the General Conditions.

Nothing in this Article shall create any obligation on the part of the Owner to pay to or to see to the payment of any sums to any Subcontractor.

Art. 45. Arbitration.—Subject to the provisions of Article 10, all questions in dispute under this contract shall be submitted to arbitration at the choice of either party to the dispute. The Contractor agrees to push the work vigorously during arbitration proceedings.

The demand for arbitration shall be filed in writing with the Architect, in the case of an appeal from his decision, within ten days of its receipt and in any other case within a reasonable time after cause thereof and in no case later than the time of final payment, except as to questions arising under Article 16. If the Architect fails to make a decision within a reasonable time, an appeal to arbitration may be taken as if his decision had been rendered against the party appealing.

No one shall be nominated or act as an arbitrator who is in any way financially interested in this contract or in the business affairs of either the Owner, Contractor or Architect.

The general procedure shall conform to the laws of the State in which the work is to be erected. Unless otherwise provided by such laws, the parties may agree upon one arbitrator; otherwise there shall be three, one named, in writing, by each party to this contract, to the other party and to the Architect, and the third chosen by these two arbitrators, or if they fail to select a third within ten days, then he shall be chosen by the presiding officer of the Bar Association nearest to the location of the work. Should the party demanding arbitration fail to name an arbitrator within ten days of his demand, his right to arbitration shall lapse. Should the other party fail to choose an arbitrator within said ten days, then such presiding officer shall appoint such arbitrator. Should either party refuse or neglect to supply the arbitrators with any papers or information demanded in writing, the arbitrators are empowered by both parties to proceed ex parte.

The arbitrators shall act with promptness. If there be one arbitrator his decision shall be binding; if three the decision of any two shall be binding. Such decision shall be a condition precedent to any right of legal action, and wherever permitted by law it may be filed in Court to carry it into effect.

The arbitrators, if they deem that the case demands it, are authorized to award to the party whose contention is sustained such sums as they shall deem proper for the time, expense and trouble incident to the appeal and, if the appeal was taken without reasonable cause, damages for delay. The arbitrators shall fix their own compensation, unless otherwise provided by agreement, and shall assess the costs and charges of the arbitration upon either or both parties.

The award of the arbitrators must be in writing and, if in writing, it shall not be open to objection on account of the form of the proceedings or the award, unless otherwise provided by the laws of the State in which the work is to be erected.

In the event of such laws providing on any matter covered by this article otherwise than as hereinbefore specified, the method of procedure throughout and the legal effect of the award shall be wholly in accordance with the said State laws, it being intended hereby to lay down a principle of action to be followed, leaving its local application to be adapted to the legal requirements of the place in which the work is to be erected.

THE STANDARD FORM OF BOND

FOR USE IN CONNECTION WITH THE THIRD EDITION OF THE STANDARD
FORM OF AGREEMENT AND GENERAL CONDITIONS OF THE CONTRACT.

This form has been approved by the National Association of Builders' Exchanges, the National Association of Master Plumbers, the National Association of Sheet Metal Contractors of the United States, the National Electrical
Contractors' Association of the United States, the National Association of
Marble Dealers, and the Heating and Piping Contractors' National Association.

KNOW ALL MEN: That we..................

(Here insert the name and address or legal title of the Contractor.)

....

....

hereinafter called the Principal, and..................

(Here insert the name and address or legal title of one or more sureties.)

....

....and

....

....and

....

hereinafter called the Surety or Sureties, are held and firmly bound unto

(Here insert the name and address or legal title of the Owner.)

....

....

hereinafter called the Owner, in the sum of

....

.................................($..................)

for the payment whereof the Principal and the Surety or Sureties bind themselves,
their heirs, executors, administrators, successors and assigns, jointly and severally,
firmly, by these presents.

Whereas, the Principal has, by means of a written Agreement, dated..................

...............................entered into a contract with the Owner for

....

a copy of which Agreement is by reference made a part hereof;

Now, Therefore, the Condition of this Obligation is such that if the Principal shall faithfully perform the Contract on his part, and satisfy all claims and demands, incurred for the same, and shall fully indemnify and save harmless the Owner from all cost and damage which he may suffer by reason of failure so to do, and shall fully reimburse and repay the Owner all outlay and expense which the Owner may incur in making good any such default, and shall pay all persons who have contracts directly with the Principal for labor or materials, then this obligation shall be null and void; otherwise it shall remain in full force and effect.

Provided, however, that no suit, action or proceeding by reason of any default whatever shall be brought on this Bond after..months from the day on which the final payment under the Contract falls due.

And Provided, that any alterations which may be made in the terms of the Contract, or in the work to be done under it, or the giving by the Owner of any extension of time for the performance of the Contract, or any other forbearance on the part of either the Owner or the Principal to the other shall not in any way release the Principal and the Surety or Sureties, or either or any of them, their heirs, executors, administrators, successors or assigns from their liability here-under, notice to the Surety or Sureties of any such alteration, extension or for-bearance being hereby waived.

Signed and Sealed this..day of........................19.......

In Presence of

....
.... } as to ....(SEAL)
....

....
.... } as to ....(SEAL)
....

....
.... } as to ....(SEAL)
....

....
.... } as to ....(SEAL)
....

THE STANDARD FORM OF AGREEMENT BETWEEN CONTRACTOR AND SUBCONTRACTOR

FOR USE IN CONNECTION WITH THE THIRD EDITION OF THE STANDARD
FORM OF AGREEMENT AND GENERAL CONDITIONS OF THE CONTRACT,

This form has been approved by the National Association of Builders' Exchanges, the National Association of Master Plumbers, the National Association of Sheet Metal Contractors of the United States, the National Electrical Contractors' Association of the United States, the National Association of Marble Dealers, and the Heating and Piping Contractors' National Association.

THIS AGREEMENT, made this   day of   19
by and between   hereinafter called
the Subcontractor and
hereinafter called the Contractor.

WITNESSETH, That the Subcontractor and Contractor for the considerations hereinafter named agree as follows:

Section 1. The Subcontractor agrees to furnish all material and perform all work as described in Section 2 hereof for (Here name the kind of building.)

for (Here insert the name of the Owner.)

hereinafter called the Owner, at (Here insert the location of the work.)

in accordance with the General Conditions of the Contract between the Owner and the Contractor, and in accordance with the Drawings and the Specifications prepared by
hereinafter called the Architect, all of which General Conditions, Drawings and Specifications signed by the parties thereto or identified by the Architect, form a part of a Contract between the Contractor and the Owner dated
, 19   and hereby become a part of this Contract.

Section 2. The Subcontractor and the Contractor agree that the materials to be furnished and work to be done by the Subcontractor are (Here insert a precise description of the work, preferably by reference to the numbers of the Drawings and the pages of the Specifications.)

Section 3. The Subcontractor agrees to complete the several portions and the whole of the work herein sublet by the time or times following:

(Here insert the date or dates and if there be liquidated damages state them.)

Section 4. The Contractor agrees to pay the Subcontractor for the performance of his work the sum of

($)

in current funds, subject to additions and deductions for changes as may be agreed upon, and to make payments on account thereof in accordance with Section 5 hereof.

Section 5. The Contractor and Subcontractor agree to be bound by the terms of the General Conditions, Drawings and Specifications as far as applicable to this subcontract, and also by the following provisions:

The Subcontractor agrees:

(*a*) To be bound to the Contractor by the terms of the General Conditions, Drawings and Specifications, and to assume toward him all the obligations and responsibilities that he, by those documents, assumes toward the Owner.

(*b*) To submit to the Contractor applications for payment in such reasonable time as to enable the Contractor to apply for payment under his contract.

(*c*) To make all claims for extras, for extensions of time and for damages for delays or otherwise, to the Contractor in the manner provided in the General Conditions for like claims by the Contractor upon the Owner, except that the time for making claims for extra cost is one week.

The Contractor agrees.

(*d*) To be bound to the Subcontractor by all the obligations that the Owner assumes to the Contractor under the General Conditions, Drawings and Specifications, and by all the provisions thereof affording remedies and redress to the Contractor from the Owner.

(*e*) To pay the Subcontractor, upon the issuance of certificates, if issued under a schedule of values, the amount allowed to the Contractor on account of the Subcontractor's work to the extent of the Subcontractor's interest therein.

(*f*) To pay the Subcontractor, upon the issuance of certificates, if issued otherwise than as in (*e*), so that at all times his total payments shall be as large in proportion to the value of the work done by him as the total amount certified to the Contractor is to the value of the work done by him.

(*g*) To pay the Subcontractor to such extent as may be provided by the Contract Documents or the Subcontract, if either of these provides for earlier or larger payments than the above.

(*h*) To pay the Subcontractor on demand for his work or materials as far as executed and fixed in place, less the retained percentage, at the time the certificate should issue, even though the Architect fails to issue it for any cause not the fault of the Subcontractor.

(*j*) To pay the Subcontractor a just share of any fire insurance money received by him, the Contractor, under the General Conditions.

(*k*) To make no demand for liquidated damages or penalty for delay in any sum in excess of such amount as may be specifically named in the Subcontract.

(*l*) That no claim for services rendered or materials furnished by the Contractor to the Subcontractor shall be valid unless written notice thereof is given by the Contractor to the Subcontractor during the first ten days of the calendar month following that in which the claim originated.

(*m*) To give the Subcontractor an opportunity to be present and to submit evidence in any arbitration involving his rights.

(*n*) To name as arbitrator under the General Conditions, the person nominated by the Subcontractor if the sole cause of dispute is the work, materials, rights or responsibilities of the Subcontractor; or, if of the Subcontractor and any other Subcontractor jointly, to name as such arbitrator the person upon whom they agree.

The Contractor and the Subcontractor agree that:

(*o*) In the matter of arbitration, their rights and obligations and all procedure shall be analogous to those set forth in the General Conditions.

Nothing herein shall create any obligation on the part of the Owner to pay or to see to the payment of any sums to any Subcontractor.

AGREEMENT BETWEEN

....*Subcontractor*

...............................*Contractor*

Finally.—The Subcontractor and Contractor, for themselves, their heirs, successors, executors, administrators and assigns, do hereby agree to the full performance of the covenants herein contained.

IN WITNESS WHEREOF they have hereunto set their hands the day and date first above written.

In Presence of

_____
_____
_____ *Subcontractor.*

_____
_____ *Contractor*

...............................*Owner*

...............................*Architect*

Contract Price $..............................

STANDARD FORM OF ACCEPTANCE OF SUBCONTRACTOR'S PROPOSAL

FOR USE IN CONNECTION WITH THE THIRD EDITION OF THE STANDARD
FORM OF AGREEMENT AND GENERAL CONDITIONS OF THE CONTRACT.

This form has been approved by the National Association of Builders' Exchanges, the National Association of Master Plumbers, the National Association of Sheet Metal Contractors of the United States, the National Electrical Contractors' Association of the United States, the National Association of Marble Dealers, and the Heating and Piping Contractors' National Association, the Building Trades Employers' Association of the City of New York.

COPYRIGHT 1915, BY THE AMERICAN INSTITUTE OF ARCHITECTS, THE OCTAGON HOUSE, WASHINGTON, D. C.

DEAR SIR: Having entered into a contract with (Here insert the name and address or corporate title of the Owner)

for the erection of   (Here insert the kind of work and the place at which it is to be erected.)

in accordance with plans and specifications prepared by   (Here insert the name and address of the Architect.)

and in accordance with the General Conditions of the Contract prefixed to the specifications, the **undersigned** hereby accepts your proposal of   (Here insert date.)
to provide all the materials and do all the work of   (Here insert the kind of work to be done, as plumbing, roofing, etc., accurately describing by number, page, etc., the drawings and specifications governing such work.)

The Undersigned agrees to pay you in current funds for the faithful performance of the subcontract established by this acceptance of your proposal the sum of

(\$)

Our relations in respect of this subcontract are to be governed by the plans and specifications named above, by the General Conditions of the Contract as far as applicable to the work thus sublet and especially by Article 44 of those conditions printed on the reverse hereof.

Very truly yours,

Article 44 of the General Conditions of the Contract.

Relations of Contractor and Subcontractor.—The Contractor agrees to bind every Subcontractor and every Subcontractor agrees to be bound, by the terms of the General Conditions, Drawings and Specifications, as far as applicable to his work, including the following provisions of this Article, unless specifically noted to the contrary in a subcontract approved in writing as adequate by the Owner or Architect. This does not apply to minor subcontracts.

The Subcontractor agrees:

(*a*) To be bound to the Contractor by the terms of the General Conditions, Drawings and Specifications, and to assume toward him all the obligations and responsibilities that he, by those documents, assumes toward the Owner.

(*b*) To submit to the Contractor applications for payment in such reasonable time as to enable the Contractor to apply for payment under Article 26 of the General Conditions.

(*c*) To make all claims for extras, for extensions of time and for damages for delays or otherwise, to the Contractor in the manner provided in the General Conditions for like claims by the Contractor upon the Owner, except that the time for making claims for extra cost as under Article 25 of the General Conditions, is one week.

The Contractor agrees:

(*d*) To be bound to the Subcontractor by all the obligations that the Owner assumes to the Contractor under the General Conditions, Drawings and Specifications, and by all the provisions thereof affording remedies and redress to the Contractor from the Owner.

(*e*) To pay the Subcontractor, upon the issuance of certificates, if issued under the schedule of values described in Article 26 of the General Conditions, the amount allowed to the Contractor on account of the Subcontractor's work to the extent of the Subcontractor's interest therein.

(*f*) To pay the Subcontractor, upon the issuance of certificates, if issued otherwise than as in (*e*), so that at all times his total payments shall be as large in proportion to the value of the work done by him as the total amount certified to the Contractor is to the value of the work done, by him.

(*g*) To pay the Subcontractor to such extent as may be provided by the Contract Documents or the subcontract,

if either of these provides for earlier or larger payments than the above.

(*h*) To pay the Subcontractor on demand for his work or materials as far as executed and fixed in place, less the retained percentage, at the time the certificate should issue, even though the Architect fails to issue it for any cause not the fault of the Subcontractor.

(*j*) To pay the Subcontractor a just share of any fire insurance money received by him, the Contractor, under Article 21 of the General Conditions.

(*k*) To make no demand for liquidated damages or penalty for delay in any sum in excess of such amount as may be specifically named in the subcontract

(*l*) That no claim for services rendered or materials furnished by the Contractor to the Subcontractor shall be valid unless written notice thereof is given by the Contractor to the Subcontractor during the first ten days of the calendar month following that in which the claim originated.

(*m*) To give the Subcontractor an opportunity to be present and to submit evidence in any arbitration involving his rights.

(*n*) To name as arbitrator under Article 45 of the General Conditions, the person nominated by the Subcontractor if the sole cause of dispute is the work, materials, rights or responsibilities of the Subcontractor; or, if of the Subcontractor and any other subcontractor jointly, to name as such arbitrator the person upon whom they agree.

The Contractor and the Subcontractor agree that—

(*o*) In the matter of arbitration, their rights and obligations and all procedure shall be analogous to those set forth in Article 45 of the General Conditions.

Nothing in this Article shall create any obligation on the part of the Owner to pay to or to see to the payment of any sums to any subcontractor.

The Subcontractor entering into this agreement should be sure that not merely the above Article 44, but the full text of the General Conditions of the Contract as signed by the Owner and Contractor is known to him, since such full text, though not herein repeated, is binding on him.

NOTES ON THE STANDARD DOCUMENTS

The Construction of the Documents.

An Agreement, Drawings and Specifications are the necessary parts of a building contract. Many conditions of a general character may be placed at will in the Agreement or in the Specifications. It is, however, wise to assemble them in a single document and, since they have as much bearing on the Drawings as on the Specifications, and even more on the business relations of the contracting parties, they are properly called the "General Conditions of the Contract." As the Agreement, General Conditions, Drawings and Specifications are the constituent elements of the contract and are acknowledged as such in the Agreement, they are correctly termed the Contract Documents. Statements made in any one of them are just as binding as if made in the Agreement.

The Institute's forms, although intended for use in actual practice, should also be regarded as a code of reference representing the judgment of the Institute as to what constitutes good practice and as such they may be drawn upon by architects in improving their own forms. Although the forms are suited for use in connection with a single or general contract, they are equally applicable to an operation conducted under separate contracts.

Notes on the Agreement.

As the laws relative to the following matters vary in the several States, and as the statements made below are true only in a broad way, the provisions of the laws of the state in which the building is to be erected should be ascertained from counsel, and the details of the contract documents should be arranged in conformity therewith.

Date of the Agreement.

Agreements executed on Sunday are generally void by statute.

Payments for materials delivered but not incorporated in the work.

On page 2 the definite system of payment which was printed on the Cover of the second edition, is now printed in the body of the agreement and a blank line is left to permit the easy insertion, when desired, of a clause covering payments for materials delivered but not incorporated in the work.

Names of the Contracting Parties.

Ascertain and use the exact name or legal title of the parties. In the case of an individual or a firm, the address of the place of business should follow the name.

If the best practice is to be observed, the name of each partner as well as that of the firm should be inserted at the place where the names of the contracting parties first appear in the Agreement. Thus, "John Brown, Richard Jones and William Robinson, trading as John Brown & Co." In this way the names of all the individuals who are to be made severally as well as jointly liable for the performance of the contract are indicated.

In the case of a corporation, use the exact title followed by a statement as to the place of incorporation, e. g., "Palmer Construction Co., a corporation under the laws of the State of Delaware." In the case of a voluntary association (unless some state statute authorizes the association as such to enter into contracts in its associate name) insert the names of the officers and some responsible members so that all become personally bound by their signatures.

Signatures of Contracting Parties.

See that the signatures agree exactly with the names of the parties as first written in the Agreement. In the case of a firm, the signature of the firm name by one of the partners, in nearly all cases, binds the firm and each of its members. Obviously, it does not bind special partners except to the extent of their interest. It does not bind the partners in case the contract be for something not within the scope of the firm's business.

On account of the trouble of securing the signatures of the various partners, it is usual to accept the firm name signed by one of them, and in that case the signature of a partnership should be the firm name, by ————, the name of the general partner signing, but again, if the most rigorous practice is to be followed, the signature will consist of the firm name and of that of each of the partners.

The name of a corporation should be followed by the signature of the officer duly authorized to execute a contract, e. g., "Palmer Construction Co. by Peter Palmer, President." The seal of the corporation must be attached or impressed and attested by the proper officer, e. t., "Attest, Walter Palmer, Secretary."

In the case of a voluntary association the signatures of its officers and of a sufficient number of responsible individual members to insure the carrying out of the financial obligation assumed by the contract should be secured.

Authority to Execute a Contract.

(a) By an individual. There is ordinarily no legal bar to the execution by an individual of a contract for the employment of an architect or for the execution of work upon a building.

(b) By a business corporation. It is important to know—
1. That the corporation has the right to enter into the proposed contract.
2. That it has exercised that right by legal action.
3. That the officer executing the contract has been duly authorized so to act by the corporation.

It is common practice to assume that the Agreement, if signed by the president, sealed with the corporate seal and attested by the secretary, binds the corporation. Unless the signer's authority to sign contracts for the corporation is a matter of common knowledge, however, there should be attached to the Agreement a certificate showing that general power to sign is fully vested in the one signing or else there should be attached a special certificate such as the following:

At a meeting of the Board of Directors of the ———— duly notified and held in ————————— on ———— 19—. a quorum being present, it was

VOTED: That ———————————— the ———— be and he is hereby authorized and directed in the name and on behalf of this corporation, and under its corporate seal, to execute and deliver a contract with ———— for a ———————————— at ———————————— for the sum of $———————, said contract to be in such form and subject to such conditions as said ———— shall see fit. And said ———————————— is hereby further authorized and directed in the name and on behalf of this corporation and under its corporate seal, to execute and deliver to said Owner any bond or bonds he may see fit, to secure the performance of said contract by this corporation.

A True Copy.

Attest ———————————— Secretary

(c) By any authority assuming to expend public moneys. The validity of an agreement between such bodies and an architect for his services is so charged with danger that no architect should enter into such an agreement except under advice of competent counsel.

Witnesses.

Witnesses at signing are not necessary. If there are witnesses there may be embarrassment in producing them in case of a contest, whereas, if there are none the signatures may be proved by any competent evidence. Witnesses are of use only when one of the parties claims that what purports to be his signature is a forgery.

Seals.

The attachment of the seal is a necessary part of the legal execution of a contract by a corporation.

The use of a seal or of the word "seal" with the name of an individual or firm can do no harm, but since the only significance of a seal as used in ordinary contracts is to imply a consideration, and since all of the Institute's forms of agreement recite considerations, the use of a seal, except in the case of a corporation, is quite unnecessary. A bond, however, by its very nature must be under seal.

Notes on the General Conditions of the Contract.

In some cases the Articles as printed do not include all necessary General Conditions of the Contract. The Architect will then add such others as he deems wise. Many architects include in their General Conditions one or more of the subjects named below. Most of these are better placed in the specifications for the various trades; and others, though suited for inclusion in the General Conditions, are not always needed. Among these subjects are:

Bracing building during construction,
Charges for extra copies of drawings,
Chases,
Checking by surveyor and his certificate,
Contractor to keep the work in repair,
Contractor to lay out the work, giving lines and levels,
Contractor to work overtime if required,
Fences,
Heating during construction,
Insurance against lightning, wind storms, hail and earthquake,
Keeping building and cellar free from water,
Ladders,
Lanterns,
Offices and their furniture,
Permission to use articles or methods other than those specified,
Photographs,
Protection and care of trees and shrubs,
Protective coverings in general,
Sanitary convenience,
Scaffolding,
Sheds,
Sidewalks,
Special cleaning other than "broom clean," as in Article 33,
Stoppage of work in freezing weather,
Telephone,
Temporary enclosure from weather,
Temporary stairways,
Temporary wiring, and electric lights,
Vault permits,
Watchmen.

For further information of use in connection with the General Conditions, refer to the "Handbook of Architectural Practice," published by the American Institute of Architects.

Notes on the Bond of Suretyship.

The bond of Suretyship is drawn for use with either corporate or individual sureties. If a bond is to be given, this form, without additions or omissions, should be insisted upon to insure a full measure of protection. Proper certification that those signing the bond have authority so to sign should accompany the bond.

Notes on the Invitation to Bid, Instructions to Bidders and Form of Proposal.

The Institute formerly issued the above named forms which contain much of value. Experience, however, showed that they had generally to be adapted to specific cases. They are, therefore, reproduced here so that Architects may draw from them whatever they deem useful.

Form of Invitation to Submit a Proposal.

DEAR SIR: You are invited to submit a proposal for .... Drawings, Specifications and other information may be procured from this office on and after .... All documents must be returned to this office not later than ....

To be entitled to consideration the proposal must be made upon the form provided by the Architect, which must be fully completed in accordance with the accompanying "Instructions to Bidders" and must be delivered to this office not later than ....

Very truly yours, ...

Form of Instructions to Bidders.

Proposals, to be entitled to consideration, must be made in accordance with the following instructions:

Proposals shall be made upon the form provided therefor, and all blank spaces in the form shall be fully filled; numbers shall be stated both in writing and in figures; the signature shall be in long hand; and the completed form shall be without interlineation, alteration or erasure.

Proposals shall not contain any recapitulation of the work to be done. No oral, telegraphic or telephonic proposals or modifications will be considered.

Proposals shall be addressed to the Owner, in care of the Architect, and shall be delivered to the Architect enclosed in an opaque sealed envelope addressed to him, marked "Proposal" and bearing the title of the work and the name of the Bidder.

Should a bidder find discrepancies in, or omissions from, the drawings or documents, or should he be in doubt as to their meaning, he should at once notify the Architect, who will send a written instruction to all bidders. Neither Owner nor Architect will be responsible for any oral instructions.

Before submitting a proposal, bidders should carefully examine the drawings and specifications, visit the site or work, fully inform themselves as to all existing conditions and limitations and shall include in the Proposal a sum to cover the cost of all items included in the Contract.

The competency and responsibility of bidders and of their proposed subcontractors will be considered in making the award. The Owner does not obligate himself to accept the lowest or any other bid.

Provision will be made in the Agreement for payments on account in the following words: (Insert the provision.)

Any Bulletins issued during the time of bidding are to be covered in the proposal and in closing a contract they will become a part thereof.

Form of Proposal.

(The Proposal should be dated and addressed to the Owner in care of the Architect.)

DEAR SIR: Having carefully examined the Instructions to Bidders, the General Conditions of the Contract and Specifications entitled ....

(Here insert the caption descriptive of the work as used therein.)

and the Drawings, similarly entitled, numbered .... as well as the premises and the conditions affecting the work, the Undersigned proposes to furnish all materials and labor called for by them for ....

(Here insert, in case all the work therein described is to be covered by one contract, "the entire work." In case of a partial contract insert name of the trade or trades to be covered and the numbers of the pages of the Specifications on which the work is described.)

in accordance with the said documents for the sum of .... Dollars ($........................). If he be notified of the acceptance of this proposal within .... days of the time set for the opening of bids he agrees to execute a contract for the above work, for the above stated compensation in the form of the Standard Agreement of the American Institute of Architects.

Very truly yours,

_____

SUGGESTIONS TO ARCHITECTS USING THE ABOVE FORM OF PROPOSAL.

The above form includes only such statements as will probably be required in any Proposal. Additions will usually have to be made to it. Suggestions suited to certain conditions are offered in the following notes.

If the bidder is to name the time required for completing the work, insert such a clause as the following:

The undersigned agrees, if awarded the Contract, to complete it within_____days, Sundays and whole holidays not included.

If liquidated damages are to be required, insert the following:

And further agrees that, from the compensation otherwise to be paid, the Owner may retain the sum of_____ dollars ($_____) for each day thereafter, Sundays and holidays included, that the work remains uncompleted, which sum is agreed upon as the proper measure of liquidated damages which the Owner will sustain per diem by the failure of the undersigned to complete the work at the time stipulated, and this sum is not to be construed as in any sense a penalty.

If a bond is required, insert the following:

The undersigned agrees, if awarded the Contract, to execute and deliver to the Architect within_____days after the signing of the Contract, a satisfactory bond in the form issued by the American Institute of Architects (second edition reissued 1918) and in an amount equal to the contract sum, and further agrees that if such bond be not required, he will deduct from the proposal price the sum of_____ _____dollars ($_____).

If a certified check is required, the following clause should be inserted:

The undersigned further agrees that the certified check

payable to_____Owner, accompanying this proposal, is left in escrow with the Architect; that its amount is the measure of liquidated damages which the Owner will sustain by the failure of the Undersigned to execute and deliver the above named Agreement and bond, and that if the Undersigned defaults in executing that Agreement within _____days of written notification of the award of the contract to him or in furnishing the Bond within_____ days thereafter, then the check shall become the property of the Owner, but if this proposal is not accepted within_____ days of the time set for the submission of bids, or if the Undersigned executes and delivers said Contract and Bond, the check shall be returned to him on receipt therefor.

If alternative proposals are required, they should be set forth, as for example,

Should_____be substituted for_____ the Undersigned agrees to deduct (or will require the addition of)_____dollars ($_____) from (or to) the proposed sum.

If unit prices are required as a part of the proposal, they should be set forth as, for example:

The Undersigned agrees that work added shall be computed at the following prices, and that work omitted shall be computed at_____per cent less than these prices.

Concrete foundations_____per cubic yard,
Rough brickwork_____per thousand,
Plastering_____per yard.

If the names of subcontractors whom the Contractor proposes to employ are required as a part of the Proposal this requirement should be set forth, as, for example:

In case of obtaining the award the Undersigned will employ, subject to the Architect's approval, subcontractors in each of the several trades selected from the following list (one or more names must be inserted for each trade):

Excavation_____
Stone Masonry_____
Brickwork_____
etc., etc.

To the Users of the Standard Documents of The American Institute of Architects

IF YOU have given the new contract forms a fair trial, the results obtained are the best recommendation for their continued use. Others have found them highly satisfactory, and have so expressed themselves.

By the President of the National Association of Builders' Exchanges:

"Our endorsement of the documents is not upon the ground that they are perfect, but because they are very well considered and well balanced, and because they embody a very substantial advance over any existing building contract forms, whether the old Uniform Contract, the first edition of the Standard Documents of the Institute, or any of the forms used by architects in various cities in their practice, either with or without the approval of the local contractors' organizations.

"If I should use just one word to designate the character of the new documents and their difference from all previous documents, I should say Certainty. If I were to add another word, I should say Justice."

By a Prominent Firm of Architects:

"The Institute is certainly to be warmly commended and congratulated for its work and success in compiling these Standard Forms, and this firm begs to express its highest appreciation of the efforts expended by the Institute as a whole, and the individual members, in the labor they have performed for the benefit of the profession at large, as well as for the honest contractor and owner."

By the Secretary of the American Institute of Architects:

"The Standard Documents are designed to help the architect in his work, by eliminating the difficulties often encountered in original forms prepared in the office, by eliminating personal worry and detail clerical work connected with such forms, and by establishing in his office a business-like system on which he may rely.

"These documents represent years of thorough study and preparation by the Standing Committee on Contracts and Specifications. It is believed that they are the most useful forms ever devised to thoroughly safeguard the rights of all under a building contract."

This booklet should be saved and used for reference purposes in your office. The reprint is limited in number.

CHAPTER 33

Estimating

Since the cost of labor and material, and the conditions under which construction work is to be done are so variable, it is a difficult task to estimate with any degree of precision the cost of a building. The preparation of an estimate is an important part in the architect's or contractor's business, and upon the correctness of the estimate will depend whether the job will result in a loss, or yield a legitimate profit.

Estimating is a study in itself and considerable experience is necessary to become a good estimator. The drawings and specifications should be followed closely in estimating, each item being listed separately rather than the makeshift method of "lumping" as followed by some contractors. In addition to the architect's fee, the cost of a building is made up of:

1. Cost of materials.
2. Cost of labor.

The architect usually calculates his fee as a percentage of the cost of the building.

To illustrate how to estimate, a very small building will be considered, as the various points may be brought out without wearying the reader, thus clearly presenting the various necessary calculations.

Example.—Estimate the cost of the small garage shown in the accompanying illustration.

First estimate the cost of materials, then the cost of labor.

1. Cost of Materials

Foundation and Floor.—Calculate cu. yds. of concrete form

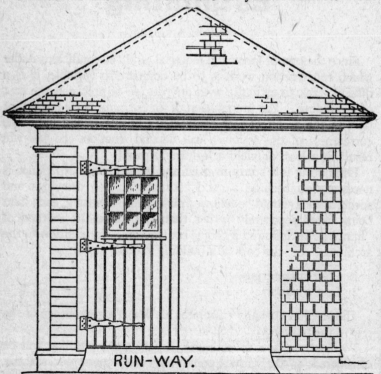

FIG. 1,684.—Front view of small garage for which estimate of cost is made in the accompanying text.

plan and end view of foundation and floor (figs. 1,685 to 1,688), thus:

Volume foundation:

Section **M** $= (8/12 \times 6/12) \times (2 \times 20 + 11 + 2', 4'' + 1', 4'')$
$= (2/3 \times 1/2) \times 54.7$ ·················· $= 18.2$ cu. ft.

Section **S** $= (1 \times 1) \times (2 \times 20 + 2 \times 11)$
$= 1 \times 62$ ·································· $= 62.$ " "

Floor $= 9/12 \{(20 - 1) \times (12 - 1)\}$
$= 3/4 \times 209$ ····························· $= 156.8$ " "

Approach, Section **L** $= 9/12 \left(\dfrac{8 + 10}{2} \times 6 \right)$

$= 2/3 \times 54$ ······························ $= 36.$ " "

Total volume of concrete ················· $= 273.$ cu. ft.

or $273. \div 27 = 10.$ cu. yds.

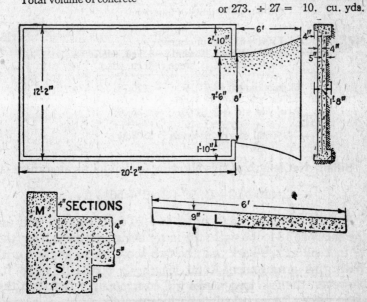

Figs. 1,685 to 1,688.—Concrete section of foundation, M, portion above floor line, S, portion below floor line; foundation, floor; L, approach for garage. Fig. 1,685, plan; fig. 1,686, end view; fig. 1,687; fig. 1,688, section of approach.

Concrete for foundation and floor is generally mixed in the proportion 1:2:4, which means 1 part cement, 2 parts sand, and 4 parts gravel or crushed stone.

A bag of cement is taken approximately as 1 cu. ft., and on this basis a 1:2:4 mixture calls for the following proportion:

1 bag cement : 2 cu. ft. sand : 4 cu. ft. stone

Now since the cement fills the voids of the sand, and the sand, the voids of the stone, if the above proportion of materials be mixed together, the volume of the above materials will be as follows:

1 bag cement+2 cu. ft. sand+4 cu. ft. stone=4½ cu. ft. concrete.

Hence to make 273 cu. ft. of concrete requires

273÷4½=61 units of mixture

or

1×61=61 bags of cement
2×61=122 cu. ft. sand (=4.5 cu. yds.)
4×61=244 cu. ft. stone (=9 cu. yds.)

61 bags cement @ $1.16	=	$70.76
4.5 cu. yds. sand @ $1.50	=	6.75
9 cu. yds. stone @ $4.00	=	36.00
Total cost of materials		$103.51

Sills.—Net length of sills allowing for lap joints at corners is:

$$2\times20+12+1', 9''+2', 9''=56\tfrac{1}{2} \text{ ft.}$$

For the two long sides, order two 20 foot lengths, and for the ends one 18 foot length, the latter being long enough for the 12 foot sill at the back and the two short pieces at the front. With this arrangement total length=2 < 20 + 18 = 58 ft. However, the two long pieces will cost more *per foot* than the short pieces; hence calculate each separately.

Board Measure Rule.—*Multiply length in ft. by width in ft. of the board and multiply this product by 1 for boards an inch or less than an inch thick, and by thickness in inches and fractions of an inch for boards over 1 inch thick.*

Accordingly, for 4 × 4 sills
2 pieces 20' long = 2 × 20 × ⁴/₁₂ × 4 = 53⅓ feet board measure (B M.)
1 piece 18' long = 18 × ⁴/₁₂ × 4 = 24 feet board measure (B. M.)

Now, if price for the 20 ft. lengths be, say. $38 per 1,000 ft. board measure, and for 18 ft. length, $36, then cost of sills will be
2 pieces 4″ × 4″ × 20', 53⅓ ft. B. M. @ $38

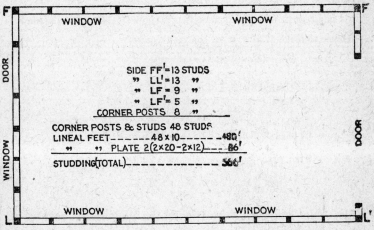

Fig. 1,689.—Plan of frame showing studs so as to count number of studs in estimate.

$$= \frac{53.3}{1,000} \text{ of } \$38 = \dots\dots\dots\dots\dots\dots \$2.03$$

and

1 piece 4″ × 4″ × 18', 24 ft. B. M. @ $36

$$= \frac{24}{1,000} \text{ of } \$36 \dots\dots\dots\dots\dots .86$$

Total cost of sills $2.89

Studding Corner Posts and Plate.—Calculate total length of 2 × 4 lumber required for studs, corner posts and plate. From fig. 1,689, number of studs (counting one under each window) is 46, and for 10 ft. studs:

total length of studding and corner posts = 48 × 10 = 480 ft.

If the plate be made two layer, then

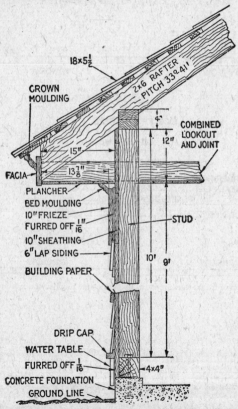

FIG. 1,690.—Elevation showing construction of water table, siding, cornice, rafters, etc., with dimensions for estimating.

length of plate (allowing for laps) = 2 (2 × 20 + 2 × 12) = 128 ft.

Combined length of stud corner posts and plate = 480 + 128 = 608 ft.

608 ft. of 2 × 4 studding = 608 × $^4/_{12}$ × 2 = 405 ft. board measure.

If the price be $24 per 1,000 ft. B. M., then

$$\text{cost of studding, corner posts and plate} = \frac{405}{1,000} \text{ of } 24 = \cdots\cdots\$9.72$$

Sheathing.—Calculate the exact surface to be covered, that is, calculate total surface and deduct openings for doors and windows; then, add $^1/_{12}$ for 12″ boards, $^1/_{10}$ for 10″ boards, ⅛ for 8″ boards, etc.

These additions are due to the fact that on account of seasoning and dressing, a 12″ board becomes about 11½″, a 10″ board, 9⅝″, an 8″ board, 7¾″, etc. The additions specified approximately allow for waste. Fig. 1,690 shows height of sheathing to be 10′ 4″, or 10.3. Accordingly calculating surface to be covered by sheathing:

Gross area sides = 2 (10.3×20) ·························	= 412	sq. ft.
Gross area ends = 2 (10.3×12) ·························	= 247	" "

Area four, 3 × 6 window openings on side,

	4 × 3 × 6 = 72	sq. ft.	
Area one, 3 × 6 window "	= 3 × 6 = 18	" "	
Area " 2½ × 6⅔ door "	= 2½ × 6⅔ = 16.7	" "	
Area " 7½ × 9 "	= 7½ × 9 = 67.5	" "	
	174.2 " "	659	" "
		deduct 174.2	" "
	Net area to be covered	484.8	" "
	Say	485	" "

Usin say 10 in. boards for sheathing add 10%, given net area for calculation 485 × 1.10 = 534 sq. ft. Amount of 1″ sheathing required = 1 × 534 = 534 ft. B. M. Price of sheathing @ $18 per 1,000 ft. B. M.:

$$\frac{534}{1,000} \text{ of } \$18 = \$9.61$$

Area of Openings

22" 1'10"	24" 2'0"	26" 2'2"	28" 2'4"	HIGH	30" 2'6"	32" 2'8"	34" 2'10"	36" 3'0"
			SQUARE FEET			SQUARE FEET		
3.67	4.00	4.33	4.67	24"=2'0"	5.00	5.33	5 67	6.00
3.82	4.17	4.51	4.86	25"=2'1"	5.21	5.56	5.90	6.25
3.97	4.33	4.69	5.06	26"=2'2"	5.42	5.78	6.14	6 50
4.12	4.50	4.87	5.25	27"=2'3"	5.62	6.00	6.37	6.75
4.28	4.67	5.05	5.44	28"=2'4"	5.83	6.22	6 61	7.00
4.43	4.83	5.24	5.64	29"=2'5"	6.04	6.44	6.85	7 25
4.58	5.00	5.42	5.83	30"=2'6"	6.25	6.67	7.08	7.50
4.74	5.17	5.60	6.03	31"=2'7"	6.46	6.89	7.32	7.75
4.89	5.33	5.78	6.22	32"=2'8"	6.67	7.11	7.55	8.00
5.04	5.50	5.96	6.42	33"=2'9"	6.87	7.33	7.79	8.25
5.19	5.67	6.14	6.61	34"=2'10"	7.08	7.55	8.03	8.50
5.35	5.83	6.32	6.80	35"=2'11"	7.29	7.78	8.26	8.75
5.50	6.00	6.50	7.00	36"=3'0"	7.50	8.00	8.50	9.00
5.65	6.17	6.68	7.19	37"=3'1"	7.71	8.22	8.73	9.25
5.80	6.33	6.86	7.39	38"=3'2"	7.91	8.44	8.97	9.50
5.96	6.50	7.04	7.58	39"=3'3"	8.12	8.66	9.21	9.75
6.11	6.67	7.22	7.78	40"=3'4"	8.33	8.89	9.44	10.00
6.26	6.83	7.40	7.97	41"=3'5"	8.54	9.11	9.68	10.25
6.42	7.00	7.58	8.16	42"=3'6"	8.75	9.33	9.91	10.50
6.57	7.17	7.76	8.36	43"=3'7"	8.96	9.55	10.15	10.75
6.72	7.33	7.94	8.55	44"=3'8"	9.16	9.77	10.39	11.00
6.87	7.50	8.12	8.75	45"=3'9"	9.37	10.00	10.62	11.25
7.03	7.67	8.30	8.94	46"=3'10"	9.58	10.22	10.86	11.50
7.18	7.83	8.40	9.14	47"=3'11"	9.79	10.44	11.09	11.75
7.33	8.00	8.66	9 33	48"=4'0"	10 00	10.66	11.33	12.00

22" 1'10"	24" 2'0"	26" 2'2"	28" 2'4"	HIGH	30" 2'6"	32" 2'8"	34" 2'10"	36" 3'0"
			SQUARE FEET			SQUARE FEET		
7.48	8.17	8.84	9.52	49"=4'1"	10.21	10.88	11.57	12.25
7.64	8.33	9.02	9.72	50"=4'2"	10.41	11.11	11.80	12.50
7.79	8.50	9.20	9.91	51"=4'3"	10.62	11.33	12.04	12.75
7.94	8.66	9.38	10.11	52"=4'4"	10.83	11.55	12.27	13.00
8.09	8.83	9.56	10.30	53"=4'5"	11.04	11.77	12.51	13.25
8.25	9.00	9.75	10.50	54"=4'6"	11.25	11.99	12.75	13.50
8.40	9.16	9.93	10.69	55"=4'7"	11.45	12.22	12.98	13.75
8.55	9.33	10.11	10.88	56"=4'8"	11.66	12.44	13.22	14 00
8.71	9.50	10.29	11.06	57"=4'9"	11.87	12.66	13.45	14.25
8.86	9.66	10.47	11.27	58"=4'10"	12 08	12.88	13.69	14.50
9.01	9.83	10.65	11.47	59"=4'11"	12.29	13.10	13.93	14.75
9.16	10.00	10.83	11.66	60"=5'0"	12.50	13.33	14.16	15.00
9.32	10.16	11.01	11.86	61"=5'1"	12.70	13.55	14.40	15.25
9.47	10.33	11.19	12.05	62"=5'2"	12.91	13.77	14.63	15.50
9.62	10.50	11.37	12.24	63"=5'3"	13.12	13.99	14.87	15.75
9.77	10.66	11.55	12.44	64"=5'4"	13.33	14.21	15.11	16.00
9.93	10.83	11.73	12.63	65"=5'5"	13.54	14.44	15.34	16.25
10.08	11.00	11.91	12.83	66"=5'6"	13.74	14.66	15.58	16.50
10.23	11.16	12.09	13.02	67"=5'7"	13.95	14.88	15.81	16.75
10.39	11.33	12.27	13.22	68"=5'8"	14.16	15.10	16.05	17.00
10.54	11.50	12.45	13.41	69"=5'9"	14.37	15.32	16.29	17.25
10.69	11.66	12.63	13.60	70"=5'10"	14.58	15.55	16.52	17.50
10.84	11.83	12.81	13.80	71"=5'11"	14.79	15.77	16.76	17.75
11.00	12.00	13.00	14.00	72"=6'0"	15.00	16.00	17.00	18.00

Explanation—For the square feet in an opening 36 by 58 inches read in the 36-inch column opposite 58 in the center 14.50.

Building Paper.—"Rosin sized" paper is the cheapest but is not water proof. Dry felt is used where better protection from cold is desired. The cheaper grades are made of wood fibre and rosin, and the better grades of wool. Tar felt is used where moisture is to be resisted. As it is desirable to resist both moisture and cold in the garage use best grade of tar felt.

Building papers are sold by the pound, coming regularly 12, 15, and 20 lbs. to the 100 sq. ft., and in rolls of various widths

Using the heavy 20 lb. paper:

$$\text{Total weight of paper} = 20 \times \frac{485}{100} = 97 \text{ lbs.}$$

$$\text{Price of paper @ say } 1\frac{1}{2}\text{c. per lb.} = 97 \times .015 = \$1.46$$

Water Table.—This is a piece of finished lumber size 1×6 extending all around the building except at doors.

$$\text{Net length } 2 \times 20 + 2 \times 12 - (2\frac{1}{2} + 7\frac{1}{2}) = 54 \text{ ft.}$$

Price 54 lineal ft. 1×6 finished @ $4\frac{1}{2}$c. per foot = $\$2.43$.

Drip Cap.—The net length of drip cap will be same as that of water table.

Price 54 lineal ft. $2''$ drip cap @ 2c. per foot = $\$1.08$.

Lap Siding.—For bevel or lap siding calculate the exact surface, deducting for window and door openings; this gives net surface to be covered by the siding. Now since part of each siding plank overlaps the adjoining plank, add 25% for $6''$ siding when laid $4\frac{1}{2}''$ to the weather; 50% for $4''$ siding.

The net area to be covered may be taken as for the sheathing less area taken up by frieze and sheathing above plancher.

Height sheathing 10.3 ft.; height siding = $10.3 - 1' \ 10'' = 10.3 - 1.8 =$ 8.5 ft. Accordingly

$$\text{area siding} = 485 \times \frac{8.5}{10.3} = 400 \text{ sq. ft.}$$

Using 6″ siding laid 4½″ to the weather add 25% to this area

$$400 \times 1.25 = 500 \text{ sq. ft.}$$

from which, quantity of siding required is

$$^{6}/_{12} \times 500 = 250 \text{ ft. B. M.}$$

Price of siding @ $33 per 1,000 ft. B. M.

$$\frac{250}{1,000} \text{ of } \$33 \dots\dots\dots\dots\dots\dots\dots\dots\dots\dots\dots\dots\dots\$8.25$$

Frieze.—This is the finished plank which forms an ornamental border all around the building at the upper limit of the siding, windows and doors.

Length of frieze = $2 \times 20 + 2 \times 12 \times 64$ ft.

Price of 64 ft. of 1×10 frieze @ 8c. per foot = $64 \times .08 = \$5.12$

Plancher.—This horizontal area of finished planking runs all around the building as shown in figs. 1,684 and ,1690. As seen in fig. 1,690, it is 15 ins. wide. Hence area to be covered is:

$$\tfrac{15}{12}\left\{2 \times 20 + 4 \times \tfrac{15}{12} + 2 \times 12\right\} = 86.25 \text{ sq. ft.}$$

This will be the quantity B. M.

Price of 86.25 ft. B. M. of $\frac{3}{4} \times 3\frac{1}{4}$ frieze @ $56 per 1,000 is

$$\frac{86.25}{1,000} \text{ of } \$56 = \dots\dots\dots\dots\dots\dots\dots\dots\dots\dots\dots\$4.83$$

Fascia.—This extends all around the building, hence:

$$2 \left(20 + \tfrac{30}{16}\right) + 2 \left(12 + \tfrac{30}{16}\right) = 72 \text{ ft.}$$

Price of 72 lineal ft. of 6 in. fascia @ 5c. per ft. is

$$72 \times .05 = \dots\dots\dots\dots\dots\dots\dots\dots\dots\dots\dots\dots\$3.60$$

Bed and Crown Mouldings.—Both of these like the fascia extend all around the building but are of different lengths.

length bed moulding 2 × 20 + 2 × 12 = 64 ft. + 2′ 6″   66′ 6″
length crown moulding same as fascia = 72 ft. + 2′ 6″   74′ 6″

Thus to above neat measurements 4% has been added for cutting.

Price 66′ 6″ lineal ft. bed moulding @ 4c. per ft. = 66.5 × .04 = $2.66

Price 74′ 6″ lineal ft. crown moulding @ 4c. per ft. = 74.5 × .04 = $2.98.

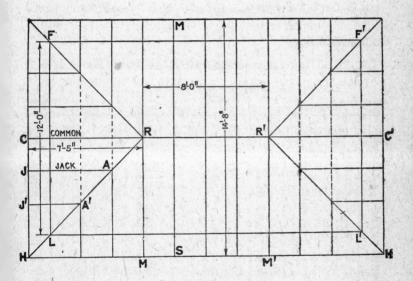

Fig. 1,691.—Skeleton plan of roof to estimate rafters.

Rafters.—There are three kinds of rafters used: hip rafters, hip jack rafters, and common rafters. For ⅓ pitch (33°):

Length of hip rafters per ft. run of common rafter = 18.78   (1)

Length of common or jack rafters per ft. run of common rafter = 14.42 (2)

Hip rafters

In fig. 1,691, the total run of common rafter CR (including tail) is 7′ 4″ and allowing for extra stock for vertical cut at end, call run, say, 8 ft. then total run of the 4 hips is 4 × 8 = 32 ft.

Multiplying by the factor in (1)

Total length of 4 hip rafters is

$$32 \times \frac{18.78}{12} = \dots\dots\dots\dots\dots\dots\dots 50 \text{ ft.}$$

Common rafters

Length of run for common rafters as found above is 8 ft.

Rafters and Gables

	FOURTH PITCH				THIRD PITCH				HALF PITCH			
Width of Building	Length of Rafter		From Plate to Comb		Area of Two Gables	Length of Rafter		From Plate to Comb		Area of Two Gables	Length of Rafter		From Plate to Comb		Area of Two Gables
	ft.	in.	ft.	in.		ft	in.	ft.	in.		ft.	in.	ft.	in.	
6	3	4	1	6	9	3	7	2	0	12	4	3	3	0	18
7	3	11	1	9	12	4	0	2	4	16	5	0	3	6	25
8	4	6	2	0	16	4	10	2	8	21	5	8	4	0	32
9	5	0	2	3	20	5	5	3	0	27	6	5	4	6	41
10	5	7	2	6	25	6	0	3	4	33	7	1	5	0	50
12	6	8	3	0	36	7	2	4	0	48	8	6	6	0	72
14	7	10	3	6	49	8	5	4	8	65	9	11	7	0	98
16	9	0	4	0	64	9	7	5	4	85	11	4	8	0	128
18	10	1	4	6	81	10	10	6	0	108	12	9	9	0	162
20	11	2	5	0	100	12	0	6	8	133	14	2	10	0	200
22	12	4	5	6	121	13	2	7	4	161	15	7	11	0	242
24	13	5	6	0	144	14	5	8	0	192	17	0	12	0	288
26	14	6	6	6	169	15	7	8	8	225	18	6	13	0	338
28	15	8	7	0	196	16	10	9	4	261	19	11	14	0	392
30	16	9	7	6	225	18	0	10	0	300	21	4	15	0	450
32	17	11	8	0	256	19	2	10	8	341	22	9	16	0	512

To the lengths of rafters above given, must be added the desired projection for cornice. Add also to make stock lengths.

For length of rafter on one-way roofs, take the rafter given for double the width thus: The rafter for a one-way roof on a building 10 feet wide, 4th pitch is that given for 20 feet wide or 11 feet, 2 inches.

In area of gable above given no allowance is made for waste or laps.

To verify above or obtain length of rafters for buildings of other widths than above given multiply the width of building by .559 for 4th pitch; by .6 for 3d pitch and by .71 for half pitch.

There are 12 common rafters as counted in fig. 1,691; hence total run of all the rafters is:

$$8 \times 12 = 96 \text{ ft.}$$

Multiplying by the factor in (2)

Total length of 12 common rafters is

$$96 \times \frac{14.42}{12} = \text{.....................} 115 \text{ ft.}$$

Jack rafters

Taking one corner in fig. 1,691, by measurement run of JA, + run of J'A', = 8', 7" and allowing for tail cuts call it 9½ ft. Since there are 4 jack rafters at each corner, total run for all the 16 jacks is:

$$(2 \times 9\tfrac{1}{2}) \times 4 = 76 \text{ ft.}$$

Multiplying by factor in (2), total length of 16 jacks is

$$76 \times \frac{14.42}{12} = \text{.....................} 91 \text{ ft.}$$

Total stock for all rafters is 50 + 115 + 91 = 256 ft. which, using 2 × 6 rafters amounts to

$$256 \times {}^{6}/_{12} \times 2 = 256 \text{ ft. B. M.}$$

Price of 256 ft. B. M. of 2 × 6 rafters @ $24 per 1,000 ft. B. M. is

$$\frac{256}{1,000} \text{ of } \$24 = \text{.....................} \$6.14$$

Combined Look Outs and Joists.—One of these is nailed to each pair of common rafters and jacks extending across the building and also fastened to the studs, serving as support and nail surface for plancher and ceiling. By count in fig. 1,691 there are 9 of these combined look out and joists each as MS, 14', 8" long; in addition there are two end pieces LF, and L'F', each 12 ft. long.

$$14\tfrac{2}{3}' \times 9 = 132 \text{ ft.}$$
$$12' \times 2 = 24 \text{ ft.}$$
$$\text{Total length} = 156 \text{ ft.}$$

Using 1×4 stock amounts to

$$156 \times \tfrac{1}{3} \times 1 = 52 \text{ ft. B. M.}$$

Price of 52 ft. B. M. of 1×4 combined look outs and joists @ $25 per 1,000 ft. B. M. is

$$\frac{52}{1,000} \text{ of } \$25 = \dots\dots\dots\dots\dots\dots\dots\$1.30$$

Ceiling and Walls.—For sides and ends the calculation for area to be covered as made for sheathing will be close enough; this was found to be 485 sq. ft.

Add to this area of overhead surface which is (working to inside dimensions, that is deducting 10″ from outside dimensions)

Capacity, in bushels, of cribs or bins, each Eight feet high in the clear.

		WIDTH						WIDTH		
3	8	10	12	14	Length	16	18	22	26	30
		BUSHELS						BUSHELS		
77	206	257	309	360	4	411	463	566	669	771
96	257	321	386	450	5	514	579	707	836	964
116	309	386	463	540	6	617	694	849	1003	1157
135	360	450	540	630	7	720	810	990	1170	1350
154	411	514	617	720	8	823	926	1131	1337	1543
174	463	579	694	810	9	926	1041	1273	1504	1736
193	514	643	771	900	10	1029	1157	1414	1671	1928
231	617	771	926	1080	12	1234	1388	1697	2006	2314
270	720	890	1080	1260	14	1440	1620	1980	2340	2700
309	823	1029	1234	1440	16	1646	1851	2263	2674	3086
347	926	1157	1388	1620	18	1851	2083	2546	3008	3471
386	1029	1286	1543	1800	20	2057	2314	2828	3343	3857
424	1131	1414	1697	1980	22	2263	2546	3111	3677	4243
463	1233	1543	1851	2160	24	2468	2777	3394	4011	4628
501	1337	1671	2006	2340	26	2674	3008	3677	4345	5014
540	1440	1800	2160	2520	28	2880	3240	3960	4680	5400
579	1543	1928	2314	2700	30	3086	3471	4243	5014	5785
617	1646	2057	2468	2880	32	3291	3703	4525	5348	6171

How large a bin shall I build to hold 800 bushels? is a very common question. To answer this and similar ones instantly is the object of above table, thus: How long a bin 8 feet wide and 8 feet high is required to hold 800 bushels of oats? Run down the 8-foot column until 823, the nearest amount to 800 bushels, is reached, and opposite, in the center column headed length, is 16, the length required.

For ear corn divide above quantities by 2; *i.e.*, a bin 8x8x16 will hold only 411 bushels ear corn. For bins 10 feet high add ¼ to above.

$$11' 2'' \times 19' 2'' = 11.17' \times 19.17' = 214 \text{ sq. ft.}$$

making a total area of

$$485 + 214 = 699 \text{ sq. ft.}$$

If say $3\frac{1}{4}''$ tongue and groove ceiling be used, increase the area by 25% to allow for lap obtaining

$$\text{gross area } 699 \times 1.25 = 874 \text{ ft.}$$

Price of 874 ft. B. M. $\frac{3}{4} \times 3\frac{1}{4}$ M. & B. ceiling @ $42.50 per 1,000 ft. B. M. is

$$\frac{874}{1,000} \times \$42.50 = \cdots\cdots\cdots\cdots\cdots\cdots\cdots \$37.15$$

Roof Boards.—Since the building is symmetrical with respect to its axes, consider only one half in calculating area, multiplying result by 2.

In fig. 1,691 area triangular sections CRH, and C'R'H', is equal to the area of square whose side is equal to the length of the common rafter.

Length of common rafter, using factor 14.42 previously given, and dimension CR, in fig. 1,691, is

$$7' 5'' \times \frac{14.42}{12} = 7.42 \times \frac{14.42}{12} = 8.9$$

and area sections CRH and C'R'H' is 8.9×8.9 = 79 sq. ft.
area of triangular sections HRM and H'R'M' =
area triangular section CRH and C'R'H'   = 79 " "
area rectangle RMM'R' = MM' $\times$ length of

common rafter, $= 8' \times 7.41 \times \dfrac{14.42}{12} = \cdots\cdots\cdots\cdots \dfrac{71}{229}$ " "

                                          Half area roof

total area roof $229 \times 2 = 458$ sq. ft.

If boards 3'' wide be used spaced $5\frac{1}{2}''$ centers, this will give $5\frac{1}{2} - 3 = 2\frac{1}{2}$ in. spaces, and the portion of roof left uncovered by this spacing will be

$$\frac{2.5}{5.5} \text{ of } 100\% = 45\%$$

hence in finding B. M. deduct 45% of roof area, that is

$$45\% \text{ of } 458 = 206 \text{ sq. ft.}$$

which deducted from total area or

$$458 - 206 = 252 \text{ sq. ft.}$$

The boards being 1 in. thick, 252 is also the amount board measure.

Price 252 ft. B. M. of 1 × 3 roof boards @ $29 per 1,000 ft. B. M. is

$$\frac{252}{1,000} \text{ of } \$29 = \cdots\cdots\cdots\cdots\cdots\cdots\cdots\$7.31$$

Shingles.—Ordinary wood shingles are furnished in random widths, but 1,000 shingles are equivalent to 1,000 shingles each 4 ins. wide. Dimension shingles are sawed to a uniform width, being either 4, 5, or 6 ins. wide.

A bunch of shingles contains the equivalent of 250 shingles of 4" average width.

When estimating the number of shingles to cover a roof the spacing of the shingles *"to weather"* must be considered, that is, the distance each shingle is exposed.

Another item to be considered is the *waste* in doubling the first course and in laying. This will amount to 8% for a plain roof and 12% for a hip roof.

The following table will be of value in estimating shingles:

Shingle Table

Distance laid to weather	Actual number per square		
	Without waste	Plain roof 8% waste	Hip roof 12% waste
4	900	972	1008
4½	800	864	896
5	720	778	806
5½	655	707	734
6	600	648	672

Estimates of shingles in this table as seen in the heading are based upon the square; that is, a square area whose sides are 10 ft. A square then is an area of $10 \times 10 = 100$ sq. ft.

The area to be covered is as found for roof boards (without deduction) 458 sq. ft. which is equivalent to

$$458 \div 100 = 4.58 \text{ squares}$$

Now using 18″ shingles, which allows a spacing of $5\frac{1}{2}$″ to weather and allowing 12% waste for hip roof as per last column in table, 734 shingles are required per square or, for the entire roof

$$734 \times 4.58 = 3.362 \text{ shingles}$$

this is equivalent to

$$3,362 \div 250 = 13 \text{ bundles}$$

The $5\frac{1}{2}$ spacing requires 18″ shingles. Accordingly, using 18 in., say "No. 1 Perfection" shingles, @ \$9.75 per M, then price of shingles is

$$\frac{13}{4} \times \$9.75 = \dots\dots\dots\dots\dots\dots\dots\$31.69$$

Mill Work.—Such parts as doors, windows, are usually and most economically bought from the mill rather than made on the job. In fact it would not be practical to make these parts without the special machinery used in sash door and blind factories.

Windows.—There are four, 2′ 4″ $\times$ 4′ 10″ windows. Prices for these are obtained from dealers, or as listed:

price of frame	\$ 4.00
price of 2 sash @ \$2.75	5.50
extras, weights, pulley, etc.	.75
	\$10.25

Price 4 windows @ \$10.25 = $10.25 \times 4 = \$41.00$.

Doors.—The cost of the small door in rear will be about as follows:

frame.................................$3.50

The price of the door is sometimes estimated on basis per sq. ft. Accordingly for 2′ 6″ × 6′ 8″ door, area = $2\frac{1}{2}′ \times 6\frac{2}{3}′$ = 16.7 sq. ft. A good quality paneled door with sash @ 55¢. per sq. ft. will be

16.7 × .55 = ·· $ 9.19
Frame... 3.50
Hardware (lock, hinges, etc.) 1.75
Price small rear door complete $14.44

The price of large door will vary considerably, depending on construction and material. For double door hinged medium quality, figure:

Frame....................... $ 8.50
Two doors @ $19.50 each.......... 39.00
Hardware (lock, hinges, etc.)....... 2.50

Large doors complete............. $50.00 $50.00

All doors and frame complete..................... $64.44

Shutters.—The windows should be provided with shutters as a matter of security and for insulation in cold weather. Ornamental paneled shutters made of clear Western cedar at, say, $4.25, per pair will amount to:

4.25 × 4 = ·· $17.00
hardware at 50c. per window, add

.50 × 4 = ·· 2.00

Price all shutters complete $19.00

Nails.—By aid of the table following the quantity of nails may be quickly estimated for the various items in construction.

Nail Table

Materials	Unit	Quantity nails required in lbs.	Size	Kind
Joists and sills......	per 1,000 ft. B. M.	25	20d	common
Studding..........	" " " "	15	10"	"
Rafters...........	" " " "	15	10"	"
Sheathing, siding....	" " " "	20	8"	"
Cornice...........	" " lineal feet	25	8"	finish
Shingling..........	" M (1,000)	4	4"	common
Bevel siding.......	" 1,000 ft. B. M.	18	6"	"
Ceiling, wainscoting.	" " " "	20	6"	"
Floors, pine........	" " " "	30	8"	"
Floors, hard wood...	" " " "	30	6"	"
Base board.........	" " " "	12	8"	finish
Window trim one side		$\frac{3}{4}$	8"	"
Door trim one side..		$\frac{3}{4}$	8"	"
Lath..............	" 1,000	8	3"	common pine
Lattice for porches..	" 1,000 sq. ft.	20	3"	"
Balustrade..........	" " lineal ft.	18	6"	casing

Estimating quantity of nails for each item:

Sills

77 ft. B. M.   20*d* common nails

nails required $= \dfrac{77}{1,000}$ of 25 lbs. = ... 1.9 lbs

Studding and Plate

392 ft. B. M.   10*d* common nails

nails required $= \dfrac{392}{1,000}$ of 15 lbs. = ... 5.9 "

Sheathing

402 ft. B. M.   8*d* common nails

nails required $= \dfrac{402}{1,000}$ of 20 lbs. = ... 8.0 "

Forward 15.8 "

Nails, brought forward 15.8 **lbs.**

Water table

54 lineal ft.   8d finish nails

nails required = $\frac{54}{1,000}$ of 18 lbs. = ... 1 "

Drip Cap

54 lineal ft.   8d finishing nails

nails required same as water table.............. 1 "

Lap siding

198 ft. B. M.   8d common nails

nails required = $\frac{198}{1,000}$ of 20 lbs. = ... 1.4 "

Cornice

Length of cornice

$$= 2\left(20 + \frac{30}{15}\right) + 2\left(12 + \frac{30}{15}\right) = 72 \text{ lineal ft.}$$

8d finish nails

nails required = $\frac{72}{1,000}$ of 25 lbs. = ... 1.8 "

Rafters

256 ft. B. M.   10d common nails

nails required = $\frac{256}{1,000}$ of 15 lbs. = ... 3.8 "

Combined look outs and joists

52 ft. B. M.   10d common nails

nails required = $\frac{52}{1,000}$ of 15 lbs. = ... 7.8 "

Forward 32.6 "

Nails, brought forward 32.6 lbs.

Ceiling and wall

770 ft. B. M.   6*d* common nails

nails required $= \dfrac{770}{1,000}$ of 20 lbs. = ... 15.4 "

Roof boards

254 ft. B. M.   8*d* common nails

nails required $= \dfrac{254}{1,000}$ of 20 lbs. = ... 5.1 "

Shingles

3,362 shingles   4*d* common nails

nails required $= \dfrac{3.362}{1,000}$ of 4 lbs. = ... 13.5 "

Total nails required 66.6 "

Price of 66.6 lbs. nails @ 5c. per lb. = ...$3.33

Paint.—Take roughly as surface to be covered the area found by multiplying height from ground to crown moulding by distance around building. Calling the first factor 10 ft., then

exterior area to be painted = 10 × (2 × 20 + 2 × 12) = 640 sq. ft.

For three coats of paint on wood one gallon of paint should cover from 175 to 200 sq. ft., of surface. If dark colored paint, such as gray, tan, buff, drab, etc., be used in three coat work on weather boarding or matched boards, one gallon of paint should cover from 200 to 225 sq. ft. On a basis of say 200 sq. ft. per gallon for 3 coats:

Paint required = 640 ÷ 200 = 3.2 gals.

Price 3 gals. paint @ $2.50 per gal. = ...$7.50

Estimating for the ceiling and walls, the area as found is 770 sq. ft.

If three coats of varnish be applied, one gallon of good spar finishing varnish should cover from 150 to 175 sq. ft. of surface. On a basis of 150 sq. ft. per gal. for 3 coats:

Varnish required = 770 ÷ 150 = 5.1 gals.

Price 5 gals. varnish @ $4.00 per gal. = ...$20.00

2. Cost of Labor

In estimating the cost of labor the estimator should tabulate the time required for each item on basis of hours required per 1,000 ft. B. M., as given in the accompanying tables. Then the cost can be easily figured knowing the scale of wages paid in the locality of the building at the time of erection.

The accompanying tables are based upon the work of one carpenter of average ability. Where a number of carpenters are employed under one foreman the time allowances given in the tables can be reduced in some instances as much as 50%. These tables which follow are as given by Prof. Ira Samuel Griffith of the University of Missouri:

Time Table for Framing and Covering

	Hours per 1,000 *ft. B. M.*
Sills and plates 6″ × 8″, no gains or mortises	20
" " " " × " gains no mortises	40
" " " " × " gains and mortises	60
Joists and box sills	20
Studding 2 × 4	32
" 2 × 6	23
Rafters 2 × 4, plain gable roof	40
" " × " hip roof add 5% to 30% for each hip or valley	
" 2 × 6, plain gable roof	27
" " × " hip roof add 5% to 30% for each hip or valley	
Sheathing, square edged, horizontal walls	16
" " " " diagonal "	19
" 6 " matched walls	24
" 6 " " " diagonal	32
" for floors, sub floors, square edged	10
" " " " " square edged diagonal	12
Roof sheathing, plain gable roof	13
" " hip roof	20

Table—*Continued.*

	Hours per 1,000 *lineal ft.*
Cornices..	400 to 800
Water table, 3 member................................	220
Corner boards...	73
Belt..	195

	Hours per 1,000 *shingles*
Shingling, plain roof new work........................	3½
" hips and valleys add 5% for each hip or valley	
" old work, add 20% for labor of removing old shingles	
" side walls plain...............................	5½
" " " fancy..............................	8

	Hours per 1,000 *ft. B. M.*
Siding, bevel 6"....................................	35
" " 4"....................................	42
" shiplap.......................................	27
" drop, when window and door casings and corner boards are placed over siding.................................	20
" drop, when jointed between casings and corner board......	32
Surfaced barn boards.................................	11½
Ceiling store..	53
Wainscoating, cut, put up, finished with cap and ¼ round, in a dwelling..	46

Time for Excavating.—Where it is necessary to excavate for trenches, piers and footings in either sand or loamy soil, and when the excavations extend to a depth of not over 5 or 6 ft., a man should excavate and throw out of the trench from ⅞ to 1 cu. yd. of sand or loamy soil per hour or at the rate of 7 to 8 cu. yds. per 8 hour day. The above quantities do not include the time for back filling which will have to be added.

Excavation for Foundation and Floor.—Roughly, call the volume to be excavated equal to ¾ volume of the concrete.

Accordingly:

$$\text{¾ of 10 cu. yds.} = 7.5 \text{ hours}$$
(assuming 1 cu. yd. excavated per hr.)

This together with back fill, leveling, etc., call 10 hours
Cost 10 hours, laborer @ 85c. per hour = $8.50

Cost of Concrete Work.—As found the quantity of concrete required is 10 cu. yds. If the concrete be mixed by hand with only one mixing board and shovelled directly from the mixing board into the forms or trenches, it will require from 3¼ to 3½ hours labor for one man to mix and deposit one cu. yd. of concrete. On a basis of 3½ hrs. per cu. yd.:

$$\text{Time} = 10 \times 3\tfrac{1}{2} = 35 \text{ hrs.}$$
Cost concrete work @ 90c. per hr. = .90 × 35 = ...$31.50

Cost of Carpenter Work.—With aid of the time table the various items are estimated as below. Where the exact item is not given in the table, an approximation is made. First the entire time for construction is estimated and then cost of same figured rather than cost of each separate item.

Sills

77 ft. B. M. @ 30 hrs. per 1,000 ft. B. M.

$$\text{Time} = \frac{77}{1,000} \text{ of 30 hrs.} = ...2.3 \text{ hrs}$$

Studding, corner posts and plate

392 ft. B. M. @ 32 hrs. per 1,000 ft. B. M.

$$\text{Time} = \frac{392}{1,000} \text{ of 32 hrs.} = ...12.5 \text{ “}$$

Sheathing

442 ft. B. M. @ 16 hrs. per 1,000 ft. B. M.

$$\text{Time} = \frac{442}{1,000} \text{ of 16 hrs.} = ...7.1 \text{ “}$$

Forward 21.9 “

Labor, brought forward 21.9 hrs.

Building paper

Not given in table but allow for this, say.............. 1 "

Water table and drip cap

54 lineal ft. @ 220 hrs. per 1,000 lineal ft.

$$\text{Time} = \frac{54}{1,000} \text{ of } 220 \text{ hrs.} = \text{.....................} 11.9 \text{ "}$$

Lap siding

464 ft. B. M. @ 42 hrs. per 1,000 ft. B. M.

$$\text{Time} = \frac{464}{1,000} \text{ of } 42 \text{ hrs.} = \text{.....................} 19.5 \text{ "}$$

Cornice

74 lineal ft. @ 160 hrs. per 1,000 lineal ft.

$$\text{Time} = \frac{74}{1,000} \text{ of } 160 \text{ hrs.} = \text{.....................} 11.8 \text{ "}$$

Rafters

256 ft. B. M. @ 27 hrs. (+ 20%) per 1,000 ft. B. M.

$$\text{Time} = \frac{256}{1,000} \text{ of } 27 \text{ hrs.} + 20\% = \text{.................} 8.3 \text{ "}$$

Combined look outs and joists

52 ft. B. M. @ 32 hrs. per 1,000 ft. B. M.

$$\text{Time} = \frac{52}{1,000} \text{ of } 32 \text{ hrs.} = \text{.....................} 1.7 \text{ "}$$

Ceiling

770 ft. B. M. @ 53 hrs. per 1,000 ft. B. M.

$$\text{Time} = \frac{770}{1,000} \text{ of } 53 \text{ hrs.} = \text{.....................} 40.8 \text{ "}$$

Forward 116.9 "

Labor, brought forward 116.9 hrs.

Roof boards

255 ft. B. M. @ 20 hrs. per 1,000 ft. B. M.

Time = $\dfrac{255}{1,000}$ of 20 hrs. = ... 5.1 "

Shingles

3,362 shingles @ 3½ hours + 20% per 1,000

Time = $\dfrac{3,362}{1,000}$ of 3½ hrs. + 20% = ... 14.2 "

Windows and shutters

4 windows with shutters @ 2 hrs. each

Time = 4 × 2 = ... 8. "

Doors

single @ 6 hrs.; double @ 10 hrs.

Time = 6 + 10 = ... 16. "

Painting and varnishing

Total area to be covered = 640 + 616 = 1,256 sq. ft.

On new wood work, weather boarding, ceiling, etc., where three coats of paint and varnish are to be applied, a painter should complete about 53 to 58 sq. ft. of surface per hour. Taking an average for the exterior and interior work of, say, 55 per sq. ft. per hour for the three coats, then:

Time of painting and varnishing = 1,256 ÷ 55 = ...22.8 "

Total labor except foundation = 183 "

Cost carpentry work, painting, etc., @ 80¢. per hr. = 183 × .8 = ... \$146.40

Cost of Garage = cost of materials + cost of labor.

Summary

Cost of Materials

Concrete................................... $103.51

Lumber and nails

Sills..	$2.89
Studs, posts, plate............................	9.41
Sheathing...................................	9.61
Building paper...............................	1.46
Water table..................................	2.43
Drip cups...................................	1.08
Lap siding	8.25
Frieze	5.12
Plancher....................................	4.59
Fascia	3.60
Bed and crown moulding......................	5.64
Rafters	6.14
Combined lookouts and joists..................	1.30
Ceiling and walls.............................	37.15
Roof boards.................................	7.31
Shingles	31.69
Windows....................................	41.00
Doors	64.44
Shutters....................................	19.00
Nails.......................................	3.33
Paint.......................................	7.50
Varnish	20.00

$292.94   292.94

Cost of Materials............. $396.45

Brought forward, $396.45

Hardware

5 window latches @ 35c	1.75	
5 sets sash pulleys, weights and cords at $1.25 per set	6.25	
Rear door locks and hinges	1.50	
Two pair main door hinges @ $1.75 per pair	3.50	
Main door bolts and lock	3.00	
4 pairs shutter catches @ 15c. per pair	.60	
4 pairs shutter butts @ 8c. per pair	.32	
	16.92	16.92
		$413.37

Cost of Labor

Foundation	excavation	$8.50	
	concrete work	31.50	
Carpenter work and painting		146.90	
		186.90	186.90
			$600.27
		say	$600

Total cost of materials and labor, $600

To this must be added if an architect be employed to design the garage, his fee at 3% of cost of constructoin, making a total of:

$$\$600 + 3\% \text{ of } 600 = \$618$$

Also, must be added cost of electric wiring if electricity be used for illumination (see page 798).

Example of Form for Carpentry Costs.—The following form, ased by a practical carpenter, and published in the Correspondence Department of "The American Carpenter and Builder," should suggest means whereby the data just given may be made more readily available for estimating purposes.

It must be remembered in interpreting all such data that costs will vary greatly with conditions. A carpenter, for illustration, who gives his time and attention to general carpentry cannot lay shingles with the speed of a shingling specialist.

Again, a carpenter cannot make windows and door frames by hand with the same speed that these can be made by machinery in a mill. The prices

Materials in Place at 80c. per Hour

Various Materials	Ft. per 8 hrs. 2 men	hrs. per 1,000 ft.	Cost of labor		Nails	
			M ft.	L. or Sq.	Lbs.	Size
Joists and sills........	810	20	$16.00	.....	25	20d
Studding, placed......	540	30	24.00	.....	15	10d
Rafters..............	405	40	32.00	.....	15	10d
Sheathing, vertical....	675	24	19.20	.....	20	8d
Sheathing, diagonal....	505	32	25.60	.....	20	8d
Bevel siding..........	462	35	28.00	.....	18	6d
Cornices..............	40	160	128.00	.....	18	8d
Shingling, new roofs...	3,600	4½	3.60	.30-L	4	4d
Lathing for plaster....	2,476	7	5.60	.....	8	3d
Lattice for porches....	1,002	16	12.80	.....	20	3d
Balustrade for porches.	32	500	400.00	.37½-L	18	6d
Baseboards, 8″ pine ...	194	83	66.40	.6¼-L	12	8d
Baseboards, 8″ hardwood..............	97	166	132.80	.12½-L	..	...
Floors, laid, pine......	462	35	28.00	.....	30	8d
Floors, laid, hardwood.	90	180	144.00	.13¾-L	30	6d
Floors, cleaned, hardwood..............	90	180	144.00	.13¾-L	..	...
Wainscoting, pine.....	48	.....	.....	.25¾-L	20	6d
Paneling, pine........	32	.....	.....	.37½-Sq.	..	...
Paneling, hardwood....	19	.....	.....	.62½-Sq.	..	...
Porches and verandas..	..	.....	.....	1.50-L	18	8d

M = 1,000 ft.   L = Lineal   Sq = Sq. ft.

here given are for work done by a general carpentry mechanic. The estimator should test out these figures to see how they compare with actual working conditions in his community.

The table on preceding page is made for "country" conditions, the men working at 80¢ per hour, 9 hours a day.

The price varies in different localities and may change by labor conditions, and the estimator is governed accordingly.

Shingles are for new roofs; where hips and valleys are required add 12% additional for each one; where old shingles and nails must be removed, add again (50% to total) for this work.

The rate in the table as stated is based on 80¢ per hour. For other rates the following will apply: At 35¢ per hour add 17%; at 40¢ add 34%; at 45¢ add 51%; and at 50¢ per hour add 68%.

Number of Joists Required for Any Room

Distance Joists are Placed on Centers	Multiply Length of Floor Span by	Add Wood Joists	Result
12 inches	1	1	Number of joists required
16 inches	3/4	1	Number of joists required
20 inches	3/5	1	Number of joists required
24 inches	1/2	1	Number of joists required
30 inches	2/5	1	Number of joists required
36 inches	1/3	1	Number of joists required
42 inches	2/7	1	Number of joists required
48 inches	1/4	1	Number of joists required
54 inches	2/9	1	Number of joists required
60 inches	1/5	1	Number of joists required

Electric Wiring.—The cost of electric wiring will depend entirely upon the class of building in which the work is to be installed, the grade of materials and workmanship required, whether there are long or short runs of wire and conduit required for each outlet, toether with the method of installation.

For approximate estimating, such as the average contractor will do, it if customary to count the number of outlets of each kind in the entire job and figure them at a certain price per outlet.

It is advisable to list the number of ceiling and wall outlets, floor or wall switches, base plugs, door bells, etc.

After the total number of outlets in each building has been obtained, they should be priced at a certain price per outlet.

Average Prices of Electric Wiring.—The following are the average prices of electric outlets installed in the building ready to receive fixtures:

In cottages, bungalows or two-story residences where "knob and tube" work is permissible, the cost of installing the electric wiring should run from $3.50 to $4.00 per outlet. In store buildings and other structures where the runs are longer than is usually encountered in residential building, the cost should about average from $4.00 to $4.50 per outlet.

In cottages, bungalows, two-story residences, apartment buildings, factory buildings, warehouses, etc., of non-fireproof construction, where the wires must be placed in steel conduit, it should cost from $5.25 to $6.00 for each outlet in the job.

In high class fireproof structures, such as office buildings, stores, universities, schools, hospitals, apartment buildings, etc., where first class materials and workmanship are required, it should cost from $8.00 to $9.00 for each electric outlet in the job.

Hints on Estimating.—The art of estimating is an important asset to the carpenter, especially the contractor. The better trained and educated he is, the more proficient he is at his work. He is the more sought for because of being considered reliable authority in the buildings arts by those contemplating building.

The competent man knows there is no fixed standard of prices, beside the always fluctuating conditions in one locality, prices vary in different localities. Therefore there is no plan or scheme that can be depended upon other than the skill of the estimator who keeps posted up to the minute. This does not argue an exact science or remove the fact that must be guessed at based upon an experimental knowledge of previous calculations, and so it is that a mastery of these conditions is essential to success in contracting, whatever the work may be.

Measure and figure. Don't guess at what it is possible to determine by actual calculation.

The actual cost of a specified window, complete with sash, possibly just completed, is known.

If the estimator is to figure a like fixture for new work to be executed while the same prices prevail, he discovers the percentage of decrease or increase at the present time and fixes the price accordingly. This is the best rule to follow in all the various fixtures that are made before becoming a part of the structure, unless, of course, he have a guaranteed price from the factory making them.

Next comes that uncertainty of the cost of putting it in place, a part of the finished product involving labor on the job. In this the greatest skill must be exercised, and this skill lies in the best knowledge of the practices of labor, in groups, partners and separately. Whether under control of labor unions, whether to be skilled, intermediate in ability or common labor. Under what climatical conditions it is to be done. Are permits of municipality to be obtained? Does the material to be excavated consist of rock, earth, clay, gravel, silt or sand? Is the foundation to start on a bottom land that will require mud sills or piling? Is there any shoring to be done? Does the work involved require forms or centers? Has the architect and engineer given sufficient data to enable the estimator to complete his work in detail without inspecting the premises for general layout and conditions, accessibility, etc.?

The careful man will not wholly depend upon this without first making a personal thorough inspection, familiarizing himself with them. He does not calculate the cost of the various haulages on materials. He determines the cost of the brick (?) delivered on the job. He should know the cost per M to lay them and how many is required for the job. The same with all other materials.

By the foregoing it will be seen that conditions may develop whereby no fixed method other than itemizing may be wholly depended upon for estimating.

However, more frequently the conditions are apparent and that shorter methods may be employed whereby close approximate figures may be arrived at.

In the case of the garage estimate itemized, it is seen to be a class of work that would be computed, if by the square foot at about $2.20 per foot. If its measurements are cubed it will contain 3,360 cubic feet and would be estimated at about 16c. per cubic foot.

If the interior walls and ceiling are to be plastered or stuccoed, the value of about 30 yards must be added. Increasing the cubic foot rate to 16¾¢ per yard will allow 80¢ per yard for it.

This rule can be intelligently used for all classes of building estimates if a careful record of former contracts have been kept and compiled for reference, showing actual costs. These compared with the work in hand will

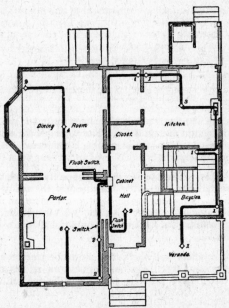

FIG. 1,692.—Wiring for heat appliances; plan of first floor. *The location* of the outlets is of importance. Usually a flush receptacle in the base board meets the requirements. Where several heating circuits are used it is essential that an appliance taking a large current be not placed on the regular lighting circuit. To guard against this possibility, special receptacles should be installed, constructed for plugs which will not fit any other receptacle.

either produce a like job or one near enough to compute. The cost of production at the time the work was done, the profits or loss and the difference in the cost for labor or material must be considered, by which it will be determined whether the price per cubic foot is plus or minus that of the job computed from.

Specifications for Interior Wiring.—The specifications for this kind of work should provide:

1. That the wiring shall be installed in accordance with the latest rules and requirements of the National Board of Fire Underwriters, the local ordinances, and the rules of the local electric light company, where current is to be taken from the public mains.

2. That no electrical device or material of any kind be used that is not approved by the Underwriters' National Electric Association, and all articles must have the name or trade mark of the manufacturer and the rating in volts and amperes or other proper units marked where they may readily be observed after the device is installed.

3. That the contractor must obtain a satisfactory certificate of inspection from the city inspector or from the inspector of the local board of fire-underwriters.

4. That if the wires are to run in a conduit system it should be so specified. When a conduit system is used, The wires should not be drawn in until all mechanical work as far as possible is completed. It is best to wait until after the plastering is dry. All conduit systems must be grounded.

5. Size of wires. The best method is to specify the size of all wires, no wire to be less than No. 14 B. & S. gauge; but if the architect do not care to do this, the following clause is sufficient, provided he can have confidence that the contractor will comply with it: "All wires must be of such size that the drop in voltage at farthest light-outlet shall not exceed 2% under maximum load."

6. Cut out cabinets and where they are to be placed; also location of main line cut out and fuse. For buildings containing not more than forty lights, one distributing point is generally sufficient, although in large houses it is often convenient to have a cut out cabinet in each story.

7. Number and kind of switches. All outlets should be marked on the plans, and the number of lights indicated by figures.

Requirements 1 and 2 are sufficient to insure a safe installation.

Approximate Cost of Wiring for Incandescent Lighting.— Approximate estimates of the cost of wiring buildings for electric lighting are usually based on the number of outlets (not lamps). The actual cost will depend upon the number of pounds of wire required, the kind and number of switches, character of cut out cabinets, etc., and the time required to do the work, so that a close estimate cannot be made without plans and

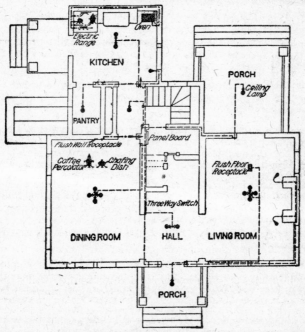

Fig. 1,693.—Plan showing one floor of a dwelling house wired with conduits. The numbers on the various outlets indicate the number of lamps supplied. The wiring is carried out on the loop system, and it will be noticed that no branches are taken off between outlets. Four circuits are used in order that there may not be more than ten lamps on any one circuit.

specifications. Again, wages and prices of material vary to a considerable extent in different parts of the country, so that an estimate that would be about right for one locality would not suffice for another. The following figures (these are pre-war prices and the data are retained for purposes of comparison of relative values), however, will enable anyone to form an approximate idea of what any proposed wiring job will cost.

Count cost of labor as not more than one-third the cost of the installation.

For knob and tube work in new houses of less than seventeen outlets or twenty five lamps, with no switches except main switch and a rough cut out box lined with asbestos, allow $1.50 per outlet.

For same class of work, from 25 to 100 lamps, allow $1.75 to $2.00 per outlet.

The extra labor involved in wiring old buildings will add from 30% to 50% to the above figures.

For each switch loop with a single pole snap switch, add from $1.50 to $1.75.

For each switch loop with single pole push button switch, add from $2.25 to $2.50.

For each lamp controlled by duplex or three point switches, add from $5.00 to $6.00.

For each hardwood cut out cabinet with door and lock, add from $7.00 up according to number of circuits and finish.

Iron cut out cabinets cost from $8.50 up.

Ordinary exposed wiring, as in factories, can usually be run for from $1.00 to $1.75 per drop, including rosettes, cord and sockets, the cost depending very largely upon how closely the drops are spaced.

Small installations with iron armored conduit will probably cost from $5.00 to $6.00 per outlet. Large installations will cost somewhat less.

A private lighting plant of 200 lamps, wired on the concealed knob and tube system, will cost from $1,250 to $1,500, and a similar plant with 600 lamps will cost from $2,500 to $3,000. These prices include engine, dynamo switchboard, etc., complete, and wiring, but no switches for controlling lamps.

The iron armored conduit system will add about $2.75 per outlet.

None of the above estimates include the cost of fixtures except in the case of exposed wiring.

Drop cord and sockets cost about 90¢ per lamp. Single lamp fixtures may be purchased from $1.25 upwards; double lamp fixtures from $2.00

upwards. Combination fixtures cost about 25% more than straight
electric fixtures.

The price of rubber covered wire varies from $8.00 to $60.00 per 1,000
ft. according to size, and of weather-proof wire from 16¢ to 25¢ per pound.

Tables

Cost of Placing Floors by One Man

	Hours per 1,000 ft. B. M.
Floors, pine	35
Floors (yellow pine, 3¼" face, laid on sheathing, including paper between smoothing rough joints, business block)	40
Floors (yellow pine, 3¼" face, laid direct on joist, no smoothing)	26⅔
Floors, yellow pine, 3¼" face, smoothed and sanded	45
Floors, maple, 2¼" face, laid not smoothed	40
Floors, maple, 2¼" face, laid and smoothed	80
Floors, maple, 1½" face, laid and well smoothed	107
Floors, oak, fine floor, glued, smoothed, scraped, sand papered	320

Cost of Bridging and Furring

	Hours per 1,000 lineal ft.
Bridging	65
Placing plaster grounds	20

Cost of Stair Work

	Hours labor on each
Box stair, cellar or attic	25
One flight plain stair 7 room house, hand rail, balusters	40
One flight, fine stair, 9 room house, hand rail, paneled	100

Porches in General

Hours per lineal foot	5
Balustrade hours per 1,000 lineal feet	500
Lattice for porches, hours per 1,000 square feet	16 to 200

Lath

Lath, hours per 1,000 ft.	7

Actuary's Estimate Tables—To find Quantities of Lumber Required

›DING on 16 inch centers. Estimate 1 to the lineal foot: This allows for doubling at openings and at corners.

'TS AND RAFTERS on 16 inch centers. To ¾ of the length of the building add 1; thus: For a building 16x32, ¾ of 32=24, to which add 1, or 27, being the joists required, or the rafters for 1 side. Add 1 or 2 for each bearing partition.

F SHEATHING LAID SOLID. To full area of roof add 10 per cent for waste. If laid 2 inches apart ¾ of above will be required.

ARTICLE	Count Width	Face Width	Loss in Matching	To area to be covered add
›lap	12 inch	11¼	7 %	1-12
"	10 "	9¼	8⅓ "	1-10
"	8 "	7¼	11 "	1-8
"	6 "	5¼	12½ "	1-5
›oring	6 "	5¼	12½ "	1-5
"	4¼ "	3½	18 "	¼
"	4 "	3¼	19 "	⅓
"	3 "	2¼	25 "	⅓
"	2¾ "	2	27 "	⅓
"	2½ "	2	20 "	⅓
"	2 "	1½	25 "	⅓

›rop siding, ceiling, and partition same as above.

ARTICLE	Size	Exposed	To area to be covered add
Siding, beveled	½x4	3¼ inch	¼
" "	½x4	3 "	⅓
" "	½x4	2¾ "	⅓
" "	½x5	4¼ "	1-5
" "	½x5	4 "	¼
" "	½x5	3¾ "	⅓
" "	½x6	5¼ "	1-5
" "	½x6	5 "	9-40
" "	½x6	4¾ "	¼

SHINGLES

When exposed 4 inches to the weather require 9 to the square foot.
" " 4½ " " " " " 8 " " " "
" " 5 " " " " " 7 1-5" " " "
" " 5½ " " " " " 6½ " " " "
" " 6 " " " " " 6 " " " "
} Add 1-10 for Waste

CORNICES. Multiply the total lineal feet, by the combined width of planceer, frieze, and fascia thus: If the planceer is 12 inches, the frieze 8 inches, and the fascia 4 inches, the combined width is 24 inches or 2 feet b. m. to the lineal foot of cornice.

CORNER BOARDS AND OUTSIDE BASE. Estimate on same plan as cornices and then add ¼ if of 1¼ or ½ if of 1½ stuff.

BRIDGING. Multiply the total lineal feet, measuring each string in a straight line by the following:

For 2x6 2x8 or 2x10 on 16 inch centers by 2
" 2x12 16 " " " 2¼
" 2x14 16 " " " 2½
" 2x6 and 2x8 12 " " " 2
" 2x10 and 2x12 12 " " " 2¼
" 2x14 12 " " " 2⅔

LATTICE

1⅛ wide multiply the area by 12 for the lineal feet required.
1⅜ " " " " " 10 " " " " "
1¾ " " " " " 8 " " " " "

Lath

Lath when laid ⅜ inch apart, as for lime, require 1½ to the square foot, or 13½ to the square yard to which add 4% for waste, making practically 14 to the square yard. So to find the lath required increase the square feet to be lathed by ½ thus: 900 square feet require 900+½ of 900 or 1350 lath plus 4%=1404.

When laid ¼ inch apart, as for cement plasters, require 7 per cent more lath.

When there are no openings add 10 per cent to amount obtained by above.

Square Feet in the Ceiling and Four Walls of Rooms

7-Foot Ceilings

FEET WIDE 3	4	5	6	7	8	Feet Long	FEET WIDE 9	10	11	12	13	14
AREA SQUARE FEET							AREA SQUARE FEET					
93	110	127	144	161	178	3	195	212	229	246	263	280
110	128	146	164	182	200	4	218	236	254	272	290	308
127	146	165	184	203	222	5	241	260	279	298	317	336
144	164	184	204	224	244	6	264	284	304	324	344	364
161	182	203	224	245	266	7	287	308	329	350	371	392
178	200	222	244	266	288	8	310	332	354	376	398	420
195	218	241	264	287	310	9	333	356	379	402	425	448
212	236	260	284	308	332	10	356	380	404	428	452	476
229	254	279	304	329	354	11	379	404	429	454	479	504
245	272	298	324	350	376	12	402	428	454	480	506	532
263	290	317	344	371	398	13	425	452	479	506	533	560
280	308	336	364	392	420	14	448	476	504	532	560	588
297	326	355	384	415	442	15	471	500	529	558	587	616
314	344	374	404	434	464	16	494	524	554	584	614	644
331	362	393	424	455	486	17	517	548	579	610	641	672
348	380	412	444	476	508	18	540	572	604	636	668	700
365	398	431	464	497	530	19	563	596	629	662	695	728
382	416	450	484	518	552	20	586	620	654	688	722	756
399	434	469	504	539	574	21	609	644	679	714	749	784
416	452	488	524	560	596	22	632	668	704	740	776	812
433	470	507	544	581	618	23	655	692	729	766	803	840
450	488	526	564	602	640	24	678	716	754	792	830	868
467	506	545	584	623	662	25	701	740	779	818	857	896
484	524	564	604	644	684	26	724	764	804	844	884	924
501	542	583	624	665	706	27	747	788	829	870	911	952
518	560	602	644	686	728	28	770	812	854	896	938	980
535	578	621	664	707	750	29	793	836	879	922	965	1008
552	596	640	684	728	772	30	816	860	904	948	992	1036

FEET WIDE 15	16	17	18	19	20	Feet Long	FEET WIDE 21	22	23	24	25	26
AREA SQUARE FEET							AREA SQUARE FEET					
297	314	331	348	365	382	3	399	416	433	450	467	484
326	344	362	380	398	416	4	434	452	470	488	506	524
355	374	393	412	431	450	5	469	488	507	526	545	564
384	404	424	444	464	484	6	504	524	544	564	584	604
413	434	455	476	497	518	7	539	560	581	602	623	644
442	464	486	508	530	552	8	574	596	618	640	662	684
471	494	517	540	563	586	9	609	632	655	678	701	724
500	524	548	572	596	620	10	644	668	692	716	740	764
529	554	579	604	629	654	11	679	704	729	754	779	804
558	584	610	636	662	688	12	714	740	766	792	818	844
587	614	641	668	695	722	13	749	776	803	830	857	884
616	644	672	700	728	756	14	784	812	840	868	896	924
645	674	703	732	761	790	15	819	848	877	906	935	964
674	704	734	764	794	824	16	854	884	914	944	974	1004
703	734	765	796	827	858	17	889	920	951	982	1013	1044
732	764	796	828	860	892	18	924	956	988	1020	1052	1084
761	794	827	860	893	926	19	959	992	1025	1058	1091	1124
790	824	858	892	926	960	20	994	1028	1062	1096	1130	1164
819	854	889	924	959	994	21	1029	1064	1099	1134	1169	1204
848	884	920	956	992	1028	22	1064	1100	1136	1172	1208	1244
877	914	951	988	1025	1062	23	1099	1136	1173	1210	1247	1284
906	944	982	1020	1058	1096	24	1134	1172	1210	1248	1286	1324
935	974	1013	1052	1091	1130	25	1169	1208	1247	1286	1325	1364
964	1004	1044	1084	1124	1164	26	1204	1244	1284	1324	1364	1404
993	1034	1075	1116	1157	1198	27	1239	1280	1321	1362	1403	1444
1022	1064	1106	1148	1190	1232	28	1274	1316	1358	1400	1442	1484
1051	1094	1137	1180	1223	1266	29	1309	1352	1395	1438	1481	1524
1080	1124	1168	1212	1256	1300	30	1344	1388	1432	1476	1520	1564

Explanation—For the total square feet in a room 20 feet wide and 30 feet long, ceiling 7 feet high, run down the 20-ft. column and opposite 30 read 1300 square feet.

Square Feet in the Ceiling and Four Walls of Rooms

8-Foot Ceilings

3	4	5	6	7	8	Feet Long	9	10	11	12	13	14
			FEET WIDE — AREA SQUARE FEET						FEET WIDE — AREA SQUARE FEET			
105	124	143	162	181	200	3	219	238	257	276	295	314
124	144	164	184	204	224	4	244	264	284	304	324	344
143	164	185	206	227	248	5	269	290	311	332	353	374
162	184	206	228	250	272	6	294	316	338	360	382	404
181	204	227	250	273	296	7	319	342	365	388	411	434
200	224	248	272	296	320	8	344	368	392	416	440	464
219	244	269	294	319	344	9	369	394	419	444	469	494
238	264	290	316	342	368	10	394	420	446	472	498	524
257	284	311	338	365	392	11	419	446	473	500	527	554
276	304	332	360	388	416	12	444	472	500	528	556	584
295	324	353	382	411	440	13	469	498	527	556	585	614
314	344	374	404	434	464	14	494	524	554	584	614	644
333	364	395	426	457	488	15	519	550	581	612	643	674
352	384	416	448	480	512	16	544	576	608	640	672	704
371	404	437	470	503	536	17	569	602	635	668	701	734
390	424	458	492	526	560	18	594	628	662	696	730	764
409	444	479	514	549	584	19	619	654	689	724	759	794
428	464	500	536	572	608	20	644	680	716	752	788	824
447	484	521	558	595	632	21	669	706	743	780	817	854
466	504	542	580	618	656	22	694	732	770	808	846	884
485	524	563	602	641	680	23	719	758	797	836	875	914
504	544	584	624	664	704	24	744	784	824	864	904	944
523	564	605	646	687	728	25	769	810	851	892	933	974
542	584	626	668	710	752	26	794	836	878	920	962	1004
561	604	647	690	733	776	27	819	862	905	948	991	1034
580	624	668	712	756	800	28	844	888	932	976	1020	1064
599	644	689	734	779	824	29	869	914	959	1004	1049	1094
618	664	710	756	802	848	30	894	940	986	1032	1078	1124

15	16	17	18	19	20	Feet Long	21	22	23	24	25	26
			AREA SQUARE FEET						AREA SQUARE FEET			
333	352	371	390	409	428	3	447	466	485	504	523	542
364	384	404	424	444	464	4	484	504	524	544	564	584
395	416	437	458	479	500	5	521	542	563	584	605	626
426	448	470	492	514	536	6	558	580	602	624	646	668
457	480	503	526	549	572	7	595	618	641	664	687	710
488	512	536	560	584	608	8	632	656	680	704	728	752
519	544	569	594	619	644	9	669	694	719	744	769	794
550	576	602	628	654	680	10	706	732	758	784	810	836
581	608	635	662	689	716	11	743	770	797	824	851	878
612	640	668	696	724	752	12	780	808	836	864	892	920
643	672	701	730	759	788	13	817	846	875	904	933	962
674	704	734	764	794	824	14	854	884	914	944	974	1004
705	736	767	798	829	860	15	891	922	953	984	1015	1046
736	768	800	832	864	896	16	928	960	992	1024	1056	1088
767	800	833	866	899	932	17	965	998	1031	1064	1097	1130
798	832	866	900	934	968	18	1002	1036	1070	1104	1138	1172
829	864	899	934	969	1004	19	1039	1074	1109	1144	1179	1214
860	896	932	968	1004	1040	20	1076	1112	1148	1184	1220	1256
891	928	965	1002	1039	1076	21	1113	1150	1187	1224	1261	1298
922	960	998	1036	1074	1112	22	1150	1188	1226	1264	1302	1340
953	992	1031	1070	1109	1148	23	1187	1226	1265	1304	1343	1382
984	1024	1064	1104	1144	1184	24	1224	1264	1304	1344	1384	1424
1015	1056	1097	1138	1179	1220	25	1261	1302	1343	1384	1425	1466
1046	1088	1130	1172	1214	1256	26	1298	1340	1382	1424	1466	1508
1077	1120	1163	1206	1249	1292	27	1335	1378	1421	1464	1507	1550
1108	1152	1196	1240	1284	1328	28	1372	1416	1460	1504	1548	1592
1139	1184	1229	1274	1319	1364	29	1409	1454	1499	1544	1589	1634
1170	1216	1262	1308	1354	1400	30	1446	1492	1538	1584	1630	1676

Explanation—For the total square feet in a room 20 feet wide and 30 feet long, ceiling 8 feet high, run down the 20-ft. column and opposite 30 read 1400 square feet.

Square Feet in the Ceiling and Four Walls of Rooms

9-Foot Ceilings

3	4	5	6	7	8	Feet Long	9	10	11	12	13	14
117	138	159	180	201	222	3	243	254	285	306	327	348
138	160	182	204	225	248	4	270	292	314	336	358	380
159	182	205	228	251	274	5	297	320	343	366	389	412
180	204	228	252	276	300	6	324	348	372	396	420	444
201	226	251	276	301	326	7	351	376	401	426	451	476
222	248	274	300	326	352	8	378	404	430	456	482	508
243	270	297	324	351	378	9	405	432	459	486	513	540
264	292	320	348	376	404	10	432	460	488	516	544	572
285	314	343	372	401	430	11	459	488	517	546	575	604
306	336	366	396	426	456	12	486	516	546	576	606	636
327	358	389	420	451	482	13	513	544	575	606	637	668
348	380	412	444	476	508	14	540	572	604	636	668	700
369	402	435	468	501	534	15	567	600	633	666	699	732
390	424	458	492	526	560	16	594	628	662	696	730	764
411	446	481	516	551	586	17	621	656	691	726	761	796
432	468	504	540	576	612	18	648	684	720	756	792	828
453	490	527	564	601	638	19	675	712	749	786	823	860
474	512	550	588	626	664	20	702	740	778	816	854	892
495	534	573	612	651	690	21	729	768	807	846	885	924
516	556	596	636	676	716	22	756	796	836	876	916	956
537	578	619	660	701	742	23	783	824	865	906	947	983
558	600	642	684	726	768	24	810	852	894	936	978	1020
579	622	665	708	751	794	25	837	880	923	966	1009	1052
600	644	688	732	776	820	26	864	908	952	996	1040	1084
621	666	711	756	801	846	27	891	936	981	1026	1071	1116
642	688	734	780	826	872	28	918	964	1010	1056	1102	1148
663	710	757	804	851	898	29	945	992	1039	1086	1133	1180
684	732	780	828	876	924	30	972	1020	1068	1116	1164	1212

15	16	17	18	19	20	Feet Long	21	22	23	24	25	26
369	390	411	432	453	474	3	495	516	537	558	579	600
402	424	446	468	490	512	4	534	556	578	600	622	644
435	458	481	504	527	550	5	573	596	619	642	665	688
468	492	516	540	564	588	6	612	636	660	684	708	732
501	526	551	576	601	626	7	651	676	701	726	751	776
534	560	586	612	638	664	8	690	716	742	768	794	820
567	594	621	648	675	702	9	729	756	783	810	837	864
600	628	656	684	712	740	10	768	796	824	852	880	908
633	662	691	720	749	778	11	807	836	865	894	923	952
666	696	726	756	786	816	12	846	876	906	936	966	996
699	730	761	792	823	854	13	885	916	947	978	1009	1040
732	764	796	828	860	892	14	924	956	988	1020	1052	1084
765	798	831	864	897	930	15	963	996	1029	1062	1095	1128
798	832	866	900	934	968	16	1002	1036	1070	1104	1138	1172
831	866	901	936	971	1006	17	1041	1076	1111	1146	1181	1216
864	900	936	972	1008	1044	18	1080	1116	1152	1188	1224	1260
897	934	971	1008	1045	1082	19	1119	1156	1193	1230	1267	1304
930	968	1006	1044	1082	1120	20	1158	1196	1234	1272	1301	1348
963	1002	1041	1080	1119	1158	21	1197	1236	1275	1314	1353	1392
996	1036	1076	1116	1156	1196	22	1236	1276	1316	1356	1396	1436
1029	1070	1111	1152	1193	1234	23	1275	1316	1357	1398	1439	1480
1062	1104	1146	1188	1230	1272	24	1314	1356	1398	1440	1482	1524
1095	1138	1181	1224	1267	1310	25	1353	1396	1439	1482	1525	1568
1128	1172	1216	1260	1304	1348	26	1392	1436	1480	1524	1568	1612
1161	1206	1251	1296	1341	1386	27	1431	1476	1521	1566	1611	1656
1194	1240	1286	1332	1378	1424	28	1470	1516	1562	1608	1654	1700
1227	1274	1321	1368	1415	1462	29	1509	1556	1603	1650	1697	1744
1260	1308	1356	1404	1452	1500	30	1548	1596	1644	1692	1740	1788

Explanation—For the total square feet in a room 15 feet wide and 20 feet long, ceiling 9 feet high, run down the 15-ft. column and opposite 20 read 930 square feet.

Square Feet in the Ceiling and Four Walls of Rooms

11-Foot Ceilings

3	4	5	6	7	8	Feet Long	9	10	11	12	13	14
FEET WIDE — AREA SQUARE FEET							**FEET WIDE — AREA SQUARE FEET**					
141	166	191	216	241	266	3	291	316	341	366	391	416
166	192	218	244	270	296	4	322	348	374	400	426	452
191	218	245	272	299	326	5	353	380	407	434	461	488
216	244	272	300	328	356	6	384	412	440	468	496	524
241	270	299	328	357	386	7	415	444	473	502	531	560
266	296	326	356	386	416	8	446	476	506	536	566	596
291	322	353	384	415	446	9	477	508	539	570	601	632
316	348	380	412	444	476	10	508	540	572	604	636	668
341	374	407	440	473	506	11	539	572	605	638	671	704
366	400	434	468	502	536	12	570	604	638	672	706	740
391	426	461	496	531	566	13	601	636	671	706	741	776
416	452	488	524	560	596	14	632	668	705	740	776	812
441	478	515	552	589	626	15	663	700	737	774	811	848
466	504	542	580	618	656	16	694	732	770	808	846	884
491	530	569	608	647	686	17	725	764	803	842	881	920
516	556	596	636	676	716	18	756	796	836	876	916	956
541	582	623	664	705	746	19	787	828	869	910	951	992
566	608	650	692	734	776	20	818	860	902	944	986	1028
591	634	677	720	763	806	21	849	892	935	978	1021	1064
616	660	704	748	792	836	22	880	924	968	1012	1056	1100
641	686	731	776	821	866	23	911	956	1001	1046	1091	1136
666	712	758	804	850	896	24	942	988	1034	1080	1126	1172
691	738	785	832	879	926	25	973	1020	1067	1114	1161	1208
716	764	812	860	908	956	26	1004	1052	1100	1148	1196	1244
741	790	839	888	937	986	27	1035	1084	1133	1182	1231	1280
766	816	866	916	966	1016	28	1066	1116	1166	1216	1266	1316
791	842	893	944	995	1046	29	1097	1148	1199	1250	1301	1352
816	868	920	972	1024	1076	30	1128	1180	1232	1284	1336	1388

15	16	17	18	19	20	Feet Long	21	22	23	24	25	26
AREA SQUARE FEET							**AREA SQUARE FEET**					
441	466	491	516	541	566	3	591	616	641	666	691	716
478	504	530	556	582	608	4	634	660	686	712	738	764
515	542	569	596	623	650	5	677	704	731	758	785	812
552	580	608	636	664	692	6	720	748	776	804	832	860
589	618	647	676	705	734	7	763	792	821	850	879	908
626	656	686	716	746	776	8	806	836	866	896	926	956
663	694	725	756	787	818	9	849	880	911	942	973	1004
700	732	764	796	828	860	10	892	924	956	988	1020	1052
737	770	803	836	869	902	11	935	968	1001	1034	1067	1100
774	808	842	876	910	944	12	978	1012	1046	1080	1114	1148
811	846	881	916	951	986	13	1021	1056	1091	1126	1161	1196
848	884	920	956	992	1028	14	1064	1100	1136	1172	1208	1244
885	922	959	996	1033	1070	15	1107	1144	1181	1218	1255	1292
922	960	998	1036	1074	1112	16	1150	1188	1226	1264	1302	1340
959	998	1037	1076	1115	1154	17	1193	1232	1271	1310	1349	1388
996	1036	1076	1116	1156	1196	18	1236	1276	1316	1356	1396	1436
1033	1074	1115	1156	1197	1238	19	1279	1320	1361	1402	1443	1484
1070	1112	1154	1196	1238	1280	20	1322	1364	1406	1448	1490	1532
1107	1150	1193	1236	1279	1322	21	1365	1408	1451	1494	1537	1580
1144	1188	1232	1276	1320	1364	22	1408	1452	1496	1540	1584	1628
1181	1226	1271	1316	1361	1406	23	1451	1496	1541	1586	1631	1676
1218	1264	1310	1356	1402	1448	24	1494	1540	1586	1632	1678	1724
1255	1302	1349	1396	1443	1490	25	1537	1584	1631	1678	1725	1772
1292	1340	1388	1436	1484	1532	26	1580	1628	1676	1724	1772	1820
1329	1378	1427	1476	1525	1574	27	1623	1672	1721	1770	1819	1868
1366	1416	1466	1516	1566	1616	28	1666	1716	1766	1816	1866	1916
1403	1454	1505	1556	1607	1658	29	1709	1760	1811	1862	1913	1964
1440	1492	1544	1596	1648	1700	30	1752	1804	1856	1908	1960	2012

Explanation—For the total square feet in a room 23 feet wide and 27 feet long, ceiling 11 feet high, run down the 23-ft. column and opposite 27 read 1721 square feet.

The Actuary Way to Figure Roof Spaces

The exact area of any roof, regardless of its shape, no matter how it may be cut up, is accurately determined as follows: Get the exact area from outside to outside of the walls on the level of the plates on which the rafters rest and add for the different roof pitches as follows:

One-fourth pitch add to area on square..............12 per cent

One-third pitch add to area on square...............20 per cent

One-half pitch add to area on square................42 per cent

Three-eighths pitch add to area on square...........25 per cent

Five-eighths pitch add to area on square............60 per cent

Three-fourths pitch add to area on square...........80 per cent

To the results thus obtained add the cornice projection all round. This gives the roof area sufficiently accurate for all practical purposes. For illustration, take a third pitch hip-roof—building 30 by 30 or 900 square feet at the square. Adding 20 per cent, or 180, gives 1080 as the roof area, including all dormers but excluding all cornice projections. Had there been a deck 5 by 6, or 30 square feet, then 30 plus 20 per cent should be deducted or 36 feet from 1080=1044 as the roof area, exclusive of deck and cornice projections.

Depreciation

| FRAME | | | | | BRICK, Shingle Roofs | | | |
| Stores | | Dwellings | | | Dwellings | | Stores | |
Average Duration	Depreciation per Year	Average Duration	Depreciation per Year	The Constituent Parts of Buildings	Average Duration	Depreciation per Year	Average Duration	Depreciation per Year
Years	%	Years	%		Years	%	Years	%
30	3⅓	40	2½	Base...............	40	2½	30	3⅓
				Brick...............	75	1⅓	66	1½
30	3⅓	40	2½	Cornice...............	40	2½	40	2½
40	2½	50	2	Dimension lumber.......	75	1⅓	66	1⅓
25	4	30	3⅓	Doors and trim.........	30	3⅓	30	3⅓
13	8	20	5	Floors...............	20	5	13	8
13	8	20	5	Hardware.............	13	8	20	5
30	3⅓	30	3⅓	Inside blinds...........	30	3⅓	30	3⅓
16	6	16	6	Outside blinds..........	16	6	16	6
5	20	7	14	Paint, inside.........	7	14	6	16
5	20	5	20	Paint, outside..........	7	14	6	16
16	6	20	5	Plaster...............	30	3⅓	30	3⅓
20	5	20	5	Porches.............	20	5	20	5
16	6	16	6	Shingles of wood.........	16	6	16	6
40	2½	50	2	Sheathing.............	50	2	50	2
30	3⅓	30	3⅓	Siding...............				
25	4	25	4	Sills and first floor joists....	40	2½	30	3⅓
20	5	30	3⅓	Stairs...............	30	3⅓	20	5
25	4	30	3⅓	Windows.............	30	3⅓	30	3⅓

The facts in the above table were compiled by Mr. A. W. Spaulding for the Fire Underwriters' Association of the Northwest. Mr. Spaulding's investigation covered twenty-seven cities and towns in eleven western states, and it is believed that the table is as accurate as it is possible to produce This Actuary table will enable lumbermen to pass upon the value of the constituent parts of any kind of building.

Miscellaneous Labor Items

Paneling, pine, hours per 100 sq. ft.	50
Paneling, hardwood, hours per 100 sq. ft.	83
Drawers, dovetailed, hours, each	2½
Drawers, 15″ × 18″, including racks and fittings	2
Shelves (in storeroom, dadoed into compartments 18″ sq. hours p 100 sq. ft.)	62½
Shelves, pantry, no dado, hours per 100 sq. ft. shelf	37½
Closet hooks on strip of wood, 12″ apart, hours per 100 lineal feet	15
Sideboard, oak, 8′ × 8′, hours	100

CHAPTER 34

Building Suggestions

In this chapter are given a few suggestions for building various structures. In building a house the author would strongly advise against cheap and inferior construction. If limited as to price let the house be of smaller size but first class in every respect; this will give the best satisfaction in the long run.

Barn Framing.—There are several kinds of frames used in barn construction as with houses. A type known as the plank frame is used extensively. Its use is due to the scarcity of large timbers which were formerly used, and owing to the increased cost of lumber especially large timbers the plank frame will be found economical. The standard barn width is 36 ft. and of any length desired.

In construction, as shown in figs. 1,694 to 1,700, the concrete foundation may be 1 ft. thick, 2 ft. above grade so that moisture from the soil will not rot the sills. Above grade it is safe to diminish thickness of concrete to 8 ins.

The studding, sills, plates and rafters are of $2 \times 6''$ lumber (plank). Joists are $2 \times 12''$ supported on $8 \times 12''$ girders built up of $2 \times 12''$ spiked together, and set on 12 ft. centers supported by either $5''$ steel columns or $6 \times 6''$ locust posts, conveniently spaced.

Each roof arch is braced down to the mow floor and bolted at the joint, or it may be well spiked from both sides. The floor joists are *lapped* (not butted) over girders and spiked together so as to become a continuous tie in tension across the barn thereby taking up any outward thrust that is natural from such trussing. To form the lap requires that the joists for

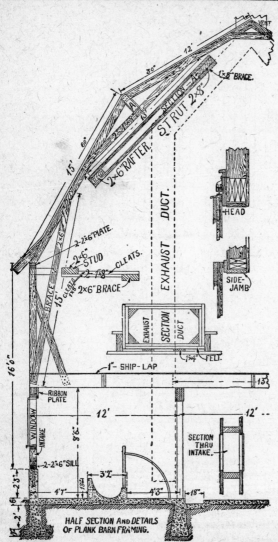

VENT

1½"×2" BRACE.

30°

SECTION 2×8.

STRUT 2×8.

2×6" RAFTER.

1½"×2" BRACE.

2-2×6" PLATE.

2×6" STUD

CLEATS.

2-1×8"

2×6" BRACE.

BRACE

EXHAUST DUCT.

HEAD

SIDE-JAMB

EXHAUST SECTION DUCT.

1½×4 FELT.

1"-SHIP-LAP

1×3

RIBBON PLATE

WINDOW

INTAKE

12'

12'

16'0"

8'6"

SECTION THRU INTAKE.

2-2×6" SILL

2'3"

3'2"

4'7"

1×4

4'3"

18"

2'

16"

HALF SECTION AND DETAILS OF PLANK BARN FRAMING.

FIGS. 1,694 to 1,700.—
Details of plank barn frame.

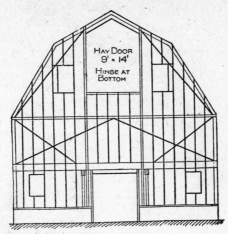

HAY DOOR
9' × 14'

HINGE AT
BOTTOM

FIG. 1,701.—Detail of end framing of barn.

FIG. 1,702.—South end elevation of barn.

center span be 13 ft. long. The outside ends must be securely spiked to studding and sill.

The side walls which are framed of the 2″ × 6″ joists are commonly 16 ft. long, from sill to plate. See section. It is most practical to frame— build together—the trusses on the floor or ground and raise them afterward. The double 2 × 6″ sill is spiked to the bottom of the studs, one at a time, and the same way for the plate. The 6″ rib plate which is the bearing for the outside end of hay mow joists are notched 1 in. into the inside face of the

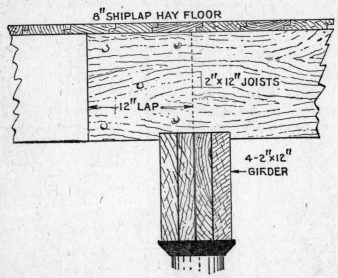

Fig. 1,703.—Detail of hay floor construction of barn.

studding. Frame out for windows, doors and vent shafts. Bore holes at exact spaces for anchor bolts that have been securely set into masonry, and you are ready to raise it.

It is recommended that the bridging be of 1 × 4″ material. They should be securely nailed when the joists are true, level and plumb. The much increased rigidity thus provided more uniformly distributes the load.

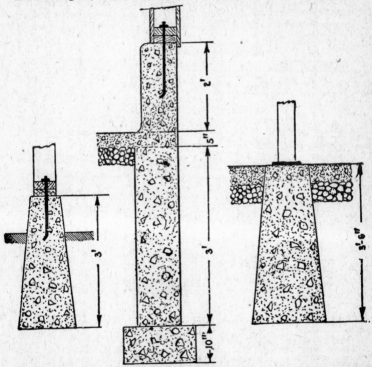

FIGS. 1,704 to 1,706.—Details of foundation of barn. Fig. 1,704, section through shed wall; fig. 1,705, section through the main wall; fig. 1,706, section of one of the piers.

Two continuous "built up" girders are seen, which, of course, must be set level. It is important when making these girders that the butt joints of the four thicknesses will not come opposite or near each other. A detail of hay floor construction shows the center span of joists to be 13 to 14 ft.

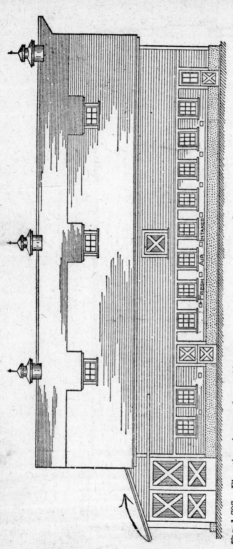

FIG. 1,707.—Elevation of east and west sides of barn.

long so as to lap the outside spans and form a tie by spiking together. Also there is a section through the main foundation walls and one of the piers and shed wall.

A cross section through horse stalls and details of ground floor framing. Note how ventilation is provided for, with intakes above the sill. These, of course, must be planned to open and close at will, and two large—in this case—12 × 26″ exhaust ducts carried to the ridge of roof into a ventilator.

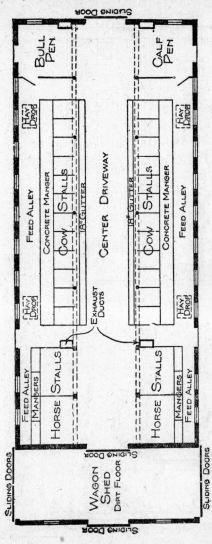

Fig. 1,708.—Main floor plan of barn showing general interior arrangement.

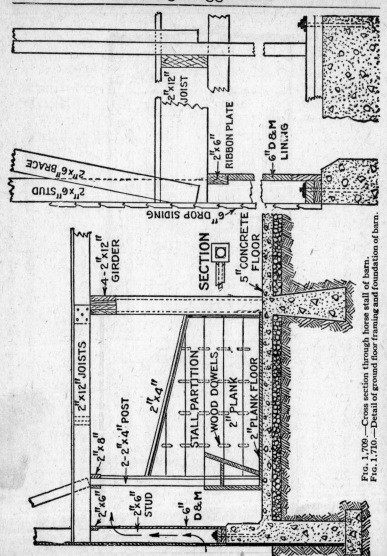

FIG. 1,709.—Cross section through horse stall of barn.
FIG. 1,710.—Detail of ground floor framing and foundation of barn.

Home Made Hot Bed.—A small hot bed is shown in fig. 1,711. The four stakes, or as many more as may be required, if one longer than 4 feet is to be built, are made long enough to be driven far enough in the ground to hold below the excavation made for the manure that should be placed below the soil.

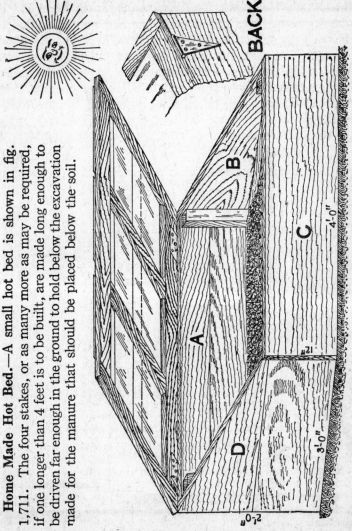

FIGS. 1,711 and 1,712.—Home made hot bed and detail of rear showing fastening of hing.

Bricked Up-Hot Bed.—This type as shown in fig. 1,713 is an improvement over the wooden hot bed and of course is much better for durability as it has no wood in or on the ground to decay. The sash, instead of being hinged moves up and down, a rabbit on the sash fits another in strips AA, which also hold them securely in position and to what ever opening they are placed without danger of being blown off by the wind. The frame being so much wider than strips AA, any water going through the slide will run out without falling inside.

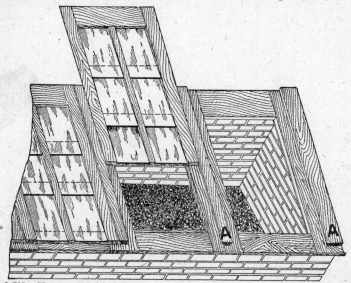

Fig. 1,713.—Home made bricked up hot bed. A, A, rabbited-pieces for holding sash.

Beginning at the bottom the glass as set in the sash rabbit, one lapping the other, the depth of lap may be varied to suit glass sizes and openings. They may be tacked in and are made tighter by puttying. For a good job the plank for frame should not be less than 1½″ thick and the sash 1¼″.

The wooden hot bed has the advantage not only of being portable. All are sunk into the ground to a depth sufficient for the required filing of manure and earth.

Boxes and Crates.—The packing or crating of household goods, furniture, etc., for removal is not usually classed as carpentry work, but the jobbing shop works up a good reputation for itself by never refusing an order, and therefore looks upon everything pertaining to woodwork and a lot of things that do not pertain to wood work as legitimate business. Many families that make a practice of moving to suburban homes for the summer months

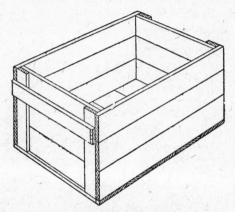

FIG. 1,714.—Proper way of using cleats at the corners of boxes.

are well able and quite willing to pay for the service of a competent man to do the packing and crating, and what follows constitute a few ideas on the subject of making crates and packing cases.

In making packing cases a very common mistake is to get them much too large. Many people procure large boxes from the dry goods merchant, probably getting a large flimsy case in which millinery, for example, has been packed. They fill this box with crockery, flatirons and preserves in glass jars and then call down maledictions upon the heads of the freight handlers because things get broken. Packing cases should be designed with a view to what is to go into them and made wherever possible of a size that can be easily handled. This, though probably using up a little more material for the job, will save money in the end.

Where dry goods boxes and such like have been procured they can be utilized by cutting them up and making them smaller, or by using the thin material of which they are composed for intermediate slats on the sides of other crates. The best way to take them to pieces is to saw through the sides close to the ends, thus wasting about an inch of each end of the sides, but obviating the chance of splitting which you are almost certain to do if you try to knock them apart in the usual way. After the sides have been cut the small pieces can be knocked from the ends and the nails withdrawn, with the result that all of the boards of the original case are in as good

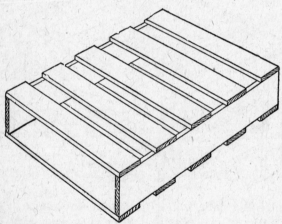

Fig. 1,715.—One form of crate.

condition as ever, excepting that the sides are an inch or so shorter than they originally were.

A packing case is a simple thing to make, but being usually constructed of narrow boards it is often necessary to use cleats at the corners of it. Inexperienced workmen frequently make the mistake of putting these cleats on the inside of the case.

The proper way of making the case is shown in fig. 1,714. The piece nailed across the cleats at the ends as shown not only serves for a handle, but in many cases prevents the freight handlers standing the package on end. The boards in the bottom of the case are put on the short way of it and the top can be fixed in the same manner, or it may be made up in the form of a lid with the boards running lengthwise and two cleats fastened across them to keep them together. These cleats also should be on the outside.

Packing cases will serve for all of the smaller household goods, such as crockery, cooking utensils, books, etc., but do not under any circumstances

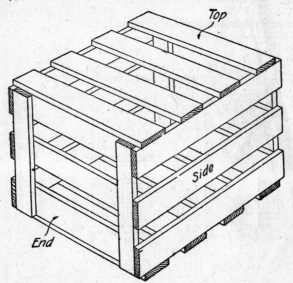

Fig. 1,716.—Another form of crate.

mix heavy with light and fragile articles. Wrap all breakables separately with paper, straw, excelsior or something which will answer a similar purpose, and pack the case full so that no amount of turning end over end will move its contents. The larger pieces of furniture with the exception of the piano, it will be more economical to crate. A case for the piano can usually be procured from the nearest dealer and this will be a much cheaper operation than making one. With the case secured, the crating of the piano simply amounts to covering it with cloths to keep out the dust and moving it

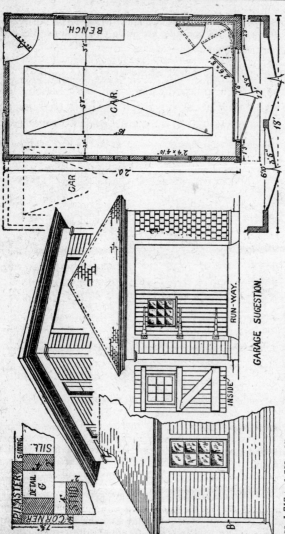

Figs. 1,717 to 1,723.—Views and details of a small garage.

into its case. It is fastened in place with two coach or lag screws, which are passed through holes provided for them in the back of the case. Notice where the screws were formerly fixed in the back of the piano as it came crated from the factory, and if the holes in the case do not suit, bore two new ones.

Although the shapes and sizes of crates vary considerably they are all made on one general principle, which is illustrated in figs. 1,715 and 1,716. If these sketches be carefully studied it will be perceived that fig. 1,716 is constructed in the same manner as fig. 1,715, but because of its greater depth the ends and sides are made of slats instead of being made solid.

Garage.—Figs. 1,717 to 1,723 show a garage for one car, being wide enough to accommodate a small work bench. By extending the width to 18 ft. as suggested by the dotted line the garage would be large enough to accommodate two cars.

The doors are built up or batten doors such as can be made on the job

FRONT.

$1000 BUNGALO. 24'x30'

FIGS. 1,724 to 1,727.—Front elevation and details of model bungalow.

and hung on strap hinges opening out in two halves. However, should space prohibit that they may be made in 3 parts, the door to the right hinged to the center one and the two carried on an overhead track to against the side wall as dotted lines show.

To allow of backing the car in the garage and to one side, conveniently, the doors are 6″ from center showing a 12″ wider space at right of door than at left.

The cheapest frame construction is to set the studding 4′ apart and cut in three rows of purlins between sill and plate, on about 2′10″ centers, varying according to height of frame and inclose with ⅞″ match boards same as door is made of with corners as at B, of broken side elevation.

The best floor construction is of cement with a slight pitch so that water will drain.

Model Bungalow.—The suggestion for a bungalow shown in

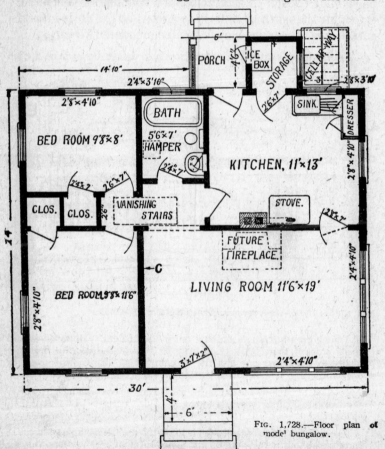

Fig. 1,728.—Floor plan of model bungalow.

figs. 1,724 to 1,729 is an example of a cheaply constructed yet durable building. There is no cellar. The girders are supported on locust posts.

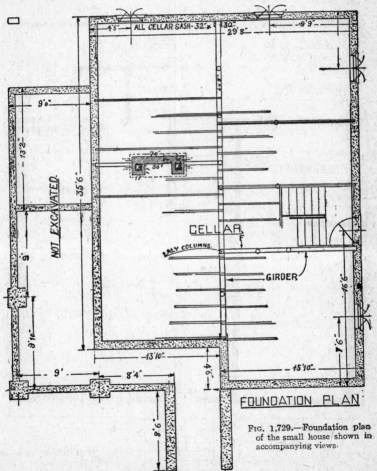

FIG. 1,729.—Foundation plan of the small house shown in accompanying views.

A cheap grade of ship lap sheathing is used and the shingles may be a No. 2 grade of red cedar of promiscuous widths,

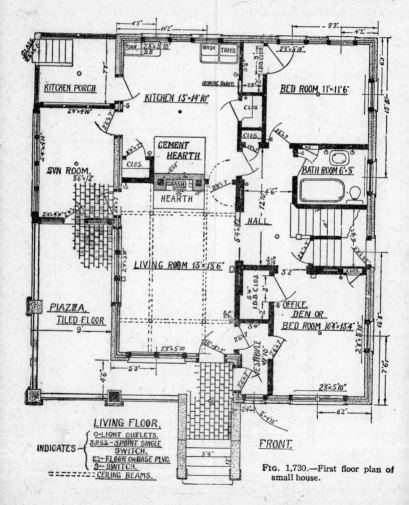

FIG. 1,730.—First floor plan of small house.

although it is very poor policy to try to save money on a roof; better get the best shingles obtainable.

The exposed ends of the rafters are dressed and hand shaped.

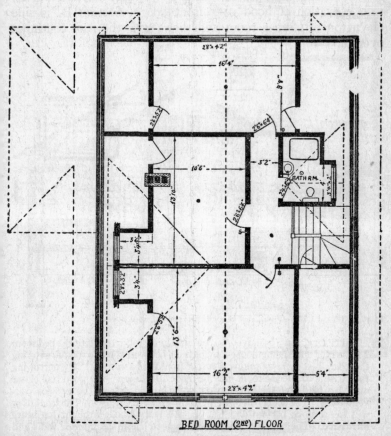

BED ROOM (2ND) FLOOR

FIG. 1,731.—Second floor plan of small house. The dotted lines show roof plan.

They are on 2 ft. centers. The floor will be laid single of matched Carolina pine, that of shorter lengths because it costs less. One third of the attic will be floored over with a cheap flooring. The trim will be of white wood or Carolina pine.

The exterior trim will be of fir or white pine. Section A is the side elevation of hood over front door. Section B, is side elevation of storage room and shows how the roof continues over it.

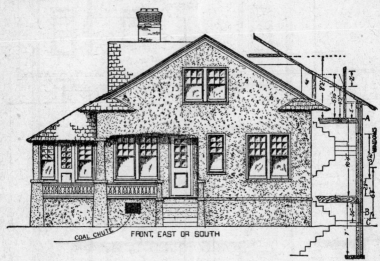

COAL CHUTE   FRONT, EAST OR SOUTH

FIGS. 1,732 and 1,733.—Front, east or south, elevation of small house.

Partition C, may be moved 2 ft. out into living room, making the bed room 2 ft. wider and sliding doors may be built between the two rooms, entering the back bed room by taking a corner from the bath room. By narrowing the closets to 20″ the room may be made 10″ deeper, or a good hall closet may be made off the hall-way or passage, and retain the present conveniences. The doors will be of fir, of two panel stock sizes. The front door will be a stock pattern 1¾″ thick. All ivory black wrought hardware furniture. The plan contemplates 3 ways to finish the interior walls and ceilings: 1, wood lath, patent wall plaster with a white skim coat hard

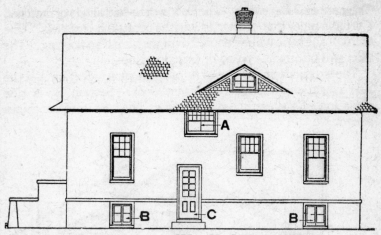

NORTH, OR EAST ELEVATION.

FIG. 1,734.—North, or east elevation of small house.

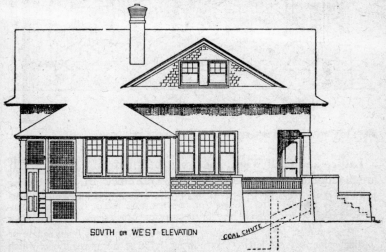

SOUTH OR WEST ELEVATION

COAL CHUTE

FIG. 1,735.—South or west elevation of small house.

finish; 2, dress the studding, use a better grade sheathing and stain interior, and patent wall board on the ceilings, panelled off with $3/8 \times 1\frac{1}{2}''$ strips, and 3, use all wall board on the interior.

Small Two Story House.—The accompanying illustrations figs. 1,730 to 1,735 show design for a small house that can be built at a reasonable price.

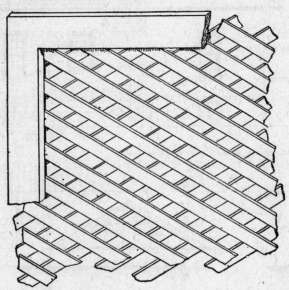

FIG. 1,736.—Diagonal lattice work.

Lattice and Grill Work.—Among the interesting items which are included in the numerous list contained in carpenters', joiners' and woodworkers' practice is the construction of the details of lattice and grill work.

The simplest form of this branch of the business is the open square or diagonal criss-cross lattice shown in fig. 1,736 of the illustrations, which consists of planed plasterers' four foot laths set diagonally and nailed top,

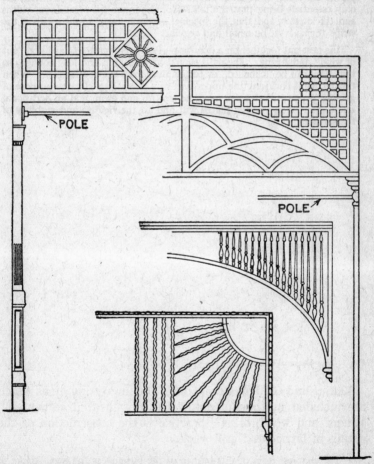

FIG. 1,737.—Example of lattice work over door.

FIGS. 1,738 to 1,740.—More examples of interior lattice work over door.

middle and bottom to a fixed frame or the underpinning of a piazza, stoop or veranda. The construction of this kind of lattice, whether the laths be placed diagonally or square, is so simple as to require little description, the only essentials being that the laths should be parallel, of uniform widths and thicknesses, and that the spacing, generally equal to the width of the strips themselves, be equal and regular.

It is best put together on a floor or perfectly flat surface so as to be "out of wind" and strong. The nails should be wire, thin and long enough, so that they can be "clinched" or turned over from the reverse side. When this lattice is enclosing the upper part of a porch, etc., for the purpose of gaining privacy, both sides must be smooth and clean and an occasional screw inserted in various places will add to the rigidity and stability of the surfaces.

CHAPTER 34A

Small House Construction

It has become increasingly evident that a careful planning is of paramount importance especially in regard to small low cost dwellings, where the capital available for design purposes is necessarily limited. In recent years there has been an ever increasing interest in the planning and design of smaller homes with the best possible room arrangement as well as an advantageous appearance.

In the low cost house, the principle of plan efficiency, economic use of materials and proper equipment which are important in any class of dwelling, becomes increasingly important. Here every square foot of space, every odd corner, every length of pipe, as well as every foot of timber must be used to the best advantage.

Due to the interest in the design and construction of such dwellings a number of plans has been developed by the *Federal Housing Administration*, Washington, D. C. and are, due to their proven popularity, reproduced on the following pages.

Construction Details House "A".—In fig. 1740A, the walls of the house may use standard 8 foot studs except on the gable sides. The framing is extremely simple, with one interior bearing partitition permitting either one span of 24 feet, supported in the center, or two spans of 12 foot joists. The plumbing is united on one stack, permitting a minimum of piping. The living room is heated directly from the heating unit. The bed-

FIG. 1740A—This dwelling may be considered the minimum house for a small family. All of the functional arrangements of a home are included, such as easy access to the bathroom from any of the other rooms, etc.

rooms are heated from a duct carried below the ceiling construction, the bathroom by the hot-water storage tank.

Figs. 1740A and 1741A shows the basic design features although a number of variations are possible. Besides utilizing different materials, variety may be achieved through variation of the character of the roof, orientation of the house, and changing the location of openings. Where it can be afforded, a porch may be added, or a garage designed in connection with the house will increase the range of variation in appearance.

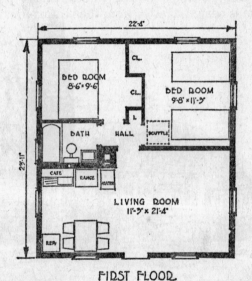

FIRST FLOOR

FIG. 1741A—Showing floor plan of house shown in fig. 1740A. The addition of a basement in a dwelling of this type is not considered practicable. If, however, this house were built with continuous foundation walls instead of on a foundation slab, it would probably cost approximately 10% more to build.

The exterior walls of the house may utilize any one or a combination of two of the materials commonly in use, such as wood siding, shingles, brick, concrete block, stucco or stone.

Construction Details House "B".—The wall construction in fig. 1742B is similar to house in fig. 1740A. Again, only one interior bearing partition is required, this time running the long dimension of the house, permitting two spans of 12 feet each, or one span of 24 foot joists supported under the main partition

FIG. 1742B—This house represents an increase in comfort over the house previously shown. Here the kitchen is separated from the living room otherwise the simplicity of the accommodation is maintained.

by a bearing member. No cutting or special framing is required except around the chimney. Plumbing is designed to permit one stack, though the length of branches varies with the alternate arrangement. The rooms, except for the one in which the heater is placed, are heated by ducts or radiators.

The same approach in exterior design is followed as in fig. 1740A. The accompanying drawings endeavor to demonstrate that attractiveness is not inconsistent with simplicity and that charm may be achieved without resort to expensive or elaborate details. This house is developed in a modern manner using wide

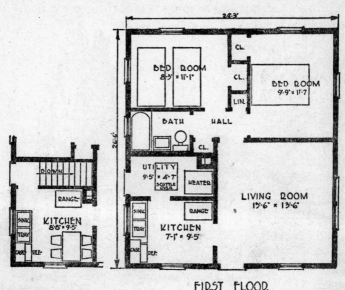

FIRST FLOOR

FIG. 1743B—Floor plan of house depicted in fig. 1742B. In this house, by utilizing a portion of the space devoted to the utility room, a stairway may be introduced and a basement added by an additional investment of 20 to 25% of the original cost.

tongue and grooved horizontal flush siding with a hipped sheet-metal roof. Other materials may be used such as stucco, brick or stone with equal effect. Here also a re-arrangement of doors and window openings may readily be made to suit individual requirements.

Construction Details House "C".—In fig. 1744C the exterior wall has been designed generally for standard lengths of stud, using balloon framing; and the floor framing has been designed to utilize 16 foot floor joists carrying between exterior bearing walls. Framing in the opposite direction will in all probability not prove as economical or provide as satisfactory a tie for the walls of the house.

FIG. 1744C—This house is provided with the same amount of accommodation as house shown in fig. 1742B, but, is a two-story house and will fill the demand of those who desire their bedrooms on the second floor.

The plumbing has been designed to permit one soil stack. A heater room has been provided on the first floor, and, if desired, laundry trays could be included in the same space.

When designing these accommodations in a two-story house, the saving by eliminating the basement is not as marked as the one-story house, and it is quite possible that, in northern climates, it would be more advisable to provide a full basement, substituting a dining room for the heater room as illustrated in the alternate plan shown.

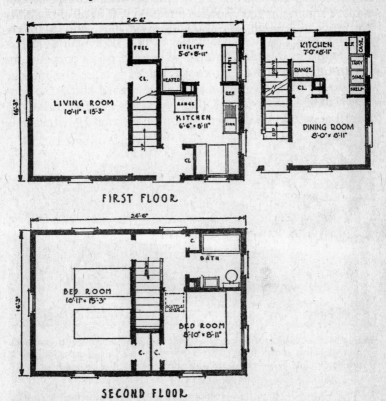

FIRST FLOOR

SECOND FLOOR

FIGS. 1745C and 1746C—Floor plans of house whose exterior is shown in fig. 1744C. If a basement be provided the alternate floor plan shown will provide for a dining room in place of the heating room and so provide for additional comfort. The second floor plan provides for two bedrooms in addition to a bathroom and closet space.

Construction Details House "D".—The framing of this house can be most economically accomplished by the use of 16 foot floor joists extending from the rear to the front walls, cut where necessary to frame around the stair opening.

The bathroom has been located directly over the utility room, permitting the use of the single soil stack and vent. An overhead hot water system adaptable to first floor operation has been shown in this plan in order to use space economically. In this installation the radiators are placed against the interior walls to permit the return piping to be carried above the concrete slab of the first floor. Other types of heating for first floor operation can be used where space for interior fuel storage is

FIG. 1747D—This house offers the same accommodation but gives an increased variety in arrangement over the plans previously shown.

not required. Where a basement is provided still greater flexibility may be had.

In the elevation of this house, the same attempt has been made as in the former to keep the roof line as low as possible in order to keep the proper relationship or proportion between the height and width of this dwelling.

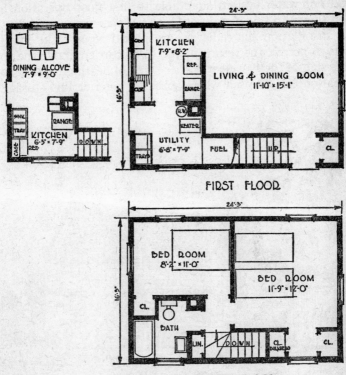

FIRST FLOOR

SECOND FLOOR

FIGS. 1748D and 1749D—These plans, with the principle outlook of the living room as well as of the bedrooms, to the rear, are particularly suitable when the lot has capacity for the development of a rear yard.

The addition of a garage, connected to the house, as indicated, adds breadth to the design and tends to diminsh the stilted quality which is so difficult to avoid in the design of small two-story structures.

While wood siding has been indicated on the drawing, it may be built of any of a number of materials, such as brick, concrete block, shingles, reinforced concrete, stucco or stone.

Construction Details House "E"—This house is designed for either a warm-air heating system with a register opening directly

FIG. 1750E—This is the most spacious of the low cost group of houses. It illustrates markedly the possibilities of an economic design for a house requiring three bedrooms. A house of this type can be framed with 20 ft. floor joists supported on a bearing member below the partition between the kitchen and the utility room.

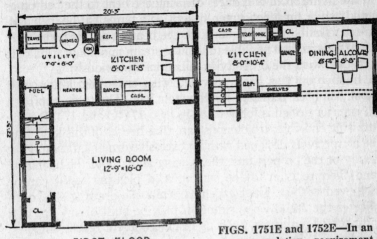

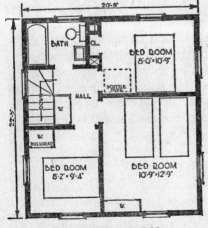

FIRST FLOOR

SECOND FLOOR

FIGS. 1751E and 1752E—In an accommodation requirement of this kind a two-story plan is preferred to the one-story plan, on account of better economy. The bathroom is located directly over the utility room, which permits one soil stack for the fixtures in the utility room, the kitchen and the bathroom.

in the living room and ducts carrying the heat to the bedrooms and bath or for a hot-water system. If a basement be included, greater flexibility in planning for the heating of this house may be had. It is then possible to include steam and adaptation of it together with the other types mentioned previously.

Each room has been provided with cross ventilation, and light has been provided for the stair hall. The same approach in exterior design is followed as in figs. 1744C and 1747D. The drawing endeavors to demonstrate that houses of this kind may be attractively designed without excessive ornamentation. By a study of the proportions, the spacing and size of the openings, and their relation to the wall area, a pleasing result can be achieved without great expense. While the drawing shown indicates the use of wood siding, it may be built of any one of a number of materials, such as brick, concrete block, shingles, reinforced concrete, stucco, stone or a combination of them. The size of the house, however, requires that the treatment of material as a feature of design be kept simple; and in no case should a combination of more than two materials be used.

This house provides an elaboration of accommodation over the dwellings previously illustrated. Even without a basement, a greater differentiation of space for living, dining, and cooking functions is permitted; it becomes possible to place the entry so as to preserve the privacy of the living room, larger bedrooms and greater privacy for the bedrooms are likewise featured.